AN
ECOLOGICAL
GLOSSARY

AN ECOLOGICAL GLOSSARY

COMPILED BY

J. RICHARD CARPENTER

NEW YORK

HAFNER PUBLISHING COMPANY

1956

Published at 31 East Tenth Street, New York 3, N. Y.

Printed in the United States of America

NOBLE OFFSET PRINTERS, INC.
400 LAFAYETTE STREET
NEW YORK 3, N. Y.

PREFACE

ECOLOGY, being the science of communities—essentially an observational study—has acquired during its existence a vocabulary rich in descriptive terms. It has been my purpose in the preparation of this Glossary to bring together and make available the more technical and restricted usages of terms which have been and are in the ecological literature. While no pretense is made that the list is by any means exhaustive, nearly all of the technical terms encountered in a diligent search of the current periodicals and texts are included. Any comment, criticism, or additions from the users of this Glossary will be of material aid in the preparation of a supplement or second edition in the future, and will of course be welcomed.

Certain other publications which will be of aid to the ecologist may be cited:

Committee on Nomenclature, Ecological Society of America, 1933—Tentative glossary of Ecological terms, compiled by the committee . . . . (Preliminary and revised mimeographed lists are being prepared yearly, notice of availability being announced in the Proceedings of the Society, published in Ecology, usually in April of each year).

Henderson, I. F. Dictionary of scientific terms. Oliver & Boyd, London. (several editions)

Jackson, B. D. 1928. A glossary of botanic terms with their derivation and accent. Duckworth, London. (second edition)

Jager, E. C. 1930. A dictionary of Greek and Latin

combining forms used in zoological names. Thomas, Springfield, Illinois.

Knox, A. 1904. Glossary of geographical and topographical terms. Stanford, London.

Parker & Smith. Dictionary of entomological terms. Paris. (in preparation)

Roller, D. 1929. The terminology of physical science. Univ. Okla. Press, Norman.

Smith, J. B. 1906. Glossary of entomology. Brooklyn Entomological Society, Brooklyn, N.Y.

In the presentation of the terms with their definitions an attempt is made to present after each term a reference to the first use of the term or to a more available work or standard text in which the term is used or discussed. Unfortunately this was not always possible and many terms have a "dictionary definition" only. Where two or more concepts are employed in the usage of a single term, the most frequently used sense (in ecology) or the usage or sense approved by the author and editor is placed first. In most cases this will be found to agree with the recommendations of the Ecological Society's Committee on Nomenclature.

To avoid unnecessary confusion the term Community is substituted in the older definitions and in citations where other than the usual usage of terms is employed (e.g., Formation, Association, etc.). The terms Association and Society are begun with capital letters when used in the community sense; small letters are used when the implication is less definite. Quotation marks are used only where the author cited explains but does not define the term.

Certain obsolete and teleologic terms are included for

the sake of completeness and for aid in interpreting the older literature. It is not meant to revive these terms of the past although some may warrant reconsideration. The use of terms implying teleology should not be tolerated.

To effect an economy of space singulars and plurals of the same term are omitted, except in cases where the form is so different as to create confusion. In certain cases the same grammatical forms are not followed in successive citations under a given term; since most of the definitions are unedited citations, the reason is apparent.

Standard abbreviations are used in the designation of the journal references and for the most part for books; frequently recurring references are given by author and date only, with the exception of quotations from Jackson's Dictionary of Botanic Terms where the designation is "J:". References by authors cited by name and date will be found in the bibliography on pages 298 ff. The name of an author appearing in parentheses with a citation indicates that the term is being defined in the sense of that author. The following system of abbreviation is used:

= indicating synonym
cf "compare"; often indicating antonym
see a cross reference to terms of similar meaning
Of/ "of or pertaining to"; a designation to place definitions of adjectives in correct grammatical style, and effect an economy of space.

It is strongly recommended that certain terms originally used for plants or animals alone be extended in usage to include all organisms. New terms certainly do have a place in the literature if they are actually needed; when introduced all new terms should be adequately defined in clear concise language in footnotes, in the text, or in a section devoted to terminology. In any event it is important that no ambiguity exist as to the exact meaning of terms as used in any ecological paper. The common names of the Communities of North America used in the Naturalist's Guide to the Americas (1926) should be used wherever possible.

The appendix includes certain tables and maps which it is hoped will serve as a useful supplement to the Glossary. Many of the maps are rapidly becoming inaccessible since the original works are out of print and it was considered advisable to bring them together in one place. Acknowledgments for the use of certain of the maps are included in the appendix.

I wish to express my appreciation to Drs. A. O. Weese, Paul B. Sears, and J. E. Weaver and to the Library staff of the Missouri Botanical Library for aid in making available certain out-of-the-way literature. I also wish to express my thanks to Dr. Weese for cooperation in the editing of the compilation, and to him and other members of the University of Oklahoma Ecology Seminar for their aid and encouragement throughout its preparation.

J. RICHARD CARPENTER
Lincoln College, Oxford

TABLE OF CONTENTS

THE DEVELOPMENT OF ECOLOGICAL NOMENCLATURE

In examining a history of the science of ecology one is impressed by the fact that prior to the beginning of the twentieth century there was little organized thought towards the construction of a definite system of ecological nomenclature. The reason is immediately obvious: Any nomenclature or system of terminology is based upon a system of concepts and it was not until the close of the nineteenth century that serious co-ordination of previously collected data and concepts was attempted. The outstanding figure in this latter movement was Eugene Warming who undertook in *Plantesamfund* (1895) to effect such a coordination. This date serves as a turning point in the history of a field of thought the literature of which was widely scattered and whose workers were for the most part widely separated.

A brief résumé of the history of ecology prior to Warming will perhaps lead to a better understanding of the place and relative lateness of the position of nomenclature in the field. Early studies on succession in peat bogs and the first serious studies on zoogeography took place in the period from 1729 to 1840 and serve as the first period in the history of ecology. Such men as Buffon, von Humboldt, A. P. deCandolle, Linnaeus, Fabricius, Darwin, Grisebach, and Ste. Hilaire characterized the period.

A second period, 1840-1870, was characterized by the application of the theories of phyto- and zoogeography, and the development of the concept of the interaction of

organisms. Workers were Steenstrup, von Post, the de-
Candolles, Dana, Haeckel, Huxley, Agassiz, Ste. Hilaire,
and Grisebach.

Following this came a ten year period from 1870 to
1880 which saw the birth of the concept of the community, considerations on physiological adaptations, and
comments on the fitness of the environment. Here we find
the names of Grisebach, A. deCandolle, Möbius, Espinas,
Forel, Wallace, Blytt, and Drude.

The next period seems to be shorter than any preceding, from 1880 to 1887-88; it was characterized by studies
on the interaction of organisms with environmental factors. S. A. Forbes, Semper, Heliprin, Sachs, von Oettin-
gin, Hult, and Drude attract our attention here and with
the men of the next period laid the foundation for many
of the present concepts of community functions.

The period 1887-88—1895 may well be termed the pre-
Warming period; significant researches here were along
the first quantitative lines, with physiological criteria
rapidly replacing the older concepts of the community.
Workers of greater importance were Bessey, Forbes, Möbius, Merriam, Andersson, Sernander, Warming, and
Schimper.

A crystallization of the ecological knowledge of the
time began with the successive appearances of the publications of Warming (1895), Schimper (1898), and Engler
(1899). Since the publication of *Plantesamfund* was in
Danish, its general effectiveness was probably somewhat
delayed, and its honors were shared somewhat with
Schimper's *Pflanzengeographie auf physiologischer Grundlage*. The influence of these works was to call attention

to the need of some sort of definite system of ecological nomenclature and classification.

This need was voiced to the scientific world by Warburg at the seventh International Geographic Congress (September 1899) at Berlin. His suggestions were (1900) that a definite and consistent principle should be followed. He pointed out that the "understandability" which Warming used for the layman should be for the scientists of all countries as well, and proposed a classification using Greek as a linguistic basis. Concerning himself only with the nomenclature of communities and considering that "biological phytogeography is now so well developed that one cannot go astray in the choice of principles and names," he suggested that an elaborate, comprehensive system of phytogeography be outlined which was to serve for once and for all. The Congress appointed a commission composed of Drude, Engler, Grabner, and Hock to work out a system to be presented before the next congress.

Flahault, stirred by Warburg's arguments and realizing that a need for clarification existed, read before the first International Botanical Congress at Paris (October 1900) a paper (1900) dealing mostly with the nomenclature of topographic and vegetational units, stressing priority in the designation of the regions, and for the most part using the vernacular in his designations. No general system of names was proposed for the actual types of communities, most of the paper being devoted to the ranking of communities and regions (as Region, Association, Society, etc.). In his words: "The great phytogeographic regions are characterized by a peculiar vegetable landscape, by a *type of vegetation* which reflects a distinct result of the reaction of climate on the plants. Good common sense has distinguished by special terms the sum of biologic characters appropriate to each of these types. Science has but to accept them."

Clements proposed in 1902 a "system of nomenclature for phytogeography" (1902) based on the habitat as a criterion using terms of Greek and Latin construction. With it was offered a system of rules in the form of a code which included the recognition of priority, and restricted the validity of proposed terms; among the restrictions were the provisions that all terms should be proposed by botanists and be compounds of the classical languages of Greek and Latin. A permanent commission of phytogeographical nomenclature was proposed to pass on all terms, the system resembling somewhat that of the systematic biologists. In 1904 Clements added a series of terms dealing with the several types of succession, and in 1905 both proposed lists were slightly modified in the glossary of *Research Methods*.

In an editorial footnote, Engler (1902, article of Clements) protested against the adoption of the principle of priority, indicating that such a system would be impracticable for concepts which might later prove erroneous.

The Vienna Congress (1905) appointed Flahault and Schröter as members of a commission to set forth propositions to be presented before the next Congress. Olsson-Seffer (1905) in the same year proposed a scheme for the construction of new terms in which clarity of meaning and conciseness of concept were the keynotes. Any attempt at rulings of priority, or of the resorting to the classical languages was discouraged; vernacular terms were considered acceptable so long as they were not linked with ambiguity.

The commission headed by Flahault and Schröter appointed by the Vienna Congress obtained by means of a form circular sent around before the Congress at Brussels, the attitudes and opinions of the principal phytogeographers of the time. Opinions and suggestions were gathered together in the *Phytogeographische Nomenklatur,* published by the Congress (1910); chief among the contributors were the committee, Harshberger, Jaccard, Diels, and a British committee composed of Tansley and Moss. Farlow and Atkinson (1910) reported that the Congress rejected Clements' proposals both in respect to priority and the proposition that the terms should be from the classical languages. "Terminology is very different from nomenclature and must be subject to change in order to bring it into harmony with the change of ideas in the interpretation of facts." A commission was again appointed to continue the work, which had really been progressing in a constructive manner, and to report at the London Congress in 1915. The War made this Congress impracticable and it was not until 1926 that the work of the Congress was resumed.

During the sixteen years which followed, nomenclature and concepts grew and metamorphosed rapidly. Terms and concepts ran the gauntlet of natural selection and public opinion, many falling out of the literature entirely. Among the more important papers on the theoretical aspect of the question appearing during this period were those of Moss (1910), Brockman-Jerosch & Rubel (1912), Pavillard (1912), Braun & Furrer (1913), Shelford (1913), Clements (1916), Samuelsson (1916), Gleason (1917), Nichols (1917), DuRietz, Fries, & Tengwall (1918), McDougall (1918), Pearsall (1918), Pavillard (1919), Clements

(1920), Hansen (1921), Klugh (1923), Nichols (1923), Yapp (1925), Cooper (1926), Pearse (1926), Shelford (1926), and Tansley & Chipp (1926). During this period the later system of Clements became more widely accepted in America and Britain; that of the earlier DuRietz school in Northern Europe, and that of the Braun-Blanquet-Rübel school in Southern Europe.

At the meeting of the fourth International Botanical Congress* at Ithaca, N.Y., 1926, the older committee (appointed in 1910) made no report, being of the opinion that recommendations of this sort should be in the hands of the younger schools of thought. Accordingly, little was done at this Congress by committees, although papers on concepts of ecological units were presented by Nichols, Gleason, DuRietz, and DelVillar. Prior to the convening of the fifth Congress several rather important contributions were made by Soo (1927), Braun-Blanquet (1928), Rübel (1928), Weaver & Clements (1929), Tansley (1920), Braun-Blanquet & Pavillard (1930), and DuRietz (1930a,b). The latter author made a particularly brilliant contribution comparing existing systems of ecological classification, proposing a compromise system, and illustrating all of the extant systems in a single comparative chart (*see* appendix I). This, together with papers by Nichols and Phillips, was presented before the Cambridge Congress in 1930. The paper of DuRietz led to a better mutual understanding on the part of the divergent schools. Phillips urged the consideration of the community as a biotic entity; his proposal met with approval by Tansley, Rübel, Salisbury, and Shantz. A commission headed by DuRietz and consisting of Cowles, Diels, Do-

---

* International Congress of Plant Sciences.

min, Gleason, Jaccard, Maire, Nordhagen, Phillips, Rübel, Stojanoff, Szafer, Tansley, and Vierhapper, was appointed with instructions to make a report before the sixth Congress to be held at Amsterdam in 1935.

Outstanding papers since the fifth Congress have been those of Phillips (1931, 1934, 1935) and Shelford (1931, 1932), and the preliminary and revised lists of terms offered by the committee on ecological nomenclature of the Ecological Society of America (1933-34). This committee has stated some "basic principles" of nomenclature (1933) which appear to be much more acceptable and workable than any other set thus far proposed (with the possible exception of Olsson-Seffer 1905). They are:

1. Natural growth of ecological nomenclature should not be hampered by rules.
2. Restricted scientific usage should not violate common literary or general scientific usage.
3. Words long used in a broad sense should not be used in a new, special meaning.
4. Uniformity of usage is desirable in the same field or in closely related fields; if a relatively new word is commonly accepted in one branch of science it should be adopted in other branches when it is needed there.
5. New words should be coined only when there is a distinct need. It is desirable that ecological literature be intelligible to as wide a field of readers as possible. It is not necessary to have a separate term for every slight difference of meaning.
6. Words are tools of thought. An exact term may aid in clarifying a clearcut distinct concept. Ambiguous or inaccurate use of terms may obscure a

definite concept. The development or formulatior of a concept may be hindered by the too early coining of new terms or definitions as well as the failure to use precise terms.

The sixth International Botanical Congress met in Amsterdam in September 1935. The twelfth International Zoological Congress met at Lisbon later in the same month, including ecology for the first time on its program. At the former Congress a sectional meeting devoted to the problems of ecological nomenclature was held in which the merits of the various systems of concepts and criteria were discussed. Concepts were decidedly at variance, and the conclusions of the section were well expressed by G. E. DuRietz: "As long as there is no general agreement in the fundamental *concepts* of phytosociology, any attempt of attaining at an agreement in the terminology of these concepts seems futile. The main thing at present appears to be to parallelize the different phytosociological systems in the right way. We must know when different systems have a certain concept in common, and what this concept is called in the different systems. And we must know the different meanings of a certain term in different systems. Above all, we must get rid of the widespread belief that there is *one* fundamental unit of phytosociology and that the term 'association' must be reserved for this unit . . . . Experiences from the phytogeographical terminology resolutions of the Brussels Congress have sufficiently demonstrated the futility of any congress resolutions which have not behind them an overwhelming majority of workers in the science concerned. A continued free discussion of phytosociological concepts and terms seems to be the best way to a future general agreement."

It is hoped that this volume will serve in clarifying the concepts and usages of the more common systems of terminology and nomenclature, and that the ultimate goal of international understanding be more rapidly reached through its use. The biotic interaction of organisms forms the basic framework for all communities. The establishment of any system of criteria or terms which omits any portion of the community in recognizing and designating communities is only a partial completion of the task. Joint action and co-operation on the part of workers in both the fields of botany and zoology—the parts of an arbitrarily divided biology—is necessary before a real international system of ecological terminology is possible.

AN
ECOLOGICAL
GLOSSARY

A

Abertos. Hardy '25:142 *Geogr. of Plants*. Liliaceous trees
resembling yuccas, forming savannahs (Brazil). *See
also* serrados, campo vero.

Abiocoen. Friederichs '30:233 = Biotop. The non-biotic
habitat.

Abrasion. The wearing away of soil. *See* appendix XII.

Abrasion platform. Flattely & Walton '22:36. A horizontal plane formed by a long continued wave action; a
portion of the continental shelf, with the continental
terrace.

Abschluss. III Int. Bot. Congr. 1910 (Drude & Beck). A
community in a condition of equilibrium with the existing habitat condition; not limited to a stable stage of a
progressive succession. *See* formation, community.

Abstract community concept. *See* association type, association, comment.

Abstract plant (as distinguished from the individual
plant). *See* sippe.

Abundance. Clements '05. The total number of individuals in an area. Braun-Blanquet & Pavillard '30. A
term expressing the relative number of individuals of
each species entering into the constitution of an area
studied, i.e., an example of the association. *See also*
density, frequency.

Abundance classes. ESA 1935. List P-3 (Braun-Blanquet & Pavillard). A scale of 5 classes in appreciation of the *relative* number of individuals of each species in a plant community.

Abyssal. Flattely & Walton '22:11. Pertaining to the area from the margin of the continental shelf to the greatest depths and bounded by the pelagic zone. *See* ocean.

Acarophytium. Mite-plant symbiotic relationship.

Accidental union. Allee '31:15 (Deegener). Groups of animals without mutual benefit for the individual members. *See* homotypical and kormogene associations.

Acclimation. Adaptation to climatic change on the part of the individual. ESA 1935. List P-3. The physiological adjustment or increased tolerance shown by an individual organism to a change in the surrounding environment. *See* Acclimatization.

Acclimatization. ESA 1935. List P-3. The adjustment or increase in tolerance shown by a species in the course of several generations in a changed environment. *See* Acclimation.

Acclimitation. Shelford '29:99. Term applied to the condition where several generations are necessary to bring about changes in an organism.

Accrescent. Of/ plants which continue growth after flowering.

Aciculignosa. Rübel '20 *Pflgesel. der Erde.* Narrow sclerophyll or coniferous vegetation. Subdivided as Aciculsilvae: the transcontinental coniferous forests (except edaphic pine forests and the Laurisilvae); and Aciculifruticeta: dwarf pine and spruce of alpine regions, and Juniper scrub of warmer and drier regions.

ESA 1935. List P-3 (Rübel). Coniferous forest with small, evergreen, needle-leaves mechanically strengthened and usually with no intercellular air spaces, able to withstand cold and drought, mostly subalpine, subarctic, and continental; elsewhere in the deciduous forest regions for edaphic reasons. G. Nadelwalder and Nadelgebusche. *See* lignosa.

Acid soil. *See* oxylic.

Acidotrophic. Feeding on acid foods.

Acospore. Clements '05. A plant with awned disseminules

Acrodomatia. J:2 Structures on plants adapted to shelter mites of supposed service to the host.

Acrophytia. Clements '02. Alpine plant communities.

Acrotropism. J:262. Movement induced by the presence of oxygen.

Actic. Klugh '23, Ecol. 4:371. Of/ seashore between the tide marks. = littoral.

Actium. Clements '02. A rocky seashore community.

Actophilus. Dwelling on rocky seashores.

-ad. Clements '05. 1. Suffix for denoting an ecad. 2. Suffix for denoting individual.

Adaptable. Clements '05. Able to form ecads.

Adaptation. Clements '05. The structural response (in plants) to stimuli. J:6. Means by which an organism adapts itself to changed surroundings. Shelford '12, Biol. Bull. 23:339. "Adaptation (in animals) is not structural, but physiological. Ecologically there is rarely reason for considering structure of motile animals separate from activity. Accordingly it seems best to reject the separate consideration of (morphological) adaptation and treat all questions of structure of motile animals as structures playing a rôle in the physiology and activity of the organism." Shelford '15, Jl. Ecol. 3:10. "Adaptation is more with reference to the vertical (stratal) conditions in which the animals live than to the climatic or other physical conditions which are usually horizontal."

Adjustment. Clements '05. The functional response to stimuli.

Adoption societies (aggregations). Allee '31:30 (Deegener) . . . . formed by mutual adoption freely entered into by both species and without recognizable advantages or noticeable harm for either.

Adsere. (Clements) That portion of a sere which precedes its convergence into another at any time before the climax stage.

Advance growth. ESA list R-1. Young trees which have sprung up in openings in the forest or under the forest canopy before cutting or before regeneration operations are begun. = advance reproduction.

Adventicous species. Clements '05. Invading from distant communities.

Adventive. Clements '05. Established temporarily. *See* ephemeral.

Aelophilous. J:8. Disseminated by wind.

Aeolian. 1. Clements. Of/ sandy soils liable to be moved rapidly by wind. 2. Wind factors.

Aerial water. J:418. Rain or dew, as distinguished from terrestrial or underground supply.

Aeromorphosis. J:417 (Turesson). 1. Change in form due to exposure to air or wind. 2. (Ivanoff). Algae living fully exposed to the air and not in the soil.

Aerophytobionts. Braun-Blanquet '32:289. Aerobic soil flora.

Aeroplankton. Braun-Blanquet '32:289. Microorganisms floating in air.

Aeroxyl. J:418 (Lindman). Trees and woody plants with an evident bole, and branches above ground. *See* geoxyl.

Aestatifruticeta. 1. J:418. Deciduous bush community. 2. Summer coppices.

Aestatisilvae. J:9, 418. Woodlands with leafage in summer; deciduous forests. *See* aestilignosa (Rübel).

Aestilignosa. Rübel '30. *Pflgesel. der Erde.* Trophophytic woodland of temperate regions. Subdivided as Aestisilvae: temperate deciduous forest; and Aestifruticeta, deciduous bush communities. *See* lignosa.

Aestival. *See* estival.

Aestivation. J:9. The manner in which the parts of a plant are folded up before expansion. Also spelled estivation (q.v.).

Agad. J:9. A beach plant.

Agamospecies. (DuRietz) An apomict population, the constituents of which, for the morphological, cytological, or other reasons, are to be considered as having common origin.

Age and Area. (Willis) "The older a species is within a region, the greater its area."

Age class. ESA 1933 List P-1. All trees in a stand or forest whose age falls within stated limits, usually divided in 20-year periods (5 years in coppice), but in old stands may be of wider range, and may be stated in extent of area or in percentage of the whole stand or forest, or, in selection forest, by number of trees. A stand in which the trees fall between the ages of 1 to 20

years should be referred to as age class 1. ESA 1934.
List R-1. A stand in which all trees originated in the
same regeneration period.

Agger arenae. Clements '02. Sand bar: silt, mud, sand,
and gravel brought down by torrents and rivers. *See*
beach.

Aggregation. 1. Clements '05. The coming together of
organisms into groups; (later papers) the process by
which germules come to be grouped together consisting
of simple aggregation and migration. Simple A. : the
grouping of germules about the parent plant. *See* colony, family. 2. Of animals. *See* Allee '31. Animal Aggregations.

Agium. Clements '05. A beach community.

Agrarian zone. J:10 (Watson) Of/ the cultivatable portion of a country.

Agrestal. J:10 (Watson). Plants growing in arable
ground. *See* culture communities.

Agrium. Clements '02. A culture community (q.v.) or
grain field.

Agrophilus. Dwelling in grain fields or culture communities.

Aigialium. Clements '02. A beach community.

Aigialophilus. Beach dwelling.

Aigicolous. J:418. Of/ inhabitants of a stony strand or
beach.

Aiophyllus. J:10. = Evergreen.

Aiphyllium. Clements '02. A broad-leaf evergreen forest
community.

Aiphyllophilus. Dwelling in broad-leaf evergreen forests.

Aiphytia. Clements '02. Stable (ultimate) communities.
See climax.

Aithallium. Clements '02. An evergreen thicket community.

Aithalophilus. Dwelling in evergreen thickets.

Alcaliotropism. J:12. Chemotropism produced by alkalies.

-ale. Clements. Suffix for colony.

Aletophytes. Warming '09:135. Mesic ruderal plants.

Alien. J:12 (Watson). Introduced plants which have become naturalized. See exotic.

Aliquote. J:12 (Linsser). The constant of temperature for a given event in the life cycle of an organism; the sum-temperature of the event divided by the sum-temperature of the year. See temperature summing, developmental rate.

-alis. Suffix denoting of or pertaining to.

Alkalitropic. Chemotropism produced by an alkali.

Allautogamia. Clements '02. Having two methods of pollenation, one usual, and the other facultative.

Alleghanian life zone (Merriam). See appendix V, VI.

Allelarkean society. Dryer '16, Geog. Rev. 2:291. A complex, interdependent, fixed, dense, civilized, economic society. Cf. autarkean society.

Allelotaxis. Allee '31:280 (Gray). The mutual depressing effect of one cell upon another. See cytotropism.

Alliance. Braun-Blanquet & Pavillard '30. "Associations and fragments of associations which show floristic and sociological affinities between themselves form an Alliance or group of Associations." = verband. Suffix: -ion.

Allochoric. J:418 (Drude). Of/ a species inhabiting two or more closely related communities in the same region, as adjoining forest and grassland. = binding influent.

Allochthonous. 1. Carpenter '28:207. *Life in Inland Waters*. Of/ material of drifted fragments of shore plants in certain lakes, preserved from total decay and accumulating in coarse grained masses on the bottom, contributing nothing to the enrichment of the waters in solution content. Cf. autochthonous. 2. J:418 (Forsaith). Of/ peat due to gradual accumulation of drifted material in still water.

Allotropic lakes. Chapman '31:318 (Birge and Juday). Lakes which receive drainage containing organic matter to add to that produced internally.

Alluvial community. J:418. A boundary zone between water and land which is subject to inundation.

Alluvium. Water deposited soil. *See* Melangeophytia, flood, floodplain.

Alpestrine. The area above timber line; approximately syn. with alpine.

Alpha. Shelford '29:183. "The prolongation of the line expressing the reciprocals of the times which fall in the limits of the equilateral hyperbola cuts the temperature axis of a velocity graph. This is the zero of the hyperbola and is the corresponding point on the velocity curve; this point has only mathematical significance and has no biological meaning."

Alpine. 1. Montane. *See* Alpestrine, corypliad, montane, orohylile. 2. Life zone (Merriam). *See* appendix V, VI.

Alpino-arctic community. A community of similar life form and frequently similar species which is repre-

AMANTHOPHILUS

the arctic and alpine regions. *See* anthelietum.

Alsad. J:14. A grove plant.

Alsium. Clements '02. A grove community; a place
grown with trees and grass. *See* parkland, savannah.

Alsophilus. Of/ grove community inhabitants.

Alternating Communities. *See* "Twin communities."

Alternation. 1. Clements '05. The heterogeneous arrangement of plant groups and communities universally
present in the vegetation. 2. Mixed succession. *See*
zonation.

Alternes. 1. Tansley & Chipp '26:53. Different communities alternating with each other where there is no
spatial change; this may be caused by alternation of
habitat, or by other causes. 2. (Clements) Alterna-
tions of dominance over the same area.

Altherbosa. Rübel '30. *Pflgesel. der Erde.* Tall herb
communities, frequently occurring where forests have
been destroyed. *See* herbosa.

Altricial. Of/ organisms which receive parental care after
birth.

Alvar. Warming '09:290 (Sernander). A type of vegetation characteristic of certain steppe-like communities of
Sweden (dwarfed perennial shrubs). *See* steppe, prairie.

Alveus. Clements '02. A sand draw. *See* sand community.

Amanthicolous. J:419. Growing in sandy plains.

Amanthium. Clements '02. A sandhill or plain community. *See* sand community.

Amanthophilus. Dwelling in sandy plains or in sandy
hills.

Amathium. Clements '05. A sandhill or sandplain community.

Ametoecious. J:15. Of/ a parasite which is confined to a single host. *See* parasite.

Ammochthad. J:16. A sandbank plant.

Ammochthium. Clements '02. A sandbank community.

Ammocolous. Hancock '11:420. Of/ dry sand inhabiting species.

Amnicolous. J:419. Growing on the sandy banks of rivers.

Amnis. Clements '02. A creek. *See* stream.

Amphichromatism, seasonal. J:339 (Lindman). The production of two or more differently colored flowers on the same stock, due to the changes of seasons. *See* aspection, coloration.

Amphichrony. J:419 (Lindman). A display of two distinct colors when in flower.

Amphicryptophytes. J:419 (Gams). Helophytes having their vegetative organs amphibious.

Amphigenesis. ESA 1934, List R-1. The union of gametes to form a zygote; an amphigenetic generation is one which forms zygotes.

Amphiphyte. J:17 (Schröter). A plant on the boundary zone of wet land, amphibious in life and hydrophytic in adaptation.

Amphoterosynhesmia. *See* synhesmia.

Anabiont. J:18 (A. Braun). Perennial, flowering and fruiting many times.

Anabiosis. J:18 (Areger). The condition of latent life, which may occur through loss of moisture.

Anadromous. Of/ fish which ascend fresh water streams to spawn, such as salmon.

Anaerophytobionts. Braun-Blanquet '32:289. Anaerobic soil flora.

Anarhizophyte. J:419. A plant able to root in soil which covers its original spot.

Ancium. Clements '02. A canyon forest community.

Ancophilus. Dwelling in a canyon forest.

Andean. Of/ the Andes mountains; equivalent to alpine. *See* montane.

Andine. Pertaining to the Andes mountains. *See* alpine.

Androconia. Modified wing scales of Lepidoptera; produce sex attractive odors.

Androecy. J:419 (Vexküll). Occurrence of purely male individuals in a species.

Androphile. A plant frequenting the neighborhood of man. *See* culture community.

Androsynhesmia. *See* synhesmia.

Anemium. Clements '05. A blowout community.

Anemochore. Clements '05. A plant distributed by wind.

Anemodium. Clements '02. A blowout community.

Anemophilous. Of/ plants pollenated by wind.

Anemophilus. Dwelling in sand draws.

Anemophobe. J:420. A plant suffering greatly from exposure to wind.

Anemoplankton. Friederichs '30:233. Organisms passively transported by wind through the air.

Anemosporic. Of/ plants disseminated by wind. *See* anemochore, wind.

Anemotaxis. Taxic orientation of an organism with reference to wind.

Anemotropism. Tropic response of organisms to wind and air currents.

Angeosere. Clements '16:289. The eosere of the cenozoic

period (= Cenosere); the climax period of the Angiosperms.

Angonekton: Friederichs '30:233. Short-lived organisms in water pools in or on earth, rocks, tree stumps, leaf axils, vessels, etc.

Anhydrobiosis. (Roubaud). Period of desiccation during which the general metabolic rate is decreased in animals about to undergo hibernation. (See Shelford '29:160, or Uvarov '31:109). The period during which the excretory organs "purify" the organism which can then resume development. See diapause, hibernation.

Annual. Pertaining to yearly occurrence of organisms or phenomena. See hornotinus, hornus, aspection, plurannual, therophyte, univoltine, perennial.

Antagonistic symbiosis. J:373. The struggle between two organisms.

Antarctogaea. Lydekker '96:26 (Sclater '74). The Australian region exclusive of New Zealand and Polynesia. See Ornithogaea, Sclater's zoological regions.

Anthecology. Robertson '22, Bot. Gaz. 73:148. Insect relationships with flowers. See pollenation adaptations.

Anthelietum. See snowflush, alpino-arctic community.

Anthesis. 1. The period of maximum physiological activity; the period of blossoming in plants. Clements '02. The period of flowering. 2. J:25. The period of pollenation.

Anthoplankton. = water bloom.

Anthracriny. J:420 (Falck). Decomposition into humus.

Anthrageny. J:420 (Falck). The formation of peat by decomposition.

Anthropeic. Nichols '23, Ecol. 4:19. Of/ human influences

upon natural conditions of a community. *See* subsere, culture community.

Anthropochorous. Of/ plants distributed through human agencies.

Anthropophilous. J:421 (Thelling). Of/ plants which follow man. *See* culture community.

Anthropophytes. = hemerophytes.

Anthropozoic characters. Braun-Blanquet & Pavillard '30. Relations of influences of man or animals. *See* culture community.

Anticryptic coloration. Pearse '26:298 (Poulton). Coloration for aggressive resemblance.

Antipleon. Clements '16:330 (Arctowski). Areas of deficiency in cycles of 2.5 years. Cf. pleon.

-anum. Clements '05. Suffix denoting layer.

Apatetic coloration. Pearse '26:298 (Poulton). Coloration of animals resembling the environment or some portion of it.

Apex time. J:421 (Bose). The time between the latent period and the recovery when a leaf moves after a shock or touch stimulus.

Aphaptotropism. J:28 (Henslow). Not influenced by touching stems or other surfaces. *See* thigmotropism, tropism.

Apheliotropism. Negative phototropism. *See* tropism.

Aphercotropism. J:421 (Henslow). The turning away from an obstruction.

Aphotic zone. The portion of bodies of water not penetrated by light (about 3000 ft.).

Aphotometric. J:421 (Weisner). Of/ leaves not affected by light.

Aphototropic. J:421. Turning away from light.

Apogeotropic. Turning away from the earth or soil.

Apomict population. A parthenogenetically produced population.

Aposematic. Pearse '26:299 (Poulton). Of/ warning colors: the giving notice to enemies of supposed distasteful or injurious qualities.

Apostrophe. Clements '05. The arrangement of the row of chloroplasts parallel to the rays of light.

Apparent noon. Clements '05. The time when the sun crosses the meridian, i.e., sun noon as distinguished from noon, standard time. See day, periods.

Approximation. J:421 (Digby). = Association.

Aquatic community. See Hydatophytia, hydrarch, lenetic, maritime, ploadostadion, stream, ocean, lake.

Aquatosere. Woodbury '33. Ecol. Monogr. 3:167. A sere beginning with a wet bare area and developing to an aquatic climax. See sere, quasi-climax.

Aquiherbosa. Rübel '30, *Pflgesel. der Erde*. Herbaceous communities of swamps and ponds. Subdiv. as Emersiherbosa, Submersiherbosa, and Sphagniherbosa. See herbosa.

Aquilonian region. (Blanford). Europe, Asia north of the Himalayas, Africa north of the tropics, and America north of about 45°. For synonomy, see maps, appendix.

Aquiprata. J:32,241. Plant communities and herbs, grasses, and bryophytes where influenced by ground water; damp meadows. See meadow.

Arbores. Clements '02. Trees.

Arbuscula. J:32. Small shrub with the aspect of a tree.

-arch. Suffix to denote -sere.

Archaeophyte. J:32 (Rikli). Weeds introduced into cultivated ground in prehistoric times. *See* ruderal, exotic.

Arctalpine. (Clements). 1.Alpine plants in the alpine zone. 2. Zone. Bray '15 Tech. Pub. 3, N.Y., Col. For. The far north beyond the limit of tree growth and in the high mountains above the timber line. Zone of the polar bear, musk-ox, reindeer, arctic poppy, dwarf willow, etc. 3. Life zone. (Merriam) That portion of the boreal life zone which is above the limits of tree growth, in altitude or latitude; the southern limit is characterized by a normal mean temperature of 50°F. during the six hottest weeks of the year. *See* appendix V, VI. 4. Faunistic zone (Wallace). Circumpolar region, limited by an isotherm of 32°F. which closely marks the tree limit. *See* appendix VII; *see also* alpinoarctic.

Arctogaea. Lydekker '96:26 (Sclater '74). A region composed of the Palaearctis, Nearctis, Oriental, and Ethiopian regions (Oriental = Indian region of Sclater '58).

Arctogaeic region. Lydekker '96:27. *See* map, appendix IX.

-ard. Clements '05. Suffix for terms dealing with water content of soils.

Ardium. Clements '05. A succession due to irrigation.

-are. 1. Clements '05. Suffix denoting community. 2. (Clements) Suffix denoting clan.

Area. 1. Waterman '22. Bot. Gaz. 74:7. The ground occupied by an individual community. 2. Braun-Blanquet & Pavillard '30. The surface containing all the known localities in which the same community occurs.

Area of normal abundance. Uvarov '31:121 (Cook '29). The area within which the limiting conditions never or rarely occur so that the insect is always present in considerable numbers and may be of economic importance every year.

Area of occasional abundance. Uvarov '31:121 (Cook '29). Areas in which the insect is always present, but becomes a pest only in certain favorable years when the limiting factors cease to exert their influence.

Area of possible abundance. Uvarov '31:121 (Cook '29). Areas in which the insect is unable to maintain a permanent population owing to annual, or almost annual occurrence of limiting conditions. Outbreaks in this area are rare and are due to the migration of the insects from one or both of the areas of possible and normal abundance.

Area of specific abundance. Uvarov '31:121. Localities where the species occurs but is constantly kept in check by limiting factors and it never becomes a pest.

Areg. J:421. 1. Sand desert. 2. Dunes in Algeria.

Arenaceous, Arenarious, Arenicolous. J:32. Of/ sandy places. *See* sand community.

Argillaceous. Of/ clay soils.

Argodromile. Klugh '23, Ecol. 4:372. Of/ slow flowing streams.

Arid transition life zone. (Merriam). *See* appendix V, VI.

Arrhenius' formula. Shelford '29:173.

$$V_2 = V_1 e \frac{\mu}{e^2} \left(\frac{t_2 - t_1}{t_2 t_1} \right)$$

Arroyo. J:422 (Spanish). A water course, especially when dry.

Arundineous. J:35. Reedy, or abounding with reeds.

Arvum. Clements '02. A grain field. *See* culture community.

-as (Clements). Patronymic suffix.

Ascolichenes. J:422. Ascomycetes in symbiosis with algae.

Aspect. 1. Clements '05. The seasonal impress on a community, e.g., the spring aspect. Clements '16:130. The seasonal changes of a community. Tansley & Chipp '26:16. Seasonal aspects are due to vegetative development and flowering of different species being confined to certain seasons of the year. Clements '16:132. A seasonal change of dominance which marks the aspects of the vegetation. *See* season, biotic. 2. ESA 1934, List R-1. The direction toward which a slope faces, as designated by the points of the compass.

Aspection. Nichols '23, Ecol. 4:14. Periodic changes in the appearance of the constituent species associated with periods of foliation and defoliation or with periods of flowering, which are reflected in the physiognomy of the community as a whole or of its constituent parts. The periods of aspection are termed seasons or aspects and are of Society (Clements) rank. The periods usually recognized are Prevernal, Vernal, Aestival, Serotinal, Autumnal, and Hiemal or Hibernal. *See* Season, biotic, *see also* diplobiont, dyschronous, anthesis, efflorescence, ephemeral, society, frutescence, hapaxanthic, heterochromatism, heterodynamous, homodynamous, meroplankton, monotonous, multivoltine, perennial, pollachanthic, polycarpic, proanthesis, pseudoephemer, triduus, diacmic.

Assembly. Fide Shelford '30. The smallest of community units, such as those occupying microhabitats such as dead animals, fallen logs; including aphis colonies on particular plants, etc. Dominants of such habitats are termed dominules, etc. Swynnerton '36, Trans. Roy. Ent. Soc. Lond. 84:515. The animals that are found in a community.

Association. 1. (sense of a climax) Fide Shelford '30. All of the life of a given climax area of uniform taxonomic composition. Phillips '30, Jl. Ecol. 18:201. A climax community with two or more dominants. Clements '16: 128. Climax communities which are associated regionally to constitute a formation. The associations agree with their formation in physiognomy and development, but differ in floristic composition among themselves and to some degree in habitat. Weaver and Clements '29: 45. Climax communities associated regionally to constitute formations; similar throughout extent in physiognomy, in ecological structure, and in general floristic composition. 2. (sense including climax and developmental stages) Woodbury '33, Ecol. Monogr. 3:168. The biotic unit, characterized by its essential homogeneity of structure (at least with regard to its dominant groups), biotic composition, and physiognomy, usually involving more than one dominant, but including the entire population of a given habitat; in this sense it includes the developmental steps from initial to climax stages. 3. (sense of a community of no stated developmental rank) a.(*floristic criteria*) Warming 109:145. A community of definite floristic composition within a formation; an ecological genus. III Int. Bot. Congr. 1910:24. A plant community of definite floristic composition, presenting a uniform physiognomy and growing in uniform habitat conditions; the fundamental unit

of synecology; of any developmental rank. Shelford
'12, Biol. Bull. 23:356. Groups of strata uniform over
a considerable area, and for which the majority of
mores, consocies, and strata are characteristic. Adams
'15, Bull. Ill. St. Lab. Nat. Hist. 11:15. The animals
found living together in a given combination of environmental conditions form an animal association or a
social community, and the study of the responses of
such a community is the province of associational ecology. DuRietz '26. A plant community characterized
by its essential homogenous floristic composition, at
least as regards the dominant species, and its essential
homogeneous physiognomy. Braun-Blanquet & Pavillard '30 . . . . recognized and characterized by
its specific assemblage and principally by its characteristic species. b. (*habitat criteria*) Vestal '14,
Bot. Gaz. 58:377. An essentially uniform assemblage of plants living together in an area essentially
uniform in environmental conditions; no interrelationship of different plants is implied, nor is uniformity
taken to exclude internal local variations of either environment or vegetation. Klugh '23, Ecol. 4:369. A
community of definite biotic composition living in uniform habitat conditions. Nichols '26, Proc. Int. Congr.
Pl. Sci. 1:636. A piece of vegetation occupying a definite piece of ground and having more or less definite
spatial boundaries. Swynnerton '36, Trans. Roy. Ent.
Soc. Lond. 84:515. A major community consisting of
a definite assemblage of species with a definite habitat
and dominated by two or more species. Friederichs
'30:37. "A self-regulated population system of a given
natural biotic area." "In its general sense it may desig-

nate a community of no specific rank, and is synonymous with 'Biocoenotic connection' (qv.), or biotic
population ("Lebensgemeinschaft"). 4. (Phytosociological sense, somewhat similar to 1) DuRietz '30. An
independent stable Phytocoenosis of one or more Consociations in which one layer is dominated by a distinct
group of species bound together by strong sociological
affinities. The composition of the other layers may display very strong variation; the binding Associon also
may exhibit a very heterogenous species composition
with different dominants and in extreme cases even completely distinct species composition in various parts of
the association. Where nothing else is indicated, the
highest layer is understood to be the binding Associon.
5. (Aggregational sense) Espinas '78 (in Allee '31:6).
Accidental societies between animals of different species.
(Humboldt) "Plantes associés." Alverdes '27:14. *Social Life in Animal World*. . . . . formed by environmental factors causing a number of animals, whether
of the same or different species, to gather in one place.
(Wheeler '30) Loosely integrated, relatively unstable
systems primarily dependent on the reactions of the individuals to environmental stimuli. Allee '31:15. An
accidental union, i.e., groups of animals without mutual
benefit for the individual members. 6. (sense of structure) Clements '05. The arrangement of individuals in
vegetation.

Comment, applicable to 1, 2, 3*a* & *b*: Nichols '23,
Ecol. 4:15. "The term association should be recognized
as applicable both to the abstract vegetation concept
and to the concrete individual pieces of vegetation

(assoziations individuum) on which this concept is based."

Often considered as chief, closed, intercepted, mixed, open, passage, progressive, retrogressive, substitute, transitional, and unstable Associations. Association in the senses of DuRietz, Rübel, Shantz, Nichols, Cockayne, Clements, Braun-Blanquet, Drude, and Cajander are compared in appendix I, II. *See* associes and community. = Plantesamfund (Danish), Pflanzenverein (Warming), Genossenshaft (Kerner), Bestand (Höck) and Assoziation. Suffix: -ic.

Association-complex. Nichols '18, Tr. Conn. Acad. 22: 275. In any unit area the associations taken collectively. J:422. A union of associations to form a phytogeographical unit. Nichols '23, Ecol. 4:161. Any group of associations which occupies a definitely circumscribed area. (DuRietz). *See* appendix I.

Association fragments. (Braun-Blanquet). Varied aspects from the normal or optimal. *See also* assoziations-individuum, relict.

Association-group. (DuRietz, Drude). *See* appendix I.

Association type. Nichols '18, Tr. Conn. Acad. 22:275. Associations which are equivalent to one another. The abstract concept of a particular association. Nichols '23, Ecol. 4:156. All Associations which resemble one another in physiognomy and ecological structure, regardless of their ecological structure.

Associes. Clements '16:136. The development equivalent of the association; it corresponds to the initial and intermediate "formations" (Clements '02-04) and to the subordinate Association (Moss '10) (Tansley '11). It is based on life form, floristic composition, and habitat. (Clements) Developmental units of Consocies. (Tansley) Transitory units. Klugh '23, Ecol. 4:369. A community which is clearly and relatively rapidly developing into a (climax) Association. Weaver and Clements '29:46. The developmental equivalent of the Association; a temporary stage of development; a non-permanent community to be replaced by another in the process of development or succession. Phillips '30, Jl. Ecol. 18; 201 and Scott '34, Jl. Ecol. 22:194. A seral community with two or more dominants. Woodbury '33, Ecol. Monogr. 3:168. The developmental group which produces the association when the climax is reached; an association in the process of development. *See* socies, consocies, locies. Suffix=-is.

Associon. DuRietz '30:336. A stable synusium composed of one or more Consocions which is dominated by a definite group of species with strong Sociological Affinity. However none of the species necessarily extend throughout the entire Associon. *See* appendix II.

Associule. Clements, '36. Jl. Ecol. 24:280. A microcommunity of associes rank in a serule.

Assoziationsindividuum. A concrete example or stand (relict after man) of a given Association. *See comment* of Nichols under Associon.

Asthenobiosis. Shelford '29:160 (Roubaud). Period of autointoxication, supposedly bringing on the state of hibernation. *See* diapause.

Asymptotic populations. Pearl '25:ii, *Biol. of Pop. Growth.* Populations which have attained a size beyond which they will not increase, no matter how long it is allowed to reproduce, providing environmental conditions remain unchanged.

Atavistic form. A reversion to the primitive form; a "throwback."

Ateliosis. J:422 (Gates). Dwarfism (normal proportions but reduced size).

Athermobiosis. Shelford '29:160; Uvarov '31:109 (Roubaud). The retarding under the influence of temperature of metabolic activity in an animal about to go into hibernation, the implication being that the excretory organs "purify" the organism which can then resume development.

Atlantic type of distribution. J:38 (Watson). Of/ British plants which occur most frequently toward the west coast of England.

Atmobios. Friederichs '30:378. Organisms living in the air.

Atoll. 1. A coral island or islands consisting of a belt or coral reef surrounding the area of a supposed formerly existing island. 2. Clements '16:24 (Macmillan). Circular zones of Sphagnum due to a season of regression of the water of a pond, followed by a year of increase in area and level.

Atrophic. Chapman '31:160 (Handlirsch). Of/ organisms eating no food.

Attrita, terra. Clements '02. Bad lands.

Attrition. = abrasion. See appendix XII.

Aucuparious. J:391 (Heinig). "Attracting birds."

Aufnahme. See Sociological Relevé.

Aulophyte. J:39. One plant living in the cavity of another for shelter only, not parasitic (= Raumparasit [German]).

Aura. Clements '02. Wind.

Auroral. Carpenter '34, Proc. Okla. Acad. 14:29. Of/

the dawn or morning crepuscular period; from the first appearances and influences of daylight to the effect of the heat of the day about midmorning. *See* day, periods.

Austral. 1. Southern. 2. Life zone. (Merriam). "Covers the whole of the U.S. and Mexico except the boreal mountains and the tropical lowlands; divided into three belts: transitional, upper austral and lower austral; the transition zone is the overlap zone between the boreal and austral proper. Chapman '31:221. The northern limit is bounded by the mean daily temperature above 43°F. (corrected from Merriam's original data, the transition area is characterized by the accumulated temperatures of 10,000°F., Upper Austral, 11,500°F., and the lower Austral 18,000°F.). The southern limit is set for the transition by an isotherm for the six hottest weeks of 71.6°F., and for the Upper Austral 78.8°F. *See* appendix V, VI.

Australian region. Wallace and Lydekker. *See* appendix VII, IX. Sclater '58. Australia, with New Guinea and the adjacent islands, New Zealand, and Polynesia.

Australis. J:40. Occasionally applied to plants which are native of warmer regions even if not of the southern hemisphere.

Austro-Columbian zoological region. (Huxley). *See* Huxley's zoological regions.

Austro-Malayan region. Lydekker '96:27. *See* appendix IX.

Austroriparian life zone. (Merriam). *See* appendix V, VI.

Autallogamia. *See* allautogamia.

Autarkean society. Dryer '16, Geogr. Rev. 2:291. Simple independent, self supporting, nomadic or sparse, economic societies. Cf. allelarkean society.

Autecology. III Int. Bot. Congr., 1910. The conditions of environment and of adaptation of individual plant species. (Schröter). The relation of individual plants to their habitats. (Turesson). The ecology of the individual organism. *See* ecology.

Autephaptomenon. J:423 (Gams). Autotrophic types of plants, including those which are semi-parasitic.

Autobiology. (Gams) = Autecology.

Autochorologic. J:423,457. Applied to distribution of plants as systematic units; local botany; plant geography.

Autochthon. J:40. A native species; indigenous. Cf. ruderal, exotic.

Autochthonous. Carpenter '28:207, *Life in inland waters.* Self produced sediments of oligotrophic and eutrophic lakes. ant.: allochthonous.

Autocolony. J:423 (West). The product of a mother cell in coenobic algae. *See* clone.

Autoecious. Of/ parasites which spend their entire life history within or on a single host.

Autoecology. J:423. The environment and adaptation of a species, confined to its habitat by local conditions. *See* autecology, ecology.

Autogamous. Of/ plants which are self pollinated. = autophilous.

Autogenetics. J:457. The study of floral change. *See* phytosociology, ecology.

Autogenic. Tansley '20, Jl. Ecology, 8:118, Of/ succession due to biotic reaction.

Autonereids. J:423 (Gams). Autotrophic water plants.

Autonomous. Warming '09:6. Of/ autotrophic land plants

which possess chorophyll and, as regards nutrition, are independent of other plants.

Autonyctitrophic. J:41. Spontaneously assuming the position usual during the night. *See* day, period, photoperiodism.

Autoorthotropous. J:423. The tendency of an organ to grow in a straight line forward.

Autoparasitism. J:423. A parasite growing upon a parasite, as mistletoe upon a mistletoe. = secondary parasitism, superparasitism; *see* parasitism.

Autopelagic. J:41 (Forel). Of/ plankton which lives continuously on the surface.

Autophilous. J:423 (Moss). Self pollinated. = autogamous.

Autopotamic. J:41 (Zimmer). Of/ algae which have become adapted to living in streams; a modified form of tychopotamic plankton.

Autopotamous. Carpenter '28:171, *Life in inland waters.* Of/ forms peculiar to lakes.

Autoscoliotropous. J:423 (Czapek). Of/ the tendency to grow in a curved line.

Autotrophic lakes. Chapman '31:318 (Birge & Juday). Lakes which are dependent on internal forces for the supply of organic matter. *See* autonomous, autephaptomenon.

Average distance. ESA 1935. List P-3 (Braun-Blanquet). Equals the square root of area divided by density computed for each species.

Avicennietum. J:424. A mangrove community.

Axial Gradient. Child '24:203, *Physiol. foundations of behavior.* Quantitative gradients in specific protoplasm representing a physiological axis and direction of order and a pattern of development. Syn.: axial, metabolic, and physiological gradients.

Azonal. J:43 (Macmillan). Of/ communities lacking any resemblance to radial symmetry. *See* mictium.

B

Backshore. Flattely & Walton '22:36. The portion of a shore which is covered by water only in exceptional storms.

Badlands. Areas which are severely eroded, the gullies being relatively close together in contrast to a ravined area where the gullies are relatively separated. *See* attrita, terra, hydrotribium, tirium.

Bahada. Clements '16:315 (Huntington). Alluvial aprons at the base of mountains. *See* talus, bajada.

Bajada. ESA 1934, List R-1. Outwash slopes of southwestern mountains in the U.S., especially in Arizona and New Mexico, presenting long straight profiles. *See* talus, bahada.

Balds. (Camp '31). "There are two types of Balds which occur in the Great Smoky Mts., the 'heath' bald and the 'grassy' bald. Both types are essentially treeless, the heath being dominated by woody ericaceous species while the grassy balds appear to be consistently herbaceous."

Banados. Hardy '25:153, *Geogr. of Pl.* Shallow swamps (Paraguay). *See* swamp.

Bancroft's law. Adams '15, Bull. Ill. St. Lab. 11:10. "When the animal or community is exerting much influence, we may look upon it as producing a pressure or strain. A condition of stress is not a permanent one, because the pressure tends to cause such changes as will equalize or relieve this condition."

Bank. Hancock '11:431. The rising ground bordering a lake or river; the margin of a watercourse.

Bar. Fenneman '10:29, *Physiog. of west. U.S.* 1. A subaqueous ridge which may entirely span a bay. 2. A spit having one free end. 3. A structure which has risen above the surface of the water and has become a beach.

Bare Areas. Clements '16:41. The important areas laid bare through erosion by water are gullies, ravines, and valleys, sand draws, washes, floodplains and river islands, banks, lake and sea shores, crests and slopes, bad lands, buttes, and monadnocks. Other important factors in the creation of bare areas are wind, gravity, and ice. Primary bare areas are due to extreme conditions as to water content, possess no viable plant germules of other than pioneer species, require long and continued reaction before they are ready for climax stages, and give rise to long seres.

Bark inhabitants. *See* endophloic.

Barotaxis. Taxic response to mechanical or barometric stimulus.

Barotropism. Tropic response of organisms to change in barometric pressure.

Barren. Hancock '11:432. A tract of barren or elevated land on which grow small trees but not timber. Sears '26, Ohio Jl. Sci. 26:130. A habitat in which tree growth is scrubby, defective, or absent; used alike in cases of deficient or excessive soil moisture.

Barren ground. = tundra.

Barrier. Clements '05. A physical or biological obstacle to migration or ecesis; first used by DeCandolle, 1820. Clements '16:77. Any topographic feature or any physical or biological agency that restricts or prevents invasion.

Basal Area. 1. ESA 1933, List P-1. The area of cross section of a tree, usually expressed in square feet, and usually referring to the section at breast-height. The sum of the basal areas of trees in a forest stand is the basal area of the stand, and is usually expressed in square feet per acre. ESA 1934, List R-1. Has come to mean the sections at $4\frac{1}{2}$ ft. above the ground; occasionally may mean one-half of the total height, but is then so stated. 2. See ground cover, basal cover.

Basal cover. Sarvis '23:20, U.S.D.A. Dept. Bull. 1170. The ground surface actually covered by plants. See basal area, 2.

Basal metabolism. Shelford '29:172. Standard metabolism at 20°C. with animals of standard size, age, diet, and treatment after making a deduction for the heart and respiratory action. Basal metabolism is about 25 percent of standard metabolism.

Base leveling. See peneplain.

Bates's theory of Mimicry. Hancock '11:117 (Wallace). "The imitative species occur in the same area and occupy the same station as the imitated; are always the more defenseless, are always less numerous in individuals, and differ from the bulk of their allies; the imitation however minute is external and visible only, never extending to internal characters or to such as do not affect the external appearance. See mimicry.

Bathile. Klugh '23, Ecol. 4:372. Of/ lake bottoms of

deep water, below 25 meters. *See* benthos, ocean.

Bathybic. J:46 (Forel). Applied to the deepest plankton, or pertaining to the life on the sea bottom.

Bathyphytia. Clements '02. Lowland plant communities.

Baumschnicht. Braun-Blanquet & Pavillard '30. Tree stratum. *See* stratification.

Beach. *See* agad, agger arenae, cheradium, agium, aigialium, litus, shore.

Begleiter. Braun-Blanquet & Pavillard '30. Companion species; associates.

Behavior, dynamic. J:424. That part played by the species in the development of the community. *See* dominance.

Belisand. Clements '16:90. Heath sand having an extreme poverty in regard to soil nutrients since humus-formed acids have been removed by percolation of water.

Belt. III Int. Bot. Congr., 1910:28. The differentiation of vegetation into bands which succeed one another from the base of a mountain to the summit (altitudinal belts) or downwards from the sea level into the depths (benthos belts). Braun-Blanquet & Pavillard '30. Zones of vegetation in mountain altitudes, and those created by edaphic conditions, e.g., more or less concentric zones on the borders of lakes, streams, etc. *See* zonation.

Belt transect. J:47. A strip of a few yards or feet in width with its constituent plants recorded. *See* quadrat.

Benthic. Klugh '23, Ecol. 4:371. Of/ sea bottom; frequently divided into littoral, sublittoral, profundal, and abyssal (*see* Eggleton '31, Ecol. Monogr. 1:245). Cf. pythic, pertaining to lake bottoms. ESA 1935. List

P-3 (Johnstone). Of/ organisms which live on the bottom either of the ocean or fresh water, especially those "that are rooted, stalked, or attached in other ways to the rocks, stones, or other solid objects on the sea floor; that are sedentary or nearly so in habit; that burrow in the deposits, that crawl about sluggishly on the bottom or, at the best, have only a limited migration."

Benthos. Chapman '31:285 (Johnstone). All those organisms which live on the sea bottom either on the foreshore between the tide marks or below the low water mark down to the greatest depths known. Friederichs '30:378. Motile organisms of deep water habitats. *See* belt, benthic.

Benthos-belts. *See* belt.

Benthophyte. J:47. A plant whose habitat is at the bottom of the sea, lake, or stream. *See* benthic, pythic, lake, stream.

Bentho-potamous. Carpenter '28:172, *Life in inland waters*. Forms living on the bottom of a river or stream.

Bergmann's law (of faunistic distribution). Mell '29, Lignan Sci. Jl. 8:187. The maximum size of a species is found in the optimal region of its range.

Bestand. (German) = unit area. (Hock) = Association.

Biferae. J:424. Plant flowering twice a year. *See* aspection.

Biflorous. J:424. Flowering in autumn as well as in spring. *See* aspection.

Biliski's formula (Growth rates / space). Allee '31:115.

$$y = k \frac{\sqrt{x}}{x - 1}$$

y: size of organism, x: number of animals per unit space.

Binding species. Nichols '23, Ecol. 4:158 (Cooper). Floristically co-ordinating species which bind together an Association or community (Association type). *See* allochoric.

Biochore. Raunkiaer '34 ('08). Biological boundary lines based on Biological Spectrum data. ESA 1935. List P-3 (Koppen, Raunkiaer). Climatic boundary in biological plant geography based upon the statistics of life-forms.

Bioclimatic law. Shelford '29:5 (Hopkins). "Other conditions being equal, the variation in the time of occurrence of a given periodic event in the life activity in temperate North America is at the general average rate of 4 days to each degree of latitude, 5 degrees of longitude, and 400 feet of altitude; later northward, eastward, and upward in spring and early summer, and the reverse in late summer and autumn."

Bioclimatic zonation (Cook). *See* areas of normal, possible, occasional abundance.

Biocoenology. ESA 1935. List P-3. The study of the community including the quantitative and qualitative analysis of the community, synecology, succession, geography, and systematics of communities. This term combines well to form such words as "bryocoenology," "Phytocoenosis," etc.

Biocoenose. = Biocoenosis. 1. First used by Möbius ('77; *see* Rep. U.S.F.C. 1880 [8]:683) in sense of a climax community but "since has been used too loosely and now has no more force than community"—Shelford '32, Ecol. 13:117. J:424 (Gams). The common vegetation of a unitary habitat. Klugh '23, Ecol. 4:370. A community of living things in possession of a definite territory. Uvarov '31:160. An ecological unit comprising both the vegetable and animal population of a habitat. *See* community. 2. Bailey '25, Bot. Gaz. 80: 93. Any interrelationship between plants and animals. = symbiosis, biocoen.

Biocoenotic connection. Friederichs '30:29. A small or large community of organisms bound together by definite, although sometimes indirect relationships, as those of a plant species with phytophagous insects and their parasites. (*See* coaction.)

Biological factors. III Int. Bot. Congr., 1910:24. The influence of one plant on another (soil bacteria, shade plants, parasites, etc.) and the influence of animals (soil fauna, pollinators, dispersers, enemies, etc.).

Biological races or species. J:50. Races or species which differ only in their physiological behavior, being morphologically identical. *See* ecad, biotype.

Biological spectrum. Raunkiaer '34. A means of expressing the relative percentages of species belonging to the various life forms of plants in a given area. The "normal" spectrum for the world is:

		Percent			Percent
S	Stem succulent	1	Ch	Chamaephytes	9
E	Epiphytes	3	H	Hemicryptophytes	27
MM	Mega- and Meso-		G	Geophytes	3
	phanerophytes	17	HH	Helo- and Hydro-	
N	Nanerophytes	20		phytes	1
			Th	Therophytes	13

Braun-Blanquet & Pavillard '30. A list of the categories of life forms with the number of species of each category in the constitution of the population. *See* Biochore.

Biomass. Bogorov '34. Jl. Mar. Biol. Assoc. U. K. 19: 585. The quantity of plankton substance in weight.

Biome. A biotic community; usually applied to communities of the rank of formations.

Biomes. J:424 (Clements). Evidences of past human communities and climates.

Biometer. Shelford '29:62. Organisms which may be used as indicators of the conditions or suitability of a climate. *See* phytometer, zoometer.

Bion. J:50. An individual morphologically and physiologically independent.

Bionomics.=Autecology (used more loosely).

Biont. J:424. A living being.

Biosociology. (Du Rietz). The life of organisms in communities. = synecology; *see* ecology.

Biosphere. J:424 (Clements). The immediate part between the atmosphere and the geosphere where life is lived; vegetation is the controlling influence on land.

Biospheric. J:425 (Adams). Agency of plants in the migration of peoples.

Biotic factors. The results of interrelations of organisms to each other from an ecological viewpoint.

Biotic potential. Shelford '29:382 (Chapman). The quantitative expression of the dynamic power of a species which is pitted against the resistance of the environment. Chapman '31:182. The inherent property of an organism to survive, i.e., to increase in numbers; the potential power that an organism has to reproduce and survive in its environment. Graham '33, Ann. Ent. Soc. Am. 26:300 (Chapman). The inherent ability of an organism to reproduce and survive, within a given time, and under optimum environmental conditions.

Biotope. ESA 1935. List P-3 (Gams). The life area of the smallest space; refers to the microhabitats within the phytocoenosis, as subterranean, terrestrial, epixylic, epilithic, etc., the herb stratum, shrub stratum, etc. A tree would simultaneously exist in several biotopes, i.e., mycorrhiza, soil bacteria, etc., occupy a distinct biotype; epixylic mosses and lichens on the bark of the trunk of another biotype; while the canopy presents yet another in which epiphytes and numerous animals may exist entirely or in part. And yet, the tree as a whole occupies a certain habitat in the larger sense, i.e., the phytocoenosis is a complex of biotopes. *See* habitat.

Biotype. DuRietz '30:294. Homogenous populations composed only of genotypically identical individuals; either a clone (Klon) or a pure line. *See* ecad.

Bipolarity. Pearse '26:110 (Pfeffer). The concept that the arctic and antarctic biota are homologous and are derived from the fauna of the early tertiary.

Bird attracting. *See* aucuparius, ornitho-.

Bisect. (Shantz). The relation of root system to water penetration and the influence of developing vegetation upon it graphically represented in a double transect. Clements '16:432. The indication of the vertical and lateral relations of individuals by means of a cross-section showing the roots and the shoots in their normal position.

Blastochore. Clements '05. A plant distributed by offshoots.

Blowout. Hancock '11:432. An excavation in sandy

ground produced by action of the wind. *See* anemad, anemium, sand communities.

Bodenschicht. Braun-Blanquet & Pavillard '30. Ground stratum; *see* stratification.

Bog. Hancock '11:430. A quagmire or wet, spongy ground where any heavy body is likely to sink. Sears '26, Ohio Jl. Sci. 26:131. A depression filled or filling with peat. Needham & Lloyd '16:89. An area overgrown with sphagnum or bog moss. ESA 1933, List P-1. The term sphagnum bog is defined as that stage in the physiographic succession of an area during which its surface is entirely devoid of ordinary "hard" soil and is composed almost entirely of living sphagnum, immediately under which is a fibrous brown peat composed mainly or entirely of partially disintegrated sphagnum, the habitat exercising a distinctly selective influence on its flora. Also used in a broad sense to include acid bogs including the moor (Tansley), sphagnum bog (Rigg) and circumneutral bogs, fens at one extreme and fen moors (= transition moors [Tansley]) on the other which include many so-called swamps, tamarack bogs, cedar bogs, cedar swamps, mixed bogs, and others. It is considered by Kurz '28, Ecol. 9:56, that the presence of peat is essential for the recognition of a bog! ESA 1934, List R-1. The vegetation complex which develops in un- or imperfectly drained localities; it comprises a series of stages involving certain characteristic sedges, ericaceous shrubs, and sphagnum, invading open water or becoming established on a solid substratum, culminating, where complete development is possible, in a forest of characteristic conifer species. *See* climbing bog, muskeg, oxodic, torfaceous, swamp, marsh, moor, fen, heath.

Bog-moss xerophyte. J:531 (Clements). Plants presenting the appearance of xerophytes though growing in water.

-bole. Clements '05. Combining term for propulsion.

Bolochore. A plant distributed by propulsion.

Boreal. Northern.

Boreal Life Zone. Folsom '26:332 (Merriam). One of the three major life zones of No. Am.; it covers the northern part of the continent to the northern boundary of U.S. except on mt. ranges where it comes further south. Subdivided into arctic-alpine, Hudsonian, and Canadian. Chapman '31:221 (Merriam). The governing temperature for the southern limit, for the six hottest weeks of the year is a mean temperature of 64°F. See appendix V, VI.

Boschveld. Hardy '25:239, *Geogr. of Plants*. Parkland of northern Transvaal.

Bradycarpic. J:425. Fruiting after winter, in the second season after flowering. See aspection.

Bradyspore. J:425. (Ulrich). A plant which disperses its seeds slowly.

Breast height. ESA 1934, List R-1. A height of 4½ feet above the average ground surface or above the root collar, the diameters of standing trees being ordinarily measured at this height (abbreviation d.b.h.).

Bromatium. A swelling on a fungus tended by ants and serving as a source of food for the latter.

Bronzing. J:426 (Harshberger). A form of sun-scorch, due to want of moisture in the soil, or deficit in root action during hot dry periods. See sun.

Brood. For suggestions on the use of this term (in such forms as cicadas, etc.) *see* Prell '30, Ann. Ent. Soc. Am. 23:27.

Brook. Hancock '11:430. A natural stream of water smaller than a river or creek. *See* stream.

Brotiocolous. Hancock '11:420. Inhabiting man's houses. *See* culture community.

Brotion = Brotium. Clements '05. A succession caused by man. = subsere.

Brotochores. Clements '05. Dispersion by man.

Browse. *See* density of browse.

Buffalo wallow. Barkley & Smith '34, Proc. Okla. Acad. 14:47. A depression in prairie caused by cattle hooves resulting in denudation and a loosening of dirt in the fight of cattle against insects; not of geologic formation. Jewell '27, Ecol. 8:294. Small more or less temporary bodies of standing water occupying depressions in the prairie, enlarged and packed by the wading and wallowing of bison and more recently cattle in them. *See* pond.

Buffer. 1. (field ecology). Term applied to an area surrounding an observational area whose purpose is to protect the observational area from the extremes of microclimate and effects of environment caused by disturbed areas which may be adjacent. ESA 1932. A region surrounding a nature sanctuary in which the biotic community (especially the vegetation) is only partly modified by man. It is a region of partial protection of nature and may be zoned to afford suitable range for roaming animals under full protection. 2. (chemical). Shelford '29:92. Chemicals such as bicarbonates and acid phosphates which are able to neutralize strong acids with a small change in free hydrogen ions. 3. Swynnerton '36, Trans. Roy. Ent. Soc. Lond. 84:516. A species which, preferred or more available, diverts largely or temporarily, the attention of predators from other species or prey.

Bush. J:58. 1. A low shrub, branching from the ground. 2. (New Zealand). Schimper '03:480 (Hochstetter). True forest.

Bushwood. Schimper '03:162. Woodland in which shrubs are so abundant as to keep the crowns of trees from touching one another. *See* savannah.

Buttress. J:426. Plank-like growth at the base of certain trees.

C

Caa-gapu. *See* rebalsa.

Caa guazu. *See* Selva.

Caa Tinga. J:58 (Warming). Brazilian forests which are deciduous during the hot dry season. *See* sertao.

Caapuera. *See* selva.

Caatinga. *See* Sertao, caa tinga.

Caingin clearings. Pendleton '33, Lingnan Sci. Jl. 12:555. Clearings caused by the cutting out of tropical vegetation for agriculture (Philippines).

Calcipete. J:426 (Drude). Dwelling in chalky soils.

Calcipetrile. Klugh '23, Ecol. 4:374. Of/ basic rock communities.

Calina. The term applied to the fine dust occurring on the plains of New Castile, Spain.

Camnium. Clements '05. A succession due to cultivation. = subsere. *See* culture community.

Campestrian. (Seton). Of/ the northern great plains area; Arid Transition of Merriam.

Campine. Warming '09:289 (Pechuel-Loesche). Congo savannahs.

Campo. Warming '09:296. Transition area from grass-steppe to savannah. J:62. Brazilian savannahs, low open woods with ground vegetation.

Campo vero. Hardy '25:142. *Geogr. of Plants*. Treeless savannahs (= plain) in Brazil. *See* abertos, serrados, capoes.

Cañada. A small canyon.

Canadian life zone. (Merriam) Folsom '26:332. A portion of the boreal life zone exclusive of the Transcontinental coniferous forest (Hudsonian) and the beyond timberline areas (arctic-alpine). Chapman '31:221. Southern limit defined by a mean normal temperature of 64.4° for the six hottest weeks of the year. Bray '15 N.Y. St. Coll. For., Tech. Pub. 3:50. Includes the southern boreal transcontinental forest; zone of red spruce, balsam fir, paper birch, and mt. ash. *See* appendix V, VI.

Cane. J:62. The stem of reeds, large grasses and small palms.

Cannibalistic. Chapman '31:160 (Handlirsch). Of/ organisms which eat each other (i.e., of the same species).

Cañon. *See* canyon.

Canopy. J:63. The high leafy covering in woodlands, the uppermost layer in forests.

Canopy trees. J:63 (Warming). Trees having well branched crowns and abundant leafage.

Canyon. J:426. A deep gorge worn by water, between high and steep banks. Hancock '11:431. A deep gorge or gulch between high steep banks worn by water courses; occurring in the western U.S. *See* badlands, ancium, gully.

Capensis region. Diels, *Florenreiche der Erde.* Region including Cape of Good Hope.

Capoe. Palm thicket (Brazil).

Capoeira. *See* selva.

Capoes. Hollows in palm forests (Guiana, So. Am.). Hardy '25, *Geogr. of Plants.* Evergreen trees occurring in the hollows of the campos veros (Brazil).

Carnivorous. Chapman '31:160 (Handlirsch). Of/ organisms eating entire animals, especially the meat portions. Cf. cannibalistic.

Carolinian life zone. (Merriam). *See* appendix V, VI.

Carphospore. Clements '05. A plant with dissemules possessing a scaly or chaffy pappus.

Carpohylile. Klugh '23, Ecol. 4:373. Of/ a dry forest community.

Carpolochmis. Klugh '23, Ecol. 4:373. A dry thicket community.

Carpophagous. Chapman '31:161 (Handlirsch). Of/ organisms which feed on fruits and seeds.

Carpostrote. Clements '05. A plant migrating by means of fruits.

Carr. J:66 (Tansley). A community of scattered trees and shrubs progressing from fen to scrub.

Carrasco. Hardy '25:142, *Geogr. of Plants.* Low bush communities on rock wastes (Brazil).

Carse. = fen.

Castanhal. *See* selva.

Caste. One of the several life forms assumed by certain of the colonial insects; they are frequently designated by apparent occupations within the colony (as soldiers, workers, etc.); a type of polymorphism.

Casual. J:66 (Watson). Of/ occasional weeds of cultivation, which are not naturalized. *See* ruderal.

Catarobic. ESA 1935. List P-3. An adequate medium in which slow decomposition of organic material is proceeding, giving off some organic by-products into the medium and using a considerable amount of oxygen, but not enough to reduce the oxygen concentration below that required by most aerobic organisms. *See* Oligosaprobic, Polysaprobic, and Mesosaprobic.

Catchment. A unit of drainage area; a watershed.

Cave. Hancock '11:433. An underground hollow place or cavern. *See* trogocolous, cavernicolous.

Cavernarius. J:68. Growing in caves.

Cecidium. J:68. Galls produced by fungi or insects, in consequence of infection; an abnormal growth.

Ceinture. *See* zonation.

Cenophytic. J:427. = cenozoic geological era.

Cenosere. Clements '16:289. The eosere of the cenozoic geological period. = Angeosere. J:427. The geologic period marked by the change in plant dominance, from Gymnosperms to Angiosperms.

Cenosis. Klugh '23, Ecol. 4:369. A community having several dominants. = community.

Center of dispersal. An area in the range of a species which is well fitted for the species and from which it spreads in large numbers; may or may not be the center of origin or distribution.

Center of distribution. A common region where the ranges

of several often unrelated species overlap and have an environment at this point suitable for all of the species in question.

Center of origin. An area from which all of a given taxonomic group have originated and since spread; for criteria in determining such a center, *see* Adams '05, Biol. Bull. 3:115, or Ruthven '20, Geogr. Rev. 10:241.

Centrospore. Clements '05. A plant with spiny dissemules.

cH. J:427 (Atkins). Hydrogen ion concentration in soil. *See* pH.

Chain of attack. Swynnerton '36, Trans. Roy. Ent. Soc. Lond. 84:516. A series of species of animals and plants associated as attackers and attacked and regarded in the sequence in which each member of the series feeds on or destroys one or more of the other members. (*See* food chain).

Chalicad. A gravel slide plant.

Chalicium. Clements '05. A gravel slide community.

Chalicodium. Clements '02. A gravel slide community.

Chalicophilous. Dwelling on gravel slides.

Chalicosporae. J:427 (Clements). Plants disseminated by movements of earth and soil.

Chalk. *See* gypophous.

Chamaephyte. Raunkiaer '34:1,34. Plants whose surviving buds or short apices are born on shoots very close to the ground or on it. Suffruticose C.: the aerial shoots are erect and negatively geotropic; at the beginning of the unfavorable season die back to the portion bearing the surviving buds. Passive C.: shoots persistent, but procumbent. Active C. shoots persistent, transversely geotropic in light; procumbent. Cushion C.: passive chamaephytes, procumbent by virtue of weak vegetative shoots. Braun-Blanquet & Pavillard '30. Phanerogams with vegetative organs from 25-30 cm. above the soil.

Chamaephyte climate. Raunkiaer '34('08):143. "Cold Zone."

Chanar steppe. J:72 (Grisebach). Regions in Argentina predominating in legumes and composites.

Chapadas. Hardy '25:143, *Geogr. of Plants.* Flat elevated grass table lands (Brazil).

Chaparral. J:72. 1. Dry shrubby regions, the plants consisting mainly of broadleaf evergreen thorny shrubs or leafless in the summer. 2. The vegetation of such a region.

Character plants. III Int. Bot. Congr. 1910:25 (Brockman). Species occurring only in the community under consideration. = characteristic species, exclusive species.

Characteristic species. Elton '27:12, *An. Ecol.* Species which occur in particularly large numbers in a community, although not necessarily confined to it. *See* exclusive species, differential species.

Character species. ESA 1935, List P-3. Braun-Blanquet & Pavillard '30. Those species of high fidelity, i.e., of class 3 to 5, preferring, especially in, or exclusively of a certain kind of plant community. Class 5, exclusive species; class 4, selective spp.; class 3, preferential spp.; class 2, companion and indifferent spp.; class 1, accidental spp. and "strangers." *See* Fidelity.

Charophytes. J:427. Plants related or having the aspect of the genus Chara.

Chasmophile. J:428. Cranny loving plant.

Chemosynthetic. J:428. Responsive to chemical action. *See* phototropism.

Chemozoophobe. J:43. A plant which defends itself against insect or other animal attack by tannin, etc.

Chena. Clements '16:275 (Pearson). Scrub forest produced by the burning of low-country forest; possesses an undergrowth of shrubs (Ceylon).

Cheradium. Clements '02. A sand bar community.

Cheradophilus. Dwelling in sand bars. *See* sand community.

Cherogens. J:428. Continental soils developed under a small range of rainfall, permanently grass covered, as the Russian black soils.

Chersic. Warming '09:136. Of/ communities of wasteland.

Chersium. Clements '02. A dry waste community.

Chersophilus. Dwelling in dry waste lands.

Chilile. Klugh '23, Ecol. 4:372. Inshore lake bottoms, down to 6 meters. Cf. pythic.

Chilling. J:428 (Coville). Exposure of perennial plants to wintry cold, as necessary for early growth in the spring. *See* dormancy.

Chimnochlorous. J:73. Of/ plants whose thin herbaceous leaves persist through the winter.

Chimnopelagic. J:73 (Forel). Of/ plankton found on the surface of bodies of water only in winter.

Chimnophilous. J:73 (Ludwig). Of/ organisms whose chief development takes place in the winter season. *See* hiemal.

Chionic. Klugh '23, Ecol. 4:373. Of/ snow fields.

Chionium. Clements '05. A snow-plant community.

Chionophytia. Clements '02. Snow-plant communities.
Chledium. Clements '02. A waste community.
Chledophilus. Dwelling in waste places.
Chomophyte. ESA 1934, List R-1. Plants growing in fissures or crevices in rock, and on ledges where rock debris has accumulated.
Chomophytes. J:75 (Simmons). Ruderal plants.
-chore. Clements '05. Suffix for an agent of migration.
Chorologic. J:428 (Rübel). Topographic.
Chorology. III Int. Bot. Congr. 1910:22 (Jaccard). The study of migrations and of the areas of distribution. = phyto- and zoogeography.
Chott. J:428. A salt spot in the Algerian desert. *See* shot.
Chresard. Clements '05. The available water of the soil; the physiological water content.
Chronology. Braun-Blanquet & Pavillard '30. The pure and simple study of the historical order of substitution or transformations of the vegetation (e.g., pollen analysis of peat.) J:428 (Rübel). The appearance of plants in the history of the earth.
Circle of vegetation. Braun-Blanquet '32:365. The highest unit of vegetation classification in the B-B. system on a floristic basis; includes the totality of the communities and associated species that are confined (or largely so) to a natural vegetation region. *See* community, zonation.
Cisternepiphyte. J:79 (Schimper). A type of epiphyte in which the roots are mere supports or altogether suppressed, and the entire nourishment takes place by the leaves.
Cistus-maqui. J:79. A mass of mostly evergreen vegeta-

tion in the Mediterranean region largely composed of Cistus spp.

Cladina heath. J:429. Barren peaty lands with large quantities of the lichen Cladina.

Clan. Clements '16:134. . . . . composed of secondary species, is local or restricted to a few small scattered areas, is more or less permanent feature of climax communities or of consocies which exist for a long time. Woodbury '33, Ecol. Monogr. 3:166. A group of organisms (individuals, mores, or colonies) occupying a recognizable horizontal division of a unit area; similar in concept to a small "association;" = colony (Weaver & Clements). Suffix: -are. Clements, '36. Jl. Ecol. 24: 278. A small community of subordinate importance but of distinctive character, frequently the result of vegetative propagation. Cf. colony.

Class. Braun-Blanquet '32:365. Orders (q.v.) with characteristic common species.

Clastotype. J:429. A fragment from an original type. *See* relict.

Clay. *See* argillaceous, perpelic, spiladophilus, pelogenous.

Cleptobiosis. (Wheeler) = Synclopia (Allee).

Cliff. Hancock '11:433. A high steep rock; a precipice.

Climactic. Pertaining to a climax.

Climagraph. Shelford '29:18. Diagrams in which the mean monthly temperature is plotted against the mean monthly humidity (or rainfall). A line surrounding the plottings of all 12 months gives a graphic expression of the climate at any given station. Term first used by Taylor in sense of temperature/rainfall.

Climate. The sum total and general effects of meteorological factors. *See* ecoclimate, microclimate.

Climatic climax. The only true climax on land. Woodbury '33, Ecol. Monogr. 3:168. A climax in which the climate is the controlling factor. *See* edaphic climax, climax.

Climatic factors. (DuRietz) Factors of the free atmosphere. J:80. The elements resulting in a stable plant community due to climate. Nichols '17, Pl. World 20: 305. All the atmospheric conditions through whose wide spread uniformity the character of the regional climate is determined; coincident with atmospheric humidity, precipitation, temperature, and light. *See* phytobiotic factors.

Climatic formation. Nichols '23, Ecol. 4:162. A complex of associations which are linked together with one another by climate.

Climatograph. *See* climagraph.

Climax. Weaver & Clements '29:75. The community in which an area ultimately terminates; determined by climate. Cooper '26, Ecol. 7:407. A variable approaching a variable rather than a constant idea of equilibrium only. (Tansley & Chipp '26). A community of stable type no further change unless surroundings alter. Phillips '30, Jl. Ecol. 18:201. In equilibrium with the environment, relatively fixed. Adams '15, Bull. Ill. St. Lab. 11:17. A community at a relatively stable condition which is able to reproduce itself indefinitely under existing conditions. The succession leading to a climax represents the process of adjustment to the conditions of stress and the climax represents a condition of relative equilibrium. Braun-Blanquet '32:323. The culmination area of all the seres which lead to one definite climatic terminal community. Clements '16:105. Every complete sere ends in a climax; this point is reached when the occupation and reaction of a dominant are such as to exclude the invasion of another dominant. Phillips '35. . . . . is biotic, animals no less than plants playing their part. = association (Clements). *See* Phillips '35, Jl. Ecol. 23:240 for discussion. *See* aiphytia, association, eschatophyte, quasiclimax, climatic climax, edaphic climax, climactic.

Climax complex. Braun-Blanquet & Pavillard '30. The grouping together of seres of the same final climactic community . . . . generally occupies a very wide territory corresponding to a climatic region (Klimax Gebeit).

Climax units (Clements). Association, consociation, society, clan.

Climax vegetation. J:80. Vegetation growth of a mature age. DuRietz '30:250. The type of vegetation which will not undergo further change under the controlling climate; but rarely composed of a single Phytocoenosis, and more often of several (particularly in Alpine areas, of many) frequently unrelated Phytocoenose which are arranged according to the likewise variable climax habitats (Klimaxstandorten) of a given region.

Climbing bog. Needham & Lloyd '26:94. Bogs on sloping ground of plants (notably sphagnum) which hold water; proceed slowly to cover a slope by growth of the mass of living moss upward over the incline. *See* bog.

Climograph. *See* climagraph.

Clisere. Clements '16:347. The series of climax formations or zones which follow each other in a particular climatic region in consequence of a distinct change of climate.

Clistase. J:429 (Clements). The climax layer of a given stase. *See* stase.

Clistrate. (Clements). The transition strate between two climaxes. *See* strate.

Clitochore. Clements '05. A plant distributed by gravity.

Clivus. Clements '02. A slide or incline.

Clone. DuRietz '30:294. The vegetatively produced progeny of a single individual. *See* autocolony, individual, primary colony.

Closed community. Schimper '03:163. Areas in which more components cannot be admitted and numerous seedlings are continually perishing in the general conflict. (Clements) When the components are so crowded that invasion by other species is very difficult. Waller '21, Ohio St. U. Bull. 25 (9):30. "A plant community cannot be regarded as completely closed until all the levels for abstracting water, minerals, light, and air are filled with sets of species of dissimilar habits and requirements."

Closed forest. Tansley & Chipp '26:204. Closed arboreal canopy; lianes common, grasses generally absent.

Closed savannah. Schimper '03:364 (Pechuel-Löelsche). Consists of densely crowded grasses.

Cloud forest. Pearse '26:262 (Ruthven). Forests above 2200 ft. on mts.; similar to tropical rain forest but cooler and more humid.

Clusium (= Clysium). Clements '05. A succession ot plants on flooded soil.

Clysotremic. Klugh '23, Ecol. 4:372. Of/ tide pools.

Coast. Flattely & Walton '26:36. All areas landward to the water line. See beach.

Coastal. *See* shore.

Codominant. Newcomb '35, Ecol. 16:235 (Shelford). Dominant plants occurring among several dominant animals and present during the entire growing season.

Codominants. Raunkiaer '34:519. . . . . of any species are those species which may occur as Frequency Dominants within the dominance area of the given species; this may be expressed as a percentage of the observations in the region in question. Woodbury '33, Ecol. Monogr. 3:165. Any of equally dominant forms. One of several species dominating a community, no one to the exclusion of the others. *See* dominance, dominant, dominance area, crown class.

Coefficient of association. *See* Shelford '15, Jl. Ecol. 3: 12. Forbes '07, Bull. Ill. St. Lab. 7:273, or Calvert '22, Ecol. 3:163.

Coefficient of Community. ESA List P-3. (Braun-Blanquet, Jaccard) Refers to the similarity of species lists of two regions (or communities) expressed in percentage.

Coefficient of destruction. Uvarov '29:137 (Blunck). The percentage of progeny which must normally be eliminated in order to keep the progeny at a given level.

Coelenterate. J.83 (Boulger) A pitcher plant of carnivorous habit.

Coen. Friederichs '30:233. = Holocoen.

Coenobiology. *See* Biocoenology.

Coenobium. J:83. A colony of independent organisms united by a common vestment, as Volvox, Pandorina, etc.

Coenosis. Friederichs '30:27 (Klugh). A population system held together by ecological factors in a state of unstable equilibrium.

Coenosium. J̄:429 (Gams). A community of plants, further divided as biocoenosium, IsoC., permanent C., temporary C., etc. *See* community.

Coenospecies. Turessn '30. Svensk Bot. Tidskr. 24:514. A variable hybrid of two Linnean or ecospecies. *See* species.

Cognoles. Clements '16:278, Warming '09:327 (Whitford). Grasslands as a consequence of cultivation; small portions of second growth forest which have been cleared and cultivated, then abandoned and burned; also applied to grasslands of the pasture type in the Hawaiian islands.

Cold. *See* temperature.

Collinus. J:85. Growing on low hills.

Colonial. J:85. Of/ weeds of the cultivated land and about houses seldom found elsewhere. *See* ruderal, culture community.

Colonist. Clements '16:248 (Birger). Species which enter after the pioneers and replace them forming characteristic and relatively constant communities.

Colony. 1. Clements '16:134. A group of two or more species which develops in a barren area or in a community as an immediate consequence of invasion. Weaver & Clements '29:53. Initial developmental communities composed of two or more species, each of which forms colonies; if one species only were present, the individuals would constitute a family. Suffix: -ale. *See* aggregation, heteromorphic C., kenapophytes. 2. Woodbury '33, Ecol. Monogr. 3:166. A group or cluster of individuals of a mores or species living together, whether of social or associational value; an extension of the term family used in plant ecology because of its preoc-

cupied place in taxonomy. 3. Viosca '35, Jl. Am. Iris
Soc. (April). A group of plants originating from more
than one seedling and consisting of two or more clones,
more or less isolated from the other groups of plants of
the same species by minor physiographic barriers.
Clements, '36. Jl. Ecol. 24:278. A developmental clan.

Coloration. *See* anticryptic, Bates's theory, mimicry, apatetic, amphichromatism, aposematic, cryptic, epigamic,
episematic, heterochromatism, Müllerian mimicry, procryptic, pseudosematic, pseudoposematic, sematic, Wallace's rule, warning.

-colus. Clements '05. Suffix for habitat forms or dwelling
place indicators.

Commensual. 1. (Van Beneden). A table companion,
Braun-Blanquet '32:9. Those species which enter into
competition separately and their common relation consist in the fact that they simultaneously utilize the various life conditions of a habitat; unequal commensualism involves species which have different needs and
hence are not in direct competition. Warming '09:92.
The relationship which exists between species which
share with one another the supply of food material
contained in soil and air. ESA 1934, list R-1. An
organism that lives in intimate association with another
without essentially benefiting or injuring it; all close
interspecific relationships in which the host is not essentially benefited or injured. 2. Pearse '26:349. An
intimate association between two or more species in
which one or more may be benefited, but none are injured. J:85. Two organisms living in mutual benefit
relations as in the dual lichen theory where the fungus

stimulates the host alga to greater energy of function. *See* symbiosis.

Commiscuum. DuRietz '30a:387 (Danser). All individuals connected by a genetical possibility of cross breeding. *See* convivum, communal connubium.

Communal habitat. Yapp '22, Jl. Ecol. 10:1. The general habitat of any recognizable community such as an association or society.

Communal connubium. Allee '31:27 (Deegener). Groups in which mating is promiscuous. *See* polygyny, polyandry, commiscuum.

Communis J:86. Growing in society.

Community. Shelford '32, Ecol. 13:105. All of the plants and animals of an area. III Int. Bot. Congr. 1910 (Warming). Ecological units of every degree. Phillips '30, Jl. Ecol. 18:201. A general term applying to any aggregation of organisms irrespective of its successional rank. Phillips '31, Jl. Ecol. 19:1. An integrated community of which the plants and animals interact as the co-acting constituents. Fide, Shelford '30. A biotic assemblage of relatively uniform taxonomic composition and of relatively uniform facies. Shelford '25, Pub. Puget Sound Biol. Sta. 5:33. Communities must be determined by dominants rather than habitats; the limits of dominants as such are the limits of the community. ESA 1935. List P-3. A general term used to designate sociological units of all degree from the simplest (as an unrooted mat of algae) to the most complex phytocoenosis (as a multistoried rain forest). = gesellschaft, societé, lebens-gemeinschaft, abschluss, alliance, association, coenosium, province, biocoenosis. *See* above, and complex, province, isocoenosis, phytocoenosis, formation, zone, panformation, associon, socion, consociation, synusium, standort, sector. (Older definitions: Svertzov 1855. "An elementary fauna." Clements '05, Res. Methods. "A mixture of the individuals of two or more species; a group of families.")

Community composition. *See* ecological structure, dominant, dominance, subdominance, influent, subinfluent.

Community-complex. *See* complex, association-complex.

Comospore. Clements '05. A plant with hairy or silky disseminules.

Comparium. = commiscuum.

Competition. Yapp '25, Veroff. D. Geobot. Inst. Rübel 44: 691. The general struggle for existence in which the living organisms compete for a limited supply of the necessaries of life. Clements '05. The relation between plants occupying the same area and dependent upon the same physical factors; . . . . occurs whenever two organisms make demands in excess of the supply; it is a universal characteristic of communities and is absent only in initial stages of succession and is greatest when individuals or species make similar or identical demands upon the same supply at the same time.

Competition curve. Nicholson '33, Jl. An. Ecol. 3:142. A curve representing the success of an individual in terms of intensified competition.

Competitive association. Sherff '13, Bull. Ill. St. Lab. 9: 585. (Woodhead). A group of plants mutually competitive. *See* codominant.

Competitive society. J:86 (Adamson). Two or more species whose roots occupy the same level of soil.

Competitor. ESA 1935. List P-3. A species or an individual which comes in competition with others for food, oxygen, space, mates, or any other factor essential for success.

Complete specific assemblage. Braun-Blanquet & Pavillard '30. The sum total of characteristic and companion species showing a high degree of presence forms the C.S.A. of a community at its optimum development. Such an assemblage is rarely found. Cf. normal specific assemblage.

Complimentary association. J:422 (Woodhead). Two or more organisms avoid competition by developing at different times or at different depths.

Complementary society. J:86. Two or more species which root at different levels in the soil with reference to each other. Seasonal C.S. the condition of different plants using the same ground at different seasons.

Complex. 1. Adams '15, Bull. Ill. St. Lab. 11:9. Natural environments are complexes in the composition of which several factors are involved. Vestal '14, Bot. Gaz. 58: 383. The "associations" within a particular region. See association complex. 2. Braun-Blanquet & Pavillard '30. A mosaic of communities determined especially by the local diversity of geomorphic factors and repeating itself or occurring identically in diverse localities. Cf. mosaic: See concept of "Association abstract" vs. "Association concrete" Nichols '23, Ecol. 4:15. See also association-complex.

Complex, formation. J:430 (Waterman). A higher grade than formation in respect to plants. See formation.

Compositicolous. Hancock '11:420. Inhabiting composites and herbaceous plants. See phytodytes.

Conconnubium. Allee '31:27 (Deegener). The forming of groups of monogamous animals during the breeding period; forming small societies during the period of copulation.

Concresence colonies. Allee '31:16 (Deegener). Secondary colonies arising from secondary union of individuals which are entirely separate for at least a brief period; may or may not be on a genetic basis.

Concretion. Clements '16:81. Soil formation by accumulation of mineral matter into rock or marl through the activity of water plants.

Conditions, geographic. For discussion on the use of terms *see* Hubbard '32, Ohio Jl. Sci. '32:39.

Confoederata. Allee '31:30 (Deegener). Societies of unlike species united by mutual friendship or sympathy and having no other basis; probably without secure foundation according to Allee.

Conifruticeta. J:89. Forest composed of or dominated by coniferous shrubs.

Conilignosa. J:89. Dominated by trees and shrubs with typical needlelike foliage.

Conisilvae. J:89. Coniferous forests.

Conjunctive symbiosis. J:373. S. in which symbionts are intimately blended so as to form an apparently single body.

Connubium confusa. Allee '31:29 (Deegener). A society of both sexes, but of different species, brought together for the breeding season.

Connubium simplex (of metazoa). Allee '31:26 (Deegener). Grouping in which mating occurs between animals of the same species but of different sexes, or between hermaphroditic animals. ant.: communal connubium.

Conodrymium. = evergreen communities.

Conophorium. Clements '02. A coniferous forest community.

Conophorophilus. Clements '02. Dwelling in coniferous forests.

Consere. = cosere.

Consocial. 1. Of/ species consistently found together in a given society or community. 2. Species forming consociations or consocies.

Consociation. 1. Phillips '30, Jl. Ecol. 18:201. A climax community with a single dominant. Clements '16:129. A unit of the association characterized by a single dominant. Weaver & Clements '29:47. An area dominated by one of several dominants of an association more or less exclusively or at least to such an extent that it is more important than any of the others; may be due to minor variation in habitat. Klugh '23, Ecol. 4:369. A community within an association dominated by a single species. Woodbury '33, Ecol. Monogr. 3:168. A morphological part of an association characterized by the presence of but a single dominant among the balance of the biota. Clements, '36. Jl. Ecol. 24:274. A community of associational rank typically constituted by a single dominant, but also including those cases where organisms normally dominant are present in sparse distribution and have little control over the community. Cf. consociule. 2. DuRietz '30:311. A stable phytocoenosis one of whose layers displays the homogeneity of a sociation (therefore of essentially uniform species composition or at least uniform dominants), while in the remaining layers there may be a certain amount of heterogeneity; if nothing to the contrary is indicated the most homogenous layer is the highest. For comparison of the uses of this term by DuRietz, Rübel, Nichols, and Clements, *see* appendix I, II. *See also* consocies.

Consocies. Phillips '30, Jl. Ecol. 18:201. A seral community with but a single dominant. Shelford '12, Biol. Bull. 23:335. Groups of mores usually dominated by one or two of the mores concerned (a physiological criterion). Vestal '14, Bot. Gaz. 58:383. An appearance or representation of an Association characterized by one or several of its dominant species (= facies of certain English workers). Gleason ('10, Bull. Ill. St. Lab. 9 [3]:38) sets up these criteria for determining whether or not two areas are consocies of the same Association: (*a*) no obvious difference in their environments; (*b*) no evidence of succession between them; (*c*) same secondary species in each; (*d*) the dominant species in both are of the same growth form; (*e*) the dominants tend to mix in other areas with the same environment and secondary species. Weaver & Clements '29:48. A developmental consociation. Clements '05. That subdivision of a formation controlled by a facies. *See* consociation.

Consocietum. = community.

Consocion. DuRietz '30:334. A synusium with essentially uniform species composition, i.e., with frequently one or more constant dominants. *See* appendix II.

Consociule. Clements, '35. Jl. Ecol. 24:280. A microcommunity of consocial rank.

Consortism. J:90 (Reinke). = symbiosis.

Consortium. 1. J:90 (Fritsch). The intimate association of "felting" of certain algae. 2. (Reinke). The relations of lichen life. = symbiosis.

Constance. ESA 1935. List P-3 (Braun-Blanquet) An

expression of occurrence of a species in several stands of the same kind of community based (unlike presence) however, on a sample area of definite size in each stand. Constance percentages are more significant than presence percentages because variability of stand area is controlled. This is equivalent to "general constance" as distinguished from "local constance," or frequency. *See* Presence, Frequency.

Constance classes. ESA 1935. List P-3 (Braun-Blanquet) Constance percentages classified on a 5 or 10 parted scale in the same manner as frequency percentages.

Constancy. Braun-Blanquet '32:53. The consistent presence of a species in the plots of a sharply delimited area. Braun-Blanquet & Pavillard '30. A relative expression of presence; can be determined by comparing a number of sample areas of similar and large size, one in each example of a community.

Constant. III Int. Bot. Congr. 1910:25 (Brockman). Of/ species appearing in at least one half of the records of sampling of a given community.

Constructiveness. ESA 1935. List P-3 (Braun-Blanquet) Refers to the dynamogenetic value of the species in the community, or communities related in a successional manner. The species role is described as constructive, conserving, consolidating, neutral, or destructive.

Contaminate zone. *See* Mesosaprobic.

Contiguum. A continuous non-interrupted area.

Continental shelf. Flattely & Walton '22:10. The term given to the ledge usually found surrounding a continental land mass; composed of a continental terrace and abrasion platform.

Continental terrace. Flattely & Walton '22:36. The area

where the material moved across the abrasion platform is deposited; a portion of the continental shelf.

Contingent symbiosis. J:373. The condition of one plant living in the interior of another for shelter, not parasitism. = Raumparasitismus.

Control factor. Nicholson '33, Jl. An. Ecol. 3:147. A factor which responds to an increase in the density of a given species either by increasing the severity of its action against the species (as do natural enemies) or by causing intraspecific competition to decrease the chance of survival of individuals (as does supply of food, habitat, etc.).

Control, biological. The introduction and encouragement of natural enemies as a method of control of a pest (as distinguished from cultural control: crop rotation, spring plowing, etc.).

Control, experimental. Shelford '29:6. Experimental controls have all conditions the same as in the experiment except for one or more factors the effects of which it seems desirable to determine.

Controls. fide Vestal 1933. The less immediate or remote influences which determine the character and amount of factors; frequently not measurable; usually items of the physical environment or topography.

Controls, geographic. For discussion on the use of this term see Hubbard '32, Ohio Jl. Sci. 32:39.

Conversion. Clements '16:157. The consequence of destruction and subsequent progressive development often obscured by the fragmentary condition of the areas concerned. A modified sere.

Convivum. DuRietz '30a:387 (Danser). Populations prevented from hybridizing only by geographic isolation; belonging to the same commiscuum, but each forming a separate convivum.

Copiosae. III Int. Bot. Congr. 1910:25 (Drude). Species mixed with dominants in different proportions but always relatively common; an expression of frequency.

Copious. Clements '05. Of/ species in which the individuals are arranged closely but uniformly. Warming '09:139 (Drude). Species represented by individuals scattered in smaller numbers among the more abundant ones.

Coppice (copse). J:91. A small woods which is regularly cut at stated intervals, the new growth arising from the stumps.

Copraphaga, -phagous. Pearse '26:73. Eaters of feces or of molds and bacteria occurring on feces.

Copraphyte, -zoon. J:430. Flagellates growing in the fecal matter or in the alimentary canal.

Copse. Hancock '11:431. A wood of small growth; a thicket of brushwood. See coppice, woodland.

Corm. Conklin '27:8. *Gen. Morphol. of Animals*. Groups of individuals morphologically united, such as a colony of sponges, hydroids, polyzoa, or ascidians.

Corrasion. The wearing away of rock by any meteorological factor or force: running water, glacier, wind, waves, etc. See appendix IV.

Coryphad. J:431. An alpine meadow plant.

Coryphile. Klugh '23, Ecol. 4:374. Alpine meadows.

Coryphium. Clements '05. An Alpine meadow community.

Cosere. J:431 (Clements). A series of unit successions in the same spot; an organic entity.

Costase. J:431 (Clements). Two or more stases, the record of a cosere.

Costrate. J:431 (Clements). A layer of inorganic matter between stases.

Coteau. Fenneman '31:74. *Physiography of west U.S.* A range of morains, not the stratified rocks on which they rest.

Cotidal line. A line delimiting all areas covered by a tide at any given time.

Cover. Braun-Blanquet '32:31. The area covered by the individuals of one species.

Cover Classes. *See* "Dominance class."

Coverage. *See* "Dominance."

Creatospore. Clements '05. A plant with nut fruits.

Creek. Hancock '11:430. A stream of water smaller than a river and larger than a brook. Pearse '26:195. A small stream which does not flow swiftly. *See* stream.

Cremnion. = Cremnium. Clements '02. A cliff community.

Crenic. Klugh '23, Ecol. 4:372. Of/ springs and the water of their brooks adjacent to their source.

Crenicolous. J:431. Dwelling in brooks fed by springs.

Crenium. Clements '02. A spring community.

Crenophilus. Dwelling near a spring.

Crepuscular periods. The dusk periods of before sunrise and after sunset. *See* auroral, vesperal.

Critical point. Uvarov '31:8. The point at which ice crystals begin to form in insect tissue and the body of the insect rises several degrees. Usually about -10°C.

Cross-timbers. Hardy '25:97, *Geogr. of plants.* Tree islands crossing the uplands at right angles to the river systems; Texas and Oklahoma.

Crown class. ESA 1934, List R-1. All trees in an even aged forest stand occupying a similar position in the crown cover. The crown classes usually distinguished are dominant, co-dominant, intermediate, overtopped, oppressed, suppressed. *See* List R-1, or Jl. For. 15:68-101 for descriptions of the classes.

Crown cover. ESA 1934, List R-1. The canopy formed by the crowns of all the trees in a forest, or, in an uneven aged forest, by the crowns of all trees in a specified crown class. = Canopy, crown canopy, leaf canopy.

Crown density. ESA 1934, List R-1. An expression of the relation of the crown area (or cover) to the land area involved, measured by the extent of shading exercised by tree crowns with due regard to the habitat of the species, site, and age; it is usually expressed in decimal fractions of complete coverage. ESA recommends that this term be restricted to the density of individual crowns, with the substitution of Density of crown cover for crown density.

Cryophyte. J:97 (Warming). An aggregation of microphytes periodically exposed to icy water.

Cryophyte. Raunkiaer '34:1. A plant with surviving buds or shoot apices buried in the ground at a distance from the surface that varies with different species; if buried in marshy soil = helophytes; if in water = hydrophytes.

Cryoplankton. Braun-Blanquet '32:289. Protista inhabiting snow and ice; classified as phytoplankton by Raunkiaer.

Cryotropism. J:97. Movements influenced by cold or frost.

Crymic. Klugh '23, Ecol. 4:374. = tundra.

Crymium. J:97. A polar barrens community.

Crymnion, cryoplankton. J:431. The plankton of perpetual ice and snow, polar and glacial.

Crymophilus. Dwelling in polar barrens.

Crymophium. Clements '02. Polar barren community.

Cryptic coloration. Pearse '26:289 (Poulton). Coloration involving concealing resemblance. *See* Procryptic and anticryptic.

Cryptogamic society. Clements '16:133. The lowermost layer of a thicket or forest often consisting of mosses, liverworts, lichens and fungi; many of them are actually colonies in minute seres.

Cryptozoic. Pearse '26:240 (Flattely & Walton). Of/ animals which live in darkness, subterranean, or in caves.

Culled forest. ESA 1934, List R-1. A cut-over forest from which certain species or size only have been culled.

Culture community. Any community established or unduly modified from its original condition by man, or human or cultural agencies. *See* agrarian, agrestal, agophilous, androphile, anthro-, hemerophyte, arvum, brotium, camnium, ecballium, fellfield, half-culture community, hemerecology, inferagrarian, subsere, secondary successions, segetalis, semicultivated, substitute community.

Cumatophytic. J:98 (Macmillan). Of/ plant modification due to wave action.

Cushion plant. Raunkiaer '34:17. Chamaephyte with surviving shoots densely massed together and usually short in stature.

Cuspate forelands. (Fenneman) Accumulations of drift in outstanding points whose position and form are determined by waves and currents instead of by the initial contour of the shore.

Cut-over forest. ESA 1934, List R-1. Forest from which some or all of the merchantable timber has been cut. = logged over. Cf. culled forest.

Cybele. J:100. Name for an estimation of the distribution of plants in a given area. = floristic list, ecologically annotated list.

Cyriodoche. Clements '04:138. A perfect or completed succession.

Cytotropism. Allee '31:45 (Roux). The coming together of cells of a frog's egg in stage of early cleavage when artificially broken apart.

D

Dauergesellschaft. Braun-Blanquet & Pavillard '30. *See* permanent community.

Day (in sense of 24 hours). *See* diel, diurnal, intradiel.

Day (periods of). *See* auroral, vesperal, diurnal, nocturnal, autonyctitropic, photoperiodism, matutinal, meridianus, nycanthus. nyctigamous, pomeridiamus, tristes, viligae.

Day-degrees. Uvarov '31:181. The number of degrees above a threshold, e.g., of 10°C. per day times the number of days taken to accomplish a given biological phenomenon.

Daylight. Park '31, Ecol. Monogr. 1:192 (Luckiesh). Solar radiation (daylight), diffuse sky radiation (skylight), and radiation variously reflected from trees, etc., are recognized under the popular term.

DENSITY OF BROWSE 77

D. B. H. *See* breast high (diameter).

Deciduilognosa. J:105 Rübel. Communities of trees and shrubs which lose their leaves during the unfavorable periods, and usually have protected buds. *See* woodland, deciduous forest.

Deciduous forest. *See* hiemifruticeta, hiemilignosa, hiemisilvae, therophyllous, deciduilignosa, woodland.

Deckunsgrad. Braun-Blanquet :31. Used in the sense of cover or areal percentage. *See* cover, dominance.

Defertilization. = depollination.

Deformation. Clements '16:297. Changes on the surface (rapid or slow) due to flood or earthquake.

Demersa. 1. Carpenter '28:152, *Life in inland waters*. Applied to eggs which are heavy and sink to the bottom of a stream. 2. Chapman '26:285 (Johnstone) Bottom living forms (cf. benthos). *See* ocean.

Dendrium. Clements '02. An orchard community.

Dendrocola. J:432. Dwelling on trees.

Dendrogaea. Lydekker '96:26 (Sclater '74). = neotropical region. *See* Sclater's zoological regions.

Dendrophilus. Dwelling or inhabiting in orchards.

Denizen. J:106 (Watson). = exotic.

Density. Dayton '31:11, USDA, Miscl. Pub. 110. The relative degree to which vegetation covers the ground surface and often expressed in tenths. Braun-Blanquet & Pavillard '30. Determined by the exact ratio between the number of individuals of the same species observed on a certain surface and the extent of the surface. = Dichtigkeit.)

Density of Browse. (Dayton). That part of the browse (i.e. twigs, shoots, and leaves cropped by livestock from shrubs, trees, and woody vines) estimated from the ground surface covered by that portion of the browse readily available to the livestock.

Dependence. Yapp '25, Veroff. d. Geobot. Inst. Rübel 44:669. A relation between individuals, usually of different growth forms and species, in which one form derives the benefit from the association of the other, the benefit being one sided, not reciprocal. Cf. mutualism; *see* symbiosis.

Dependent communities. Braun-Blanquet & Pavillard '30. Communities of species depending on the presence of more highly evolved communities (e.g., communities of epiphytes in certain forest communities, etc.)

Depollination. J:432 (Brown). The eating or brushing off of the pollen from the anthers by insects.

Deposition. J:432. The addition of fresh soil as by floods. Retrogressive D.: the removal of freshly deposited earth by similar agencies.

Derived. Clements '05. Coming in from other communities. *See* invader, ruderal, exotic.

Desert. Hancock '11:432. Vast sandy tracts of land where evaporation exceeds rainfall. Schimper '03:163. The climatic community which originates when, because of too great a drought or cold, climatic conditions are hostile to all vegetation; transition forms between desert and woodland or grassland are termed semidesert. Warming '09:274. Very dry communities showing very sparse vegetation. *See* eremophyte, eremic, eremium, reg, areg, erg, hamada, khor, litorilignosa, medanos, mobile D., sicciD. travesias, deserta.

Deserta. Rübel '30, *Pflgesel. der Erde*. Regions with little or no vegetation, embracing desert, steppe, tundra, dunes, and fell field. Subdivided into Sicci-D, Frigori-

D, Mobili-D, Rupi-D, and Saxi-D.

Desiccation. A drying out adaptation for existence during unfavorable periods. *See* dormancy, anhydrobiosis, xerotropism.

Desmoplankton. J:108 (Forel). Plankton united into bands or ribbons.

Detrivorous. Chapman '31:160 (Handlirsch). Organisms which feed on animal waste, parts of the integument, etc. (scales, hair, feathers, wax, silk).

Development. Shelford '31, Ecol. 12:465. The growth of communities where no succession occurs. 2. Phillips '35. Jl. Ecol. 23:213. The growth of communities both where no succession occurs and where succession is an outstanding fact. *See* Jl. Ecol. 23:214.

Developmental index. *See* developmental unit (Janisch).

Developmental rates. *See* aliquote, Krogh's law, Arrhenius formula, Van't Hoff formula, medial temperature, medial humidity, subitane development, velocity, Webber's law.

Developmental total. Shelford '29:192, 369. . . . . the sum of the developmental units at the time of completion of a stage in the life history or a certain amount of activity; . . . . the number of temperature-humidity-time developmental units required to complete a stage or life cycle; not a constant but varies with the rainfall of a season, with other weather factors, and with the generation and the individual animal.

Developmental unit. Shelford '29:369. The difference of development between that produced in one hour at a given degree of medial temperature. and that amount produced at the next degree as shown by the difference in time to complete a given stage . . . . the amount of development produced for one hour in conjunction with a mean temp. (°C.) operating for one hour in conjunction with a mean variable amount of atmospheric moisture, and an average amount of air movement, other forces being average. Uvarov '31:23. The reciprocal value of the length of development; "unity/length of time" represents the fraction of the whole development which takes place per unit of time. Janisch '30 (in Uvarov '31:24). The reciprocal value (1/time of total development) expresses the relative velocity of the development and the line based on these values is called the velocity line or index line; any point on it is the developmental index for the given temperature.

Dew point. (Huxley). "When a body of moist air is cooled, the point of saturation is gradually reached; when saturated, any further cooling causes a deposition of dew; this temperature is known as the D.P.

Diacmic. J:109. Plankton having two maximum periods. *See* aspection.

Diageic. 1. J:109. Plants producing stolons beneath the ground. 2. J:433 (Vahl). Plants whose shoots protrude through the soil.

Diaphototropism. J:110. The act of self-placing at right angles to incident light.

Diatropic. J:110. Organs which place themselves transversely to the operating force.

Dichtigkeit. *See* density.

Diel. Carpenter '34, Proc. Okla. Acad. 14:29. Referring to the day in the sense of the 24 hours.

Dientomophily. J:112. The habit of a plant species of which some forms are adapted for insect pollenation by a different species than are the others.

Differential species. Braun-Blanquet '32:59. Species which
appear only in one or two societies but cannot be said
to be designated as characteristic species of any association. Cf. characteristic species.

Diphotic. Clements '05. The two surfaces equally lighted.

Diplobiont. J:433. A plant flowering or fruiting twice
each season. *See* aspection.

Dipterid. J:115. "Fly flowers," those chiefly visited by
diptera.

Directive species. Swynnerton '36, Trans. Roy. Ent. Soc.
84:517. Species the presence of which, instead of acting as a buffer, will tend to draw predators to a site in
which they will also find a species of prey that otherwise might have escaped.

Disclimax. Clements, '36. Jl. Ecol. 24:265. A climax
which is the consequence of disturbance by man or domestic animals.

Diserotisation. Moreau '35, Jl. Animal Ecol., 4:180,
(Huxley & Howard). The phenomenon of cold interfer-
ing with and ultimately inhibiting the process of coitus.

Disjunctive symbiosis. J:116 (Frank). Cases in which
symbionsts do not form an associated organism, but are
temporarily associated, as in the case of insects pollen-
izing plants. *See* symbiosis.

Dispersion. ESA 1935. List P-3. A term referring to the
gregariousness of plants, whether species stand close together in mass formation or are more or less isolated
and scattered. See hypodisperse, hyperdisperse, sociability.

Dissemination. Suffix -chore, -bole. *See* disseminule.

Disseminule. Clements '05. A seed, fruit, or spore modified for migration.

Dissophyte. J:117 (Clements). A plant with xerophytic leaves and stems, and a mesophytic root.

Distribution. Woodbury '33, Ecol. Monogr. 3:169. The geographic localities within the area of a range.

District. Braun-Blanquet '32:355. Characterized by the presence of communities and species which are rare or lacking in adjacent areas.

Ditch. Hancock '11:430. A trench made in the earth by digging for draining the land.

Diurnal. 1. Carpenter '34, Proc. Okla. Acad. 14:29. Of/ that portion of the day which is free from nocturnal and crepuscular influences (chiefly decreased light and increased humidity). 2. Pertaining to daily occurring phenomena. *See* diel.

Diurnation. Carpenter '34, Proc. Okla. Acad. 14:29. The phenomenon of diel (daily) fluctuation in community composition, i.e., within the confines of a single 24 hour day; equivalent to aspection and annuation, the fluctuations from season to season and year to year, respectively.

Divergence. Clements '16. "Initial stages on rock, in water, and on dune sand are identical or similar throughout the northern hemisphere although the climaxes vary widely; this is a consequence of the fact that few species are able to grow in extreme conditions; as a consequence, a few communities form the pioneer and initial stages of the development of a number of climax communities. The result is that the corresponding seres diverge as soon as the point where the effect of the various climates begins to be felt."

-doche. J:117 (Clements) suffix for succession. *See* sere, -arch.

Dollo's dictum. Haviland '26:141. An organism never reverts exactly to its original form, even if returned to its original environment. *See* new place effect (Collins).

Domin. Shelford '35, Ecol. Monogr., 5:259 (Clements). An organism exhibiting a weak type of dominance such as that of the larger pelagic animals. *See* Vedomin.

Dominance. 1. The degree of influence a species exerts over a community. 2. J:434. Preponderance in surface occupied. Braun-Blanquet & Pavillard '30. The extent of the area occupied or covered by the individuals of each species. fide Weese '35. The relation of a dominant to the community of which it is a part. Nichols '23, Ecol. 4:11. Organisms that characterize the community in its larger aspects; they receive the full impact of the environment and so alter it as to affect the habits of their associates; they are usually plants on the land and animals in the water; they typify the life-form of the community and are usually preponderant either numerically or in mass effect. The relation of a dominant (q.v.) to the community of which it is a part.

Dominance area. Raunkiaer '34:519. The region or regions throughout which a species occurs as a frequency dominant (with a frequency-of-occurrence per cent greater than 80 per cent as determined by sample area studies). *See also* codominance (Raunkiaer), dominant, dominance.

Dominance Classes. ESA 1935. List P-3 (Braun-Blanquet) The coverage percentages of the species are separated into 5 classes, most commonly as follows: 1-5%, 6-25%, 26-50%, 51-75%, and 76-100%.

Dominance, degrees of. *See* dominant, subdominant, codominant, influent, major-, minor-, and sub- influents, dominule, Vedomin.

Dominant. 1. An organism which controls the habitat. Jones '26, Ecol. 7:503. An organism so outstandingly well adjusted to a given set of conditions that it becomes controlling wherever these conditions occur. Woodbury '33, Ecol. Monogr. 3:165. An organism that controls the habitat at any stage of development; those that receive the full impact of the environment and so alter it as to affect the habitats of their associates. fide Shelford '30. Dominants control the habitat; they are usually plants on land and animals in the sea and fresh water beyond a light penetration path of about 30 meters in clear water, but may be either in shallower water. J:118. The chief constituent of a plant community. 2. DuRietz '30:307. A species which alone or with several other equally important species forms the principal part of the vegetation of its layer. 3. Nichols '23, Ecol. 4:13. Species which typify the dominant life form. 4. (Clements) Genera which have persisted through geologic times to the present. 5. *See* crown class.

Dominant. Newcomb '35. Ecol. 16:235 (Shelford) . . . . control the habitat biota, being of outstanding abundance or conspicuous influence in the community throughout the entire active or growing season.

Dominant. Nichols '23, Ecol. 4:11. Organisms that characterize the community in its larger aspects; they receive the full impact of the environment and so alter it as to affect the habits of their associates; they are usually plants on the land and animals in the water; they typify the life form of the community and are usually preponderant either numerically or in mass effect.

Dominant percentage. Raunkiaer '34:527. The number of dominants expressed as a percentage of the number of species; the numerical percentage of the dominants.

Dominanz. Braun-Blanquet '32:31. Used in the sense of cover or areal percentage. *See* dominance.

Dominule. The dominant of a microhabitat, such as a fallen log, a carcass, etc. Clements, '36. Jl. Ecol. 24: 280. A dominant organism in any community in a serule.

Dormancy. Shelford '29:150. The case where activity or development (insofar as casual observation is concerned) is spontaneously arrested. This term should be restricted insofar as possible to (*a*) conditions in which further development cannot be induced without internal physiological change; and to (*b*) sleep or inanition in which the normal physiological processes of the active animal are substituted by others characteristically different. *See* (in a broader sense) anabiosis, asthenobiosis, athermobiosis, desiccation, hibernation, diapause, estivation, hibernacula, hypnoplasy, induced dormancy, quiescence.

Down. 1. Clements '02. A dune. *See* sand communities. 2. A tract of open upland.

Drainage. *See* ochetium, erosion.

Draw. *See* alveus.

Dreen. Wright '32, Ecol. Monogr. 2:118. Woodland swamp separating marginal islands from the mainland.

Drimium. Clements '02. An alkali plain or salt basin community.

Drimophilus. Salt loving.

Driodad. A plant of a dry thicket.

Driodium. Clements '05. A dry thicket community.

Dromotropism. J:119. The tropisinity of climbing plants which results in their spiral growth.

Drosphile. J:434 (Errera). Pollenated by dew.

Drought. A period of interrupted or reduction of water supply due to a period of no effective rainfall. J:119. A want of rain hindering plant growth; Physical D.: exists when the soil contains very little free water; Physiological D. (Warming) exists when the soil contains considerable amounts of water which by reason of the character of the soil or weak osmotic force of the roots cannot be used by the plant.

Dryad. J:119. A shade plant.

Dsaengael. Hardy '25:48, *Geogr. of Plants.* Loose scrub land with scattered trees (Arabia).

Duff. USDA, Miscl. Pub. 70. The decomposed and partly decomposed vegetable matter making up part of the forest floor; composed of litter, or humus. ESA 1933, List P-1. A layer of unincorporated humus, distinctly delimited from the mineral soil. The top layer of only partly decomposed dead vegetable material forming a mat or carpet covering the ground. Includes "litter" and "humus." *See* necron, europhyta.

Dulobia. Allee '31:30 (Deegener). A situation illustrated by slave making ants which raid other colonies and carry off the young, which in time take over the routine work of the colony into which they are carried, receiving in return the advantages of being members of the given societies.

Dumetum. J:120. A thicket.

Dumi. Clements '02. Bushes. *See* thicket.

Dune. Hancock '11:433. A hill of drifting sand usually

formed on the shore or coast, but often carried far inland by the prevailing winds. *See* sand communities, thinic, tumulus, xerophorbium.

Dung. *See* copra-, fimetarius.

Duriherbosa. Rübel '30. *Pflgesel. der Erde.* Grasses and herbs which die down in winter; include the continental grasslands of Eurasia and America. *See* herbosa.

Durifruticeta. J:434. Communities of macchia and garigue. *See* above. Dust. *See* calina.

Durilignosa. 1. Rübel '30, *Pflgesel. der Erde.* Broad sclerophyll vegetation. Subdiv. as Durisilvae: broad sclerophyll forest, including the oak forest of the Mediterranean, the Oak-Arbutus forest of the Pacific North America, and certain Eucalyptus forests of So. Australia; and Durifruticeta: sclerophyllous scrub of the Eucalyptus-Acacia scrub of Australia and macchia, garigue, chaparral, phrygana, or fynbosch; of great floristic diversity. 2. J:434. Hard wood plants.

Dwarfish. *See* ateliosis, nanism, stenomorph.

Dy. A soupy type of peat; muck of lake bottoms.

Dyar's rule. Taylor '31, Ann. Am. Ent. Soc. 24:465. The ratio of growth increase upon the head measurements of successive larval instars in insects; Taylor indicates that this is restricted to the Lepidoptera.

Dynamic Behavior. ESA 1935. List P-3 (Braun-Blanquet) The influence of the species on the genesis of the communities of its sere. A species may be constructive, conserving, consolidating, neutral, or destructive.

Dynamic status. Adams '15, Bull. Ill. St. Lab. 11:10. The condition of a unit or system with regard to its degree of relative equilibrium. The initial stage of the cycle is the condition of stress or pressure; the response to the pressure is the process of adjustment to the strain and leads to the condition of adjustment known as relative equilibrium.

Dyschronous. Robertson '24, Ecol. 5:393. Of/ a species, genus or family, which does not overlap in period of blooming, or a group which does not contain species which overlap in blooming periods. *See* aspection.

Dysgeogenous. J:121 (Thurmann). Plants growing on soils which do not readily yield detritus. Clements '05. Weathering with difficulty to form soil.

Dysphotic. Schimper '03:782. The dim region of aquatic environments in which most macrophytes eke out a scanty livelihood or cannot exist at all, while certain accommodating assimilating microphytes still flourish. The deeper situated benthos. *See* dissophyte.

Dysteleologic. J:121. An agent which evades the teleologic end, as a bee which obtains nectar by means which do not lead to pollenation.

Dystrophic. ESA 1933, List P-1. A type of lake in which the water usually has an acid reaction, brown color, and is often associated with peat bogs. ESA 1935. List P-3. An adjective applied to lakes with brown waters, contain much humic material in solution, poor in bottom fauna and characterized by a pronounced oxygen consumption. *See* eutrophic.

Dystropous. J:121. Of/ an injurious flower-visiting insect.

Dyticon. Friederichs '30:233. Inhabitants of the aqueous portion of partially moving media, as mud.

Dzierzon's theory. Folsom '26:286. The concept that queens of a honey bee are able to lay male or female eggs at will and that unfertilized eggs produce males and fertilized eggs produce females.

E

Ecad. 1. Clements '05. A habitat form due to adaptation. Swingle '28:30 *Syst. Botany.* A form arising by adaptation to environment. fide Shelford '30. A form of sessile animal associated with a particular habitat but presumably not fixed. *See* habitat form, habitat races, megecad, Dollo's dictum, new place effect, variad. 2. Stakman '26-7:121, *Mayo Foundation Lectures.* Racial specialization in plant disease fungi.

Ecballium. (Clements). A succession of plants after timber falling.

Ecesis. J:121. The germination and establishment of invaders. Clements '05. The phenomenon exhibited by an invading disseminule from the time it enters a new community until it becomes thoroughly established. Clements '16:68. The adjustment of the plant to a new home, and consists of germination, growth, and reproduction; it is the normal consequence of migration and results in competition. ESA 1934, List P-2. The establishment of a plant in a new location, consisting of three processes: germination, growth, and reproduction.

Echard. Clements '05. The non-available water of the soil from the standpoint of the plants.

Ecidio-climate. Swynnerton '36, Trans. Roy. Ent. Soc. Lond. 84:518. The eco-climate of a very small place. (*See* micro-climate).

Ecize. J:434. To colonize.

Ecoclimate. Uvarov '31:128. The actual climate of the individual; the sum total of the meterological factors within a habitat.

Ecoclimatic forecasting of pests. Uvarov '31:180. The forecasting of pests taking into account the physiological life history and the actual seasonal course of the weather.

Ecocline. Phillips '35. Jl. Ecol. 23:232. The aspect of slope of a community; may be xerocline or mesocline; microclimates are associated with difference in ecocline.

Ecocline. Clements, '36. Jl. Ecol. 24:280. A differentiation in community structure brought about by different slope exposures around a mountain or on two sides of a high ridge. Cf. seriation.

Ecogenesis. Clements '25, Carn Inst. Yrbk. 24:310. The origin of new forms by the ece or the environment. J:12. The origin of ecologic factors. Ecological amplitude. Lundegardh '31, *Envt. and Pl. Develt.* The aptitude of plants to live in a given variety of numbers of habitats.

Ecological-edaphic series. Sukachev '28, Jl. Ecol. 16:15. A series connected with a change of the nature of the soil within the limits of a given region.

Ecological factors. *See* media, factors, controls, phytobiotic factor.

Ecological light unit. Park '31, Ecol. Monogr. 1:222.

$$\mathrm{E\ L\ U} = \frac{PQ + (A{-}P)\ [Sq' + (1{-}Sq)]}{AQ}$$

A: unit area
A—P: shaded portion
P: sunlit portion
S: per cent of shaded area covered by light flecks

1—S: per cent of shaded area not covered by light
    flecks

q: intensity of sunlight in shaded regions

q': intensity in flecked regions

Q: intensity of daylight from unobstructed sun in the
    open parts of the unit area (or P).

Ecological optimum. Schimper '03:44. The condition of
equilibrium in which the plants have their functions in
a state of equilibrium that corresponds to the external
conditions. *See* optimum. J:121. When the surroundings offer the most favorable conditions for the life of a
given organism.

Ecological structure. Nichols '23, Ecol. 4:13. The various peculiarities of the vegetation including the growth
form and the behavior towards environmental conditions and physiological structure; all features of a
community which are of ecological importance; physiognomy is but one expression of the ecological structure. Nichols '23, Ecol. 4:11. Includes all peculiarities
in vegetation which are of ecological significance; physiognomy is but one phase of ecological structure. *See*
community composition.

Ecology. Shelford '29. The science of communities.
Haeckel '66. The science of relationships of organisms
to environment. *See* anthecological, autecology, oecology, bionomics, biosociology, phytosociology.

Economic coefficient. J:122 (Pfeffer). The weight produced by a consumption of 100 parts of the nutrient
material.

Ecoparasite. J:122 (Salmon). A specialized form of a
parasitic fungus when growing on one or more host

species to which it is confined under normal circumstances.

Ecophene. J:434 (Turesson). The reaction of ecotype to extreme habitat factors.

Ecoproterandry. J:434 (Delpino). The maturation of staminal flowers before the pistillate.

Ecoproterogyny. J:434 (Delpino). The maturation of pistillate flowers before the staminate.

Ecospecies. J:434 (Turesson). A species modified to fit its locality. Turesson '30, Svensk Bot. Tidschrift 24: 514. A species by its own right; not recognizably a recent hybrid; two ecospecies may breed together to give a coenospecific hybrid.

Ecotone. Weaver and Clements '29:53. Mixed communities formed by the over-lapping of adjoining communities in the transition areas. Clements '16: Actual transition areas on the ground between two communities, regardless of whether the latter are climax or seral. Carpenter '35, Ecol. 16 (April). First order ecotone: the general area between two major climaxes, as between forest and grassland. Second order ecotone: the actual boundary communities in ecotone of the first order, as forest edge communities in the general transition zone between deciduous forest and prairie. Swynnerton '36, Trans. Roy. Ent. Soc. Lond. 84:518. A transitional strip separating two communities. (See edge effect and interzone).

Ecronic. = estuarine.

Ectodynamic soil. Braun-Blanquet '32:256 (Glinka). Soil whose formation is predominantly conditioned by climate and the resulting vegetation.

Ectotroph. J:435. A parasite feeding from the exterior of its host.

Ectotrophic. Tansley & Chipp '26:158. Of/ mycorrhiza which do not enter the cells of the host but cluster about the outside of the rootlets of the host.

Ecotype. J:434. A habitat type of plant; a subunit of the ecospecies resulting due to the conditions of the environment. Turesson '22, Hereditas 3:211. Products arising as a result of genotypical response of an ecospecies to a particular habitat. *See* DuRietz '30a:355. ESA 1935. List P-3 (Turesson). An elementary species or race naturally selected on a basis of a certain more or less local habitat and climate from the broader "Linnaean species." These genetical groups are broader than the biotype and narrower than the species under usual treatment.

Ectendotrophic. J:434 (Melin). Combined type of parasitism, exterior and interior.

Edaphic. (Schimper). Of/ the influence of the soil on the plants growing upon it. *See* physiographic.

Edaphic characters. Braun-Blanquet & Pavillard '30. Corresponding to the physical and chemical condition of the soil.

Edaphic climax. *See* physiographic climax.

Edaphic climax association. Nichols '18, Trans. Conn. Acad. 22:275. The culminating member of any specific successional sere; in favorable situations this coincides with the regional climax association type which is the most mesophytic type of vegetation which the climate of the region permits on the upland. Nichols '23, Ecol. 4:172. An association-complex which is related to a specific physiographic area; = physiographic climax.

Edaphic factor. 1. III Int. Bot. Congr. 1910:24. Water content, nutritive content, temperature, and other physical characteristics of soil. DuRietz '26. Inorganic factors-complex of the lithosphere and the hydrosphere. 2. Nichols '17, Pl. World '20:305. All conditions which are attributable to soil or topographic agencies. Nichols '23, Ecol. 4:21. Conditions due to the physical structure or chemical composition of the soil, water, or whatever medium plants grow on or in, other than the atmosphere. *See* phytobiotic factors.

Edaphic formation. Nichols '18, Trans. Conn. Acad. 22: 275. Any association-complex which is related to a specific physiographic unit area.

Edaphic formation type. Edaphic formations correlated with a common type of physiognomic unit area.

Edaphon. Friederichs '30:376. The biota of the soil and humus layers of a community.

Edaphonekton. Friederichs '30:233. Organisms living in free soil water.

Edaphophyte. J:132 (Sclater). Plants which root in the earth, with assimilation organs in the air.

Edaphos. (France '21)—Edaphon (Friederichs '30).

Edaphotropism. Tropic responses to soil water.

Edobole. Clements '05. A plant whose seeds are scattered by propulsion through turgescence.

Edominant. Clements, '36. Jl. Ecol. 24:271. Of/ secondary or accessory species which exert little or no dominance in a community.

Edominule. Clements, '36. Jl. Ecol. 24:271. An edominant of a micro-community.

Efficient difference. Clements '05. The amount of a physical factor necessary to produce a change in the response.

Efflorescence. J:123. The season of flowering; anthesis. *See* aspection.

Einzelbelstände. An example of an association; = assoziationsindiduum.

Elective. *See* selective species.

Elementary association. Drude '19 (in Braun-Blanquet '32:25). = facies.

Elfin wood. Schimper '03:704. Alpine forest, distorted by mountain climate. = Krummholz.

Ellitoral. Warming '09:172. Of/ the coastal region below the sublittoral (i.e., below 20 fathoms) and extending as far as the light penetrates. *See* ocean.

Eluviation. J:435. Elutration, decanting the finer particles from the heavier by a stream of water.

Eluvium. J:124 (Boulger). Sand blown dunes. *See* sand communities.

Emerging belt. Schimper '03:789. The belt extending landwards from the low tide mark above the high tide mark to a distance proportionate to the force of the water. *See* ocean.

Emersiherbosa. Rübel '30, *Pflgesel. der Erde*. Communities of fens (flachmoor), sedge swamps, reed swamps, and salt marshes. *See* marsh, herbosa. Emersiprata. J:435. Upper portions of moist meadows.

Emophytic. Klugh '23, Ecol. 4:382. Submerged vegetation.

Empirical threshold. Shelford '29:370. Any threshold assumed or calculated which is not approximately correct for the organism in question. = Imaginary threshold; *See* hyperbolic zero, developmental rates.

-en. Suffix for larger societies.

Enalid. A submerged marine plant growing on the sea bottom, as eel grass.

Enaulium. Clements '02. A sand draw community.

Enaulophilus. Dwelling in sand dunes. *See* sand community.

Enclave. Vestal '18, Trans. Ill. Acad. 11:125. Openings of prairie in forest. *See* thicket.

Encyonemetum. J:126. An algal aggregation in lakes, of Spyrogyra, etc. *See* plankton.

Endemic. Dayton '31, USDA, Miscl. Pub. 110:12. Indigenous or native in a restricted locality; confined naturally to a certain limited area or region. Cf. exotic, ruderal.

Endemism. Clements '05 (deCandolle). Peculiar to a certain region, i.e., in distribution, not origin. Cf. polydemic.

Endodynamomorphic soil. Braun-Blanquet '32:256 (Glinka). Soils whose formation is chiefly conditioned by the character of the underlying soil.

Endolithophyte. Braun-Blanquet '32:289. Lichens, algae, and fungi which penetrate rocks. *See* rock communities.

Endopetrion. J:435 (Gams). Growing in the interstices of rock. *See* rock communities.

Endophloic. J:435. Of the inner bark. = bark habitat.

Endophyte. Braun-Blanquet '32:289. Organisms which penetrate their host or habitat; inferior organisms living under the surface of rocks or in the tissues of plants or living animals. *See* rock community, parasite, endolithophyte, endoxylophyte, endozoophyte.

ENVIRONMENTAL RESISTANCE 97

Endotrophic. Tansley & Chipp '26:158. Parasites or commensuals found within the cells of the host. *See* parasite.

Endoxylophyte. Braun-Blanquet '32:289. Parasites living in plants.

Endozoophyte. Braun-Blanquet '32:289. Protista living in animal organisms, frequently pathogens. *See* parasites.

Eng-forest. Schimper '03:354 (Kurz). Local term for forests of India dominated by Dipterocaprus (Eng being the local name for this tree).

Enhalid community. (Warming). Plants on the loose soils of the littoral region. *See* ocean, salt community.

Entomogamy. J:129 (Kirchner). Pollenation of flowers by insects. = entomophilous. *See* pollenation.

Entomogenous. J:129. Of/ fungi parasitic on insects.

Entomophagous. Folsom '26:373. Of/ organisms parasitic on insects.

Entomophilous. Plants pollenated by insects.

Entphyte. = endophyte.

Environment. ESA 1934, List R-1. The sum total or the resultant of all the external conditions which act upon an organism. *See* habitat.

Environmental complex. Swynnerton '36, Trans. Roy. Ent. Soc. Land. 84:518. The combination of biotic and physical factors together constituting the environment in which a plant or animal is living.

Environmental resistance. ESA 1935. List P-3 (Chapman). The restrictions imposed upon the numerical increase of a species by the physical and biological factors of the environment (e.g., by cold, dryness, parasites, predators, etc.). *See* Biotic potential.

Eoclimax. 1. (Clements). The climax of a given period
of dominance of a given plant group, e.g., Angiosperms.
See eosere. 2. The climax of the eocene geological period.

Eolian erosion. Erosion by wind. *See* appendix XII.

Eophytic. Clements '16:288 (Saporta). Phytological
epoch synchronous with the proterozoic.

Eosere. Clements '16:289. The development of vegetation during an eon or era. Major developmental series
within the climatic climax of the geological era. The
total development of a particular vegetation throughout
a period of dominance (during a geological period) of
a particular group of plants. *See* eoclimax.

Eostase. J:436 (Clements). A series of geologic layers
resulting in part from an eosere.

Eostrate. J:436 (Clements). The sum total of all strates
in the same vegetation or geological era; a succession
after a stase when the inorganic matter exceeds the
organic. The strates of all ages constitute collectively
the geostrate.

Epactile. Klugh '23, Ecol. 4:371. Upper littoral zone. *See*
ocean.

Epeirogenic. J:436. Of/ movements raising continents.
Cf. orogenic.

Ephaptomenon. ESA 1935, List P-3 (Gams). A major
life-form division referring to adnate types and including the following life-form classes: Nereides (aquatic),
Amphinereides (amphibious), Autephaptomenes and
Heterephaptomenes (aerial), Innatao (within rock,
shale, bark, etc.), Endophtes and Endokes (within living organisms as symbionts, saprophytes & parasites).

Epharmone, epharmony, epharmosis. Warming '09:2

(Vesque '82). The process of adaptation of organisms
to new conditions of environment. Hesse '30, Proc. Int.
Zool. Congr. 10:85. All morphological change that can
reasonably be considered as due to a change of environment. A form that differs from the normal or usual due
to influences of the environment. *See* ecad, biotype,
species, growth form. ESA 1935. List P-3. Adaptive
forms which may be classified as follows:
 a) Phenotypic epharmones, "reactive forms" and
    "environmental control" of Cowles;
 b) Genotypic epharmones, "congenital inherent
    forms" of Cowles, "eco-species" of Turesson;
 c) Indifferent, not epharmonic category; the "or-
    ganizations-merkmale" of Wettstein.
Ephemer. J:130 (Rikli). Introduced plants which are
 unable to exist and soon disappear.
Ephemeral. Dayton '31, USDA, Miscl. Pub. 110:12.
 Enduring for a day; evanescent; Richards '28, Jl. Ecol.
 16:292. Short lived communities on bare soil and arable land. *See* culture community.
Ephipytes. Misprint in Braun-Blanquet & Pavillard '30,
 for epiphyte.
Ephydrogamicae. J:130 (Knuth). Plants whose flowers
 are pollenated on the surface of the water.
Epibenthile. Klugh '23, Ecol. 4:371. Of/ sea bottom, low
 tide mark to 200 meters. *See* ocean.
Epibiotica. J:436. (Ridley). Survivors of a lost flora.
 See relict.
Epiclysile. Klugh '23, Ecol. 4:372. Of/ upper tide pools;
 those in which the temperature of the water rises to
 more than 3°C over that of the sea. *See* tide pools.
Epidemic. Applied to a disease or parasite which becomes

widespread and attacks large numbers of plants or animals at the same time; or to an animal which becomes excessively abundant over a considerable area.

Epigamic colors. Pearse '26:299 (Poulton). Colors displayed during courtship.

Epigeotropism. J:131 (White). Tropism resulting in growth on the surface of the soil. *See* tropism.

Epilimnile. Above the thermocline of lakes; that portion which is warm and well aerated by circulation. Chapman '31 (Birge '10). The upper layer of wind disturbed lakes.

Epilimnion. Chapman '31 (Birge '10). The upper layer of wind disturbed lakes.

Epilithophytes. J:436 (Wetter). Plants growing on stone or rock, as is the case of many lichens. *See* rock community.

Epiontology. J:132. The developmental history of plant distribution. *See* geographic distribution.

Epiparasitism. *See* superparasitism, parasite.

Epiphytes. Schimper '03:197. Plants which germinate on other plants and grow without obtaining nutriment at the cost of the substance of the host. Braun-Blanquet & Pavillard '30. Vascular plants living on other plants. *See* protoE, hemiE, nestE, tankE.

Epiphytoid. J:132 (Johow). Of/ phanerogamous parasites presumably derived from an autogamous epiphyte.

Epiphytotic. J:132 (Crozier). Of/ wide spreading diseases in plants as an epidemic.

Epiplankton. J:132. The upper portions of pelagic plankton. (Forel). Floating organisms attached to pelagic organisms.

Epirrheology. J:133. The effects of external agents on living plants.

Episematic colorations. Pearse '26:299 (Poulton). Recognition markings.

Epistrophe. Clements '05. The arrangement of the row of chloroplasts at right angles to the incident light.

Epiterranean. J:436. Of/ the above ground fruiting portion of certain plants.

Equinoctial. J:13'4. Of/ plants whose flowers expand and close at particular hours of the day. See day, periods.

Equivalent area of discovery. Nicholson '33, Jl. An. Ecol. 3:156. The area of discovery a specific parasite would require in order to control the density of the host at the same value.

Eremic. Concerning communities of desert and steppe.

Eremium. Clements '02. A desert community.

Eremophilus. Desert dwelling organisms.

Eremophytes. (Warming). Desert or steppe plants.

Eremus. Clements '02. A desert community.

Erg desert. Hardy '25:206, Geogr. of Plants. Sand dunes forming on the reg desert of the Sahara, caused by wearing down of rocks (hamada). See sand communities, desert.

Ergology. (Delpino). = Biology.

Ericetal. J:135 (Watson). Of/ plants growing on moors.

Ericilignosa. (= Ericifruticosa). Rübel '30, Pflgesel. der Erde. Ericaceous heaths, alpine and arctic heaths, Mediterranean and South African scrub, and areas of similar physiognomy in So. Am. and Australia. Usually correlated with oceanic climate and poor soil. See Lignosa.

Erine. (French). An abnormal growth on the epidermis of plants caused by certain mites of the genus Phytoptus.

Erinea. J:437. Phytoptus mites producing galls on leaf surfaces resembling fungi.

Erosion. Clements '16:39. The removal of soil or rock by wearing away of land surface; for the stages of erosion *see* Clements '16:310; *see* appendix XII. *See* fluviraption, plucking, pluvo-fluvial E., gullying, sheet E., surface E., lateral planation, ochetium, tribium, xerosion.

Errantia. Friederichs '30:233. Mobile organisms.

Eruption year. *See* outbreak.

Escape. J:135. A cultivated plant found growing as though wild, dispersed by any agency.

Eschatophyte. Hansen '21, Ecol. 2:125. Any member of a climax vegetation.

Espalier growth form. Warming '09:26. The form assumed by many sub-glacial plants in which their stems lie on the ground and are concealed frequently by the ground mosses, etc.; the tips are directed upwards.

Espinal. Warming '09:308. Maquis of Chile; thorn woodland.

Essential aggregations. Allee '31:23 (Deegener). Communities of species of similar or dissimilar animals which have a real value for the individuals composing them (the aggregational sense of society).

Esteros. Hardy '25:156, *Geogr. of Plants*. Salt wastes of W. Argentina.

Esthesis. Perception or sensibility to stimuli, also spelled aesthesis.

Estival. Clements '05. Pertaining to early summer. *See* aspection, serotinal.

Estivation. Shelford '29:150. Used in a manner similar to hibernation; the passing of the summer in an inactive state. *See* dormancy.

Estuary. A narrow arm of the sea at the lower end of a river; where the tide meets the river current.

Etage. *See* belt, zonation.

-etalia, Braun-Blanquet & Pavillard '30. Suffix to denote order.

Ete. *See* selva.

Ethiopian region. (Wallace) Africa south of the Sahara, S. Arabia, and Madagascar; the latter sometimes included in the Lemurian region or realm. *See* appendix VII.

Ethnobotany. Relating to plants which illustrate or are typical of the customs of a given race or people. *See* culture community, anthro-.

-etosum. Braun-Blanquet & Pavillard '30. Suffix to denote sub-association.

-etum. 1. Clements '05. Suffix to denote consocies. 2. Braun-Blanquet & Pavillard '30. Suffix to denote association.

Eudominant. Clements '36. Jl. Ecol. 24:260. A dominant of true prairie; applicable to dominants more or less peculiar to or typical of an association.

Eufluent. Clements '36. Jl. Ecol. 24:271. An influent more or less peculiar to or typical of an association.

Eugeopenous. Clements '05. Weathering readily to form soil.

Eugeophytes. J:437 (Massart). Plants with a resting period due to want of warmth or light.

Eulimnetic. J:137. Of/ plankton exclusively of pools.

Eupelagic. J:137. Of/ plankton confined to the ocean.

Euphemera. J:137. Flowers which open and close finally within 24 hours. Cf. ephemeral.

Euphotic. (Warming). Hydrophytes which receive an abundance of light.

Euphotometric. = euphototropic. J:137. (Weisner). Leaves which place themselves so as to obtain the maximum of diffused light, as the foliage of forests.

Euphytoid parasites. J:137 (Johow). Erect land plants, parasitic in habit.

Eupotamic. J:137 (Zimmer). Applied to the plankton of running or standing inland waters.

Europhytia. Clements '02. Leaf mold communities.

Eurotophilus. Dwelling in leaf mold. *See* duff, humus.

Eurybathic. Carpenter '28. *Life in inland waters.* Of/ species which can extend a long way vertically in water.

Eurychoric. J:137 (Drude). Plants having a wide distribution in varying climates and several plant formations.

Eurycladous. J:137 (Forel). Plankton adapted to varying conditions of salinity.

Eurycoenose. J:437 (Gams). Widely distributed, common.

Euryhaline. Carpenter '28:173, *Life in inland waters.* Of/ species peculiar to non-marine brackish water and are resistant to great changes in salinity.

Euryoecic. Not at all or broadly limited by ecological conditions of environment; ubiquitous.

Euryphagous. Pearse '26:72. Of/ animals which have a wide range of food selection. ant.; stenophagous.

Euryphotic. J:137. Adapted to light of varying intensities.

Eurysynusic. J:137 (Gams). Of/ widely distributed groups of plants. Cf. steno-.

Eurythermic. J:137. Applied to bacteria capable of enduring great heat; (Setchell). Species of wide distribution able to withstand diverse conditions of temperature. Pearse '26:34 (Semper, Möbius). Organisms having the ability of living through a wide range of temperature conditions.

Eurytope. Börner '21. Art. Biol. Reich. L.v. Forstw. 10: 413. Of/ organisms spending one or more stages in several habitats.

Eurytropic. J:434 (Solms). Wide adaptation of species to varied conditions.

Eutherophyte. Braun-Blanquet '32:289. Annual seed plants.

Eutrophic. 1. Chapman '31:305. Of/ lakes characterized by the paucity or absence of oxygen in the bottom waters. 2. Braun-Blanquet '32:76 (Thienemann). Waters poor in humus, often richest in calcium, and with a broad zone of rooted plants. 3. (Clements). Swamps rich in nutrients. 4. J:138. Plants which are adapted to live at the expense of nutritive substances present in the soil.

Eutropic.1. J:138 (Gray). Twining with the sun, i.e., left to right, dextrorse. 2. McLeod. Flowers to which only a restricted class of specialized insects can gain access.

Evanescent. Ephemeral; disappearing after a short time.

Even aged. ESA 1934, List R-1. Applied to a stand in which only small age differences appear, differences varying with the age of the stand; in young stands the age differences should not be more than 10 or 20 years; in mature stands, not more than 30-40 years.

Evergreen communities. *See* Aiophyllus, Silva sempervirens, aithallium, conilignosa, coniferfruticeta, conisilvae, conodryium, conophorium, sempervirent.

Excerpt. Torre-Bueno '31, Bull. Brooklyn Ent. Soc. 26: 229. A quotation or selection taken from an article; may be typed or written.

Exclusive species. Elton '27:11, *Animal Ecology*. The animals whose distribution is strictly determined by the type of vegetation in a community. Braun-Blanquet '32:59. Species completely or almost completely confined to one community.

Exclusiveness. *See* fidelity.

Exolithophyte. J:437 (Wetter). Mosses and lichens growing on rock.

Exotic. Of/ any non-native species; introduced. *See* ruderal. ant.:endemic.

Exotrophic. J:141. Pollenated from the anthers of the same plant.

Exponential law. Uvarov '31:30. The concept that development follows a caternary exponential curve on which the two upper critical points are the point beyond which development is not completed, and the point at which death occurs.

Exsiccation. Tansley & Chipp '26:146. The process of furthering desert conditions through human agency or change of climate.

F

Faciation. A portion of an Association in which one or
more dominants have dropped out and been replaced by
other forms, the general aspect of the community remaining unchanged. If all dominants save one drop out
and are not replaced the community becomes a Consociation. Clements '36. Jl. Ecol. 24:274. A local climatic (or micro-climatic) difference within an association characterized by one or two eudominants, or a re-
combination of the dominants of the association. *See*
appendix IIIa.
Facies. 1. A developmental community in the sense of a
Faciation. 2. Pound & Clements '98. The general
aspect of a community. 3. Braun-Blanquet '32:25. A
difference in quantity or distribution of a species especially in the dominance of certain companion species.
4. Clements '05. A dominant species of a community;
a distinct area controlled by it is a Consocies. *See*
appendix I, II, III.
Factors. Fide Vestal '33. Immediate influences affecting
organisms directly; in most instances physical forces;
factors interact and can hardly be isolated in ecological
work. J:438. Elements which contribute to produce a
result; frequently recognized subdivisions: Biotic, Climatic, Edaphic, Geodynamic (latent forces of the
earth), Lethal, Physiographic.
Facultative. Occasional, incidental or "at will"; opposed
to obligate.
False plankton. J:143 (Warming). Forms at first fixed,
afterwards broken loose and floating.
Famile. = family.

Family. Weaver & Clements '29:51. 1. Isolated groups of organisms belonging to a single species (*see* colony). Clements '16. 2. A group of plants belonging to one species; often descendants of a single plant but not necessarily. *See* clone, cenosis, aggregation.

Fastigiate trees. Raunkiaer '34:19. Trees with shoots growing erect, forming an acute angle with the stem.

Fauna hygropetrica. Carpenter '28:142. *Life in inland waters* (Thienemann). Fauna which find lodging in that film of water which surrounds the surfaces of stones not truly submerged clinging to them by surface tension.

Faunula. Friederichs '30:29. The entire animal population of a small unit area, as the intestine of a ruminant, a compost heap, or a layer of a community.

Federation. 1.DuRietz '30:316. A Phytocoenosis of one or more independent stable associations in which one layer is dominated by a definite group of species, frequently of weak sociological affinities (i.e., composed of a distinct federion). The composition of the other layers may vary widely, and the binding Federion may also exhibit a wide heterogeneity. If nothing else is indicated, the highest layer is understood to be the binding Federion. *See* appendix I, II. 2. J:144. The entire and collective plant associations of the world. = biosphere.

Federion. DuRietz '30:386. A stable synusium composed of one or more independent Associons dominated by a definite group of species held together only by a weak sociological affinity; none of the species necessarily extend throughout the entire Association.

Fellfields. J:144. Districts of dwarf, scattered plants,

chiefly cryptogams. *See* cultural communities, wastes.

Fen. 1. Hardy '25:301. *Geogr. of Plants.* Usually reed, rush, sedge, or grass marsh communities. 2. ESA 1933, List P-1. Tracts of peat relatively rich in mineral salts, alkaline in reaction, in the upper parts of the old estuaries, around fresh water lakes, and bearing plant communities distinct from those which characterize the moor soils.

Fence row. Hancock '11:432. A strip of land along the course of a fence left untilled.

Fertilization adaptations of flowers. *See* pollenation.

Feste. Braun-Blanquet '32:58. = selective species.

Field. Hancock '11:432. Open cleared land.

Field stratum. J:146 (Warming). Formed by the grass, herbs, and dwarf shrubs.

Fidelity. Braun-Blanquet & Pavillard '30. The degree to which species are confined to certain communities; types: exclusive, selective, preferential, indifferent, and accidental species. = exclusiveness, Gesellschaftstreu, Fidelité.

Fimetarius. J:146. Growing on or in dung.

Final stage. *See* stage, climax.

Fixity. Clements '05. The condition characterized by little or no response to stimuli.

Fjaeld. Michelmore '34, Jl. Ecol. 22:158. A community which occupies most of the land free from ice . . . . includes all stages between ground with abundance of isolated plants and a barren waste, where only the closest search can disclose a tiny tuft of moss under a stone. Elton '27:10. *Animal Ecology.* Arctic stony desert.

Flachmoor. = fen. *See* Emersiherbosa.

Fjeld. A barren upland plateau (Scand.) .

Flechtenserien. Braun-Blanquet & Pavillard '30. Lichen seres.

Floating. *See* natant, neuston, ploto-, vadal.

Flood. *See* floodplain, clusium, clysium, inundatal.

Floodplain. That portion of a river valley which is covered in periods of high water and is populated by biota not greatly harmed by short time immersions; soil largely alluvium.

Floristic composition. Tansley & Chipp '26:10. The compiled species lists of a number of samples of a given community. Nichols '23, Ecol. 4:11. The kinds of species included in a community; primarily it is the species which typify the dominant life-form (dominant species); but species belong to life-forms of subordinate rank (subdominant species) must be included.

Flos aquae. J:149 (Cohn). Floating algae, as Rivularia.

Fluctuans. J:364. Floating.

Fluitantes. Clements '02. Floating plants.

Flumen. Clements '02. A river. *See* stream.

Fluminalis. J:149. Of/ plants which grow in running water.

Flush. 1. A piece of moist ground where water frequently lies. 2. A sluggish channel. *See* snow flush.

Fluvatile lakes. Forbes '25, Bull. Ill. St. Nat. Hist. Surv. 15:538. Lakes which are appendages to river systems,. being situated in the river bottoms and connected with the adjacent streams by periodical overflows; their fauna is substantially that of the rivers.

Fluvial. J:149 (Crozier). Applied to plants growing on streams.

Fluviraption. Malott '28, Proc. Ind. Acad. 37:153. The act of tearing away or snatching up and carrying away by flowing or running water; exaration is the similar work of ice. *See* appendix XII, erosion.

Food. ESA 1934, List R-1. Any substance as carbohydrates, fats, or proteins, that may be used directly, or after hydrolysis, by the protoplasm for growth and repair or as a source of energy.

Food chain. Elton '27:56, *Animal Ecology*. Animals linked together by food and all dependent in the long run upon plants. ESA 1935. List P-3. A series of species in an association, each of which lives (in part at least) as a predator or parasite on the next in the series. Term used by Elton, useful in analyzing food relations between animals in an association.

Food cycle. ESA 1935, List P-3. A fairly complete analysis of the food relations between the species in an association showing where each species obtains its food and what other organisms in turn derive their food from it.

Foothill. *See* pagophytia.

Forb. An herbaceous plant, not a grass. Dayton '31:14, U.S.D.A., Miscl. Pub. 110. A weed in the stockman's sense; a non grasslike herb. (Clements). = herb.

Foredune. J:438 (Cockayne). The surface of a dune exposed to the prevalent wind. *See* sand community.

Forest. Land covered with trees, usually not greatly disturbed. Schimper '03:162. Woodland in which the trees grow in a closed condition. *See* woodland.

Forest cover. ESA 1933, List P-1. All trees and other woody plants (underbrush) covering the ground in a forest. ESA 1934, List R-1. Includes (*a*) trees and tall shrubs, (*b*) herbs and shrubs growing thereunder or in openings in forest or brush fields, (*c*) litter or fallen leaves, branches, fallen trees, and other vegetative material on the forest floor, (d) the rich humus of partly decayed vegetable matter at the surface and top layer of soil.

Forest edge. The thicket at the edge of an undisturbed forest composed of the forest reproduction and shrubs; functions as a forest wall much as does the forest canopy as a roof with respect to climatic and microclimatic factors.

Forest floor. The ground layer of a forest including dead vegetable matter, litter and the upper humus. USDA, Miscl. Pub. 70. The forest material on top of the mineral soil composed of vegetable matter that is more or less decomposed. ESA 1934, List R-1. The deposits of vegetable matter on the ground in a forest. *See* duff, litter.

Forest influences. ESA 1934, List R-1. All effects resulting from the presence of the forest upon health, climate, streamflow, and economic conditions.

Forest type. ESA 1934, List R-1. A forest stand essentially similar throughout its extent as regards composition and development under essentially similar conditions, i.e., essentially similar throughout as regards floristic composition, physiognomy, and ecological structure. The following types are recognized: temporary, permanent, climax, cover type (*see* Jl. For. 15:68, 1917).

Foreshore. Flattely & Walton '22:36. The area traversed daily by the oscillating water line of the tide.

Forewold. (Clements). = Forest edge.

Form. DuRietz '30a:342. A population of one or several biotypes occurring sporadically in a species population, not forming a distinct regional or local facies of it, and differing from the other biotypes of the species population in one or several distinct characters.

Formation. 1. (Climax-complex). Weaver and Clements '29:43. A fully developed or climax community of a natural area in which the essential climatic regions are similar or identical; the product of, under the control of, and delimited by climate. Woodbury '33, Ecol. Monogr. 3:167. The climax unit of biotic communities, usually including a group of Associations which implies the inclusion of all developmental (successful) steps within its borders; the final stage of biotic development in a climatic unit; the climatic climax of succession which terminates in the highest life forms possible with the available biota in the climate concerned. Tansley '11:9. *Types of British Veg.* The entire set of plant communities on a given type of soil, in the same geographic region, and under given climatic conditions, in spite of diversity of the dominant plant-forms in the different Associations; the whole of the natural and seminatural plant covering occupying a certain type of soil, characterized by definite plant communities and a definite flora. 2. (Phytocoenotic basis). DuRietz '30:318. A stable Phytocoenosis consisting of several independent federations, in which one layer is dominated by a definite group of species, the direct sociological affinity of the peripheral members not always recognizable; however, these are held together by an unbroken series of strong sociological affinities and by certain species traversing the essential portions of the given formation (i.e., a Phytocoenosis in which one layer is composed of a distinct formion). The composition of the other layers may vary widely, and also the binding formion

may as a whole show no floristic homogeneity at all.
If nothing else is indicated, the binding formion is understood as the highest layer. 3. (sere plus climax concept) Klugh '23, Ecol. 4:368. A set of communities
related developmentally and culminating in one or more
associations. Moss 1907:12, Rankin & Tansley 1910,
and Tansley 1910. The series of plant communities
which begins its history as an open or unstable community passing through a closed or stable community.
4. (Floristic concept). Drude 1890, Gradmann 1909,
Negri, 1914, Tansley 1911 and Moss 1907. The whole
of the natural and semi-natural plant covering occupying a certain type of soil, characterized by definite
plant communities and a definite flora; the floristic
composition is the basic and decisive criterion for the
recognition of plant Formations. 5. (Climatic vs edaphic distinction). Schimper (in III Int. Bot. Congr.
1910:26) Plant communities determined by soil qualities; two groups may be distinguished, the climatic or
territorial whose vegetative characters are controlled by
rainfall and precipitation, and edaphic or habitat Formations, the character of which is determined in the
first place by the nature of the soil. 6. (Physiognomic
criterion) Grisebach, 1838, Drude 1905, Olsson-Seffer
'05, Bot. Gaz. 39:183. An aggregation of plants characterized by a dominant species and having a definite
physiognomic aspect. DuRietz '26. An abstract type of
Association based upon physiognomy: "a life form of
communities." Schröter 1902. All of the Association
types of the entire earth which agree in their physiognomy and ecological character, while the floristic is
immaterial. Warming 1895. A community of species

all belonging to definite life forms which have become associated together by definite external (edaphic or climatic) characters of the habitat to which they are adapted; the expression of certain defined conditions of life, not concerned with floristic differences. 7. (Phytosociological criterion). Braun-Blanquet & Pavillard '30. An assemblage of Synusia whose collective physiognomy is the expression of an equilibrium more or less durable with the conditions of the habitat; the Formations of the same physiognomy can be united into groups of classes and in types of vegetation. 8. (Habitat criterion). Clements '02. The unit of vegetative covering should correspond with the unit of the earth's surface, the habitat. III Int. Bot. Congr. 1910:26. The actual expression of certain definite conditions of life; it is composed of Associations which differ in their floristic composition but are in agreement with the conditions of the habitat and secondarily as regards their growth forms. Friederichs '30:37. The biota of any given portion of a life zone, regardless of whether this unit area corresponds precisely with the habitat boundaries or not. suffix: -ium. *See* appendix I, II for a comparison of the present uses of the term.

Formation, closed. J:151. A community in which the plants are so crowded that invasion is difficult. *See* closed community.

Formation dominants. Raunkiaer '34:527. Species which occur everywhere within a Formation with a frequency percent of more than 80 percent.

Formation group. (Rübel, Shantz, DuRietz). *See* appendix II.

Formion. DuRietz '30:337. A stable Synusium composed of one or more stable and independent federions, dominated by a distinct group of species which do not always have a direct sociological affinity between their peripheral members; which are, however, held together by an unbroken series traversing a series of strong sociological affinities and by certain species traversing a series of the principal parts of the given Formion. A salient regional Facies (Hauptteile) (geographical race) of a Formion is known as a Subformion. *See* appendix II.

Fragments of Associations. Braun-Blanquet & Pavillard '30. Populations more or less incomplete, i.e., possessing only a single part of the specific assemblage.

Fremde. = strange species (Braun-Blanquet).

Frequency. Braun-Blanquet & Pavillard '30. A statistical expression obtained by arranging together the complete floristic lists of a certain number of sample areas of uniform but restricted size which are spread as far as possible over the whole extent of a single example of a community; expressed also by the ratio (in %) between the number of sample areas which contain a species and the total sample areas.

Frequency classes. ESA 1935. List P-3 (Braun-Blanquet) The frequency percentages or indices of the component species of a community divided into equal classes on a 5 or 10 parted scale.

Frequency curve. *See* Law of Frequency.

Frequency dominant. Raunkiaer. '34:493. Dominant species with the highest degree of frequency. ESA 1935. List P-3 (Raunkiaer). Species of 80-100% frequency, having a sum frequency of approximately 50% of the whole for the flora, which thus characterizes the least unit of vegetation. Uniformity of these species only is demanded of a community type, i.e., each concrete example of the community type must have these species as frequency dominants.

Frequency index. Cain '32, Ecol. Monogr. 2:479. The percentage of uniformity with which the plants of a species are distributed throughout a community.

Frequency, Law of. ESA 1935. List P-3. Distribution of the frequency percentages of the species of a community through the five classes reveals a double peak, in classes A and E. The law of distribution of frequency figures can be expressed thus: $A>B>C><D<E$.

Freshet. Hancock '11:430. An overflowing of a stream caused by a heavy rain or melted snow, usually occurring in the spring.

Frigideserta. Rübel '30. *Pflgesel. der Erde.* Cold deserts; open communities of cold arctic and alpine regions. $=$ tundra.

Frigofuges. J:152. Plants which shun low temperatures.

Fringing forest. Tansley & Chipp '26. A type of rain forest which exists as continuous belts along water courses of certain parklands.

Frost. *See* cryo-, psychro-.

Frostless season. Robbins '17, Colo. Agr. Exp. Sta. Bull. 224. The days between the last frost in the spring and the first frost in the fall.

Fruit eating. *See* carpophagous.

Frutescence. J:152. The time of maturity of fruit. *See* anthesis, aspection.

Frutice. Clements '02. Shrubs.

Fruticeta. Rübel '28, *Pflgesel. der Erde.* Scrub forests. *See* lignosa.

Fruticuli. Half shrubs.

Full water capacity of the soil. Schimper '03:84 (Mayer). The amount of water taken up by the soil.

Fully stocked. ESA 1934, List R-1. The condition of a stand containing as many trees or as much material of the species and age as the site is capable of supporting. *See* overstocked.

Furiotile lakes. Chapman '31:347. Oxbows and sloughs which are connected with the main stream at periods of high water but disconnected at low water. *See* fluvatile lakes.

Furniture. Swynnerton '36, Trans. Roy. Ent. Soc. Lond. 84:524. The objects in the home of an animal which for one purpose or other it needs or insists on having.

Fynbosch (S and SW Australia). *See* Maquis, durifruticeta.

G

Gall. *See* Cecidium, acarodomatia, erinea, gallivorous, scroll G., zoocecida, zoomorphosis.

Gallivorous. Chapman '31:161 (Handlirsch). Of/ organisms feeding in galls.

Gamobium. J:156 (Gibson). The sexual generation of organisms which show alternation of generation; the gamont generation.

Garide. Warming '09:291 (Chodat). Thorn-bushland of deciduous shrubs in the Rhone and Jura valleys.

Garigue. Warming '09:304. An open type of vegetation

in dry localities which is transitional between fellfield and woodland; composed of perennial shrubs (Mediterranean). Schimper '03:516. Waste tracts of S. France in which remnants of the former forest occur.

Gebiet. Braun-Blanquet '32:323. = a complex complex. *See* appendix I.

Genecology. J:439. Ecology concerned chiefly with species. *See* autecology.

Genetic coefficient. J:439. Dynamic behavior, the part played by the species in the development of the community. *See* aut- and synecology.

Genetical sociology. *See* syngenesis.

Genospecies. Raunkiaer ('13, '18) = Biotype (DuRietz '30).

Genossenschaft (Kerner) = Association.

-genous. Clements '05. Suffix indicating producing.

Geobenthos. Chapman '31:333. Of/ that portion of the stream, etc., bottom which is not covered by vegetation. Cf. phytobenthos.

Geobion. J:159. Plant communities of the land, as distinguished from the water.

Geobiont. J:439. Any soil nurtured plant. Cf. autotrophic.

Geobotany. J:439. Phytogeography. *See* Ecology, Phytosociology.

Geocentric. J:159 (Weisner). Opposed to geotropic (qv).

Geodiatropism. J:159. The function by which an organ places itself at right angles to the force of gravity.

Geodynamic. J:440. The influence of soils as agents.

Geodyte. Hancock '11:420. Ground inhabitant. *See* terricolous.

Geographic units. ESA 1935. List P-3 (Gams). Within the climatic zones (Klimazonen) and floral kingdoms (Florenreichen) can be recognized the following more or less standardized units: District (Distrikt, Bezirk, Territorium); Realm (Vegetationsbereich); Region (Domane, Provinz); Sector (Sektor, Zone, Unterprovinz); Subdistrict (Subdistrikt, Gau.). Each district or subdistrict is characterized by a special "climax formation" in the sense of Cowles and Clements.

Geophagous. Chapman '31:161 (Handlirsch). Organisms feeding on soil.

Geophilae. J:440 (Ivanoff). (Algae) growing on barren or mossy ground.

Geophilous. J:159. Earth loving; plants which fruit underground.

Geophytia. Clements '02:31. Land plant communities.

Geophytes. Braun-Blanquet '32:389. Earth plants; with perennating organs (buds, mycelia) buried in the substratum and therefore but little exposed to the influences of the unfavorable season. (Raunkiaer) Plants with buds more deeply buried than in the surface layer of soil. See cryptophytes.

Geosere. J:440 (Sere). The total plant succession of the geological past.

Geosphere. J:440. The earth.

Geostrate. J:440 (Clements). The entire series of strates subdivided into Ceno-, Meso-, Paleo- strates after the geologic periods.

Geosylvacolous. Hancock '11:420. Of/ ground tree inhabiting species. See terricolous.

Geotaxis. Orientation of organisms with reference to gravity.

Gesamtschaetzung. Braun-Blanquet & Pavillard '30. An expression of dominance for surfaces of considerable extent combining abundance and dominance (= estimation globale).

Geselligkeit. *See* sociability.

Gesellschaft. = community.

Gesellschaftshaushalt. *See* synecology.

Gesellschaftstreue. Braun-Blanquet '32:52. The fidelity of the ties by which plants are bound (restricted) to certain communities.

Girdle. (Gürtel). III Int. Bot. Congr. 1910:28. The bands of concentric arrangement within a formation or group of formations. Sherff '13, Bull. Ill. St. Lab. 9: 577. Zonal bands that are not concentric. = zonation.

Glacial erosion. *See* appendix IV.

Glacospore. Clements '05. A plant with viscid disseminules.

Glade. Hancock '11:431. An open passage through a woods; a grassy open or cleared space in a forest. *See* thicket, enclave.

Glareal. J:162 (Watson). Of/ plants which grow in dry exposed ground, chiefly gravel or sand.

Glen. Hancock '11:432. A depression between hills. *See* ravine.

Glykophyte. Plants forming glysogen (mostly fungi).

Gradation. 1. Clements '16:297. Includes all of the processes concerned in the moulding of the surface of the earth by the transportation of material. *See* erosion, deposition, peneplanation, appendix IV. 2. Friederichs '30:Appendix. The outbreak of a pest, including its period of increase, peak of abundance, and decrease.

Gradient. *See* axial gradient.

Gramnicolous. Hancock '11:420. Of/ grass inhabiting species. *See* phytodyte.

Grassheath. J:165. Tussock communities, peculiar to the southern hemisphere.

Grassland. Schimper '03:162. Consists essentially of perennial grasses growing in tufts; when hygrophilous termed meadow, when xeric, steppe. Tansley & Chipp '26:204. Trees and shrubs usually absent; herbaceous covering general; grasses predominate. Hancock '11: 432. Land kept in grass and not tilled. *See* prairie, plain (N. America), steppe (Eurasia), pampas (S. America), pussta (Hungary), veld (S. Africa), and alvar, chanar, cogonales, duriherbosa, eremophyte, loma, leimocolous, mallee, meadow, poic, pratal, psilicolous, siccideserta.

Grassland climate. Schimper '03:174. Frequent, even if weak, atmospheric precipitations during the vegetative season, so that the superficial soil is kept in a moist condition, and further a moderate degree of heat during the same period. Almost immaterial is the moisture of the subsoil, the dryness of the air in rest periods, and winds; a hostile item is drought during the vegetative season.

Grass-moor. J:165. Intermediate between Scirpus moors and silicious grassland, mainly of grasses, rushes, and sedges.

Grass steppe. Warming '09:274. Found where rain is moderate in amount but falls only in a few days of the year; considered by Warming as synonomous with prairie and pampas.

Grass waste. Schimper '03:592. Dry meadow where deep

rooted perennials usually dominate over the grasses; always due to edaphic influences.

Gravity. *See* clito-.

Grazing capacity. USDA, Dept. Bull. 790:16. The number of stock of a given class or classes which a range unit will support for the period of grazing allowed.

Gregariae. III Int. Bot. Congr. 1910:25 (Drude). Species occurring in groups.

Gregarious. Warming '09:139 (Drude). Of/ species whose individuals occur in small groups so as to form small unmixed collections in the main vegetation.

Grisebach's Vegetation regions (1872), *See* appendix VIII.

Ground cover. *See* Vegetation cover.

Ground form. J:166. Elementary form, as distinguished from growth form.

Group society. Nichols '23, Ecol. 4:11. A plant community within an Association which results from the local aggregation to form more or less well defined clumps or masses of any species other than those which predominate in the Association as a whole. *See* colony, clan, family, society.

Grove. Hancock '11:431. A smaller group of trees than a forest, and without underwood. *See* parkland, savannah, alsad, alsium, lucus.

Growth form. fide Shelford '30. The form assumed by individuals during growth as an immediate response to conditions of the environment. *See* epharmone, ecad, ecospecies, ecotype, species guild.

Guild. Schimper '03:192. Groups of plants having in accordance with the mode of life characteristic traits . .

. . such as lianes, epiphytes, saprophytes, parasites, etc. *See* Synusium, species guild.

Gürtelung. = Zonation.

Guts. Raunkiaer '34 ('08):154. Stony stream beds (Danish W. Indies).

Gymneosere. Clements '16:289. The eosere of the Mesozoic geological period; = mesosere.

Gynaeocentric theory. Fink '06, Pl. World 9:179. The concept placing the more important role of evolution on the female sex of plants.

Gynecogenic. J:440 (Janet). = parthenogenetic.

Gynecology. J:440 (Turesson). The ecology of species. = autecology.

Gynochore. Börner '21. Art. Biol. Reich. L.v. Forstw. 10:413. Of/ organisms distributed by wandering females or by migration movement in larval stages.

Gynopaedium Allee '31:18 (Deegener). A primary association (aggregation) composed of a mother and her offspring that remain together for a period. *See* monogynopaedia.

Gynosynhesmia. *See* synhesmia.

Gypsophilous, J:441. Organisms loving chalk.

Gypsophytia. Clements '02. Limestone communities.

Gyttja. Scandinavian term applied to the jelly like ooze of lake bottoms.

H

H-layer. *See* Humus.

Habit. J:169. The general appearance of an organism, whether erect, climbing, etc.

Habitat. 1. (Physiognomic-areal concept) Shelford '29:
71. An area and not a particular location. Dayton '31,
USDA, Miscl. Pub. 110:16. The site or environment
which a plant or animal natively occupies. ESA 1934,
List R-1. The kind of place in which a plant or animal
lives, such as a forest, grassland, marsh, etc. 2. (environmental factors concept). Tansley & Chipp '26:14.
The sum of the effective environmental conditions under which a community exists. Clements '05. The sum
of all of the forces or factors present in a given area; it
is the exact equivalent of the term environment, although the latter is commonly used in a more general
sense. Clements '16:356. A plexus of physical and biological factors which persist in a climax area as long as
the climate remains essentially unchanged, as measured
in terms of vegetation. III Int. Bot. Congr. 1910:24.
Everything related to the factors operative in a geographically defined locality as far as these factors
influence plants. Braun-Blanquet '32:21. The dwelling place of a species or of a community including all
of the operative factors (except competition) that influence the plants themselves. Yapp '22, Jl. Ecol. 10:1.
The place of abode of the plant, plant community, or
in some cases even a group or a succession of related
communities together with all factors operative within
the abode, but external to the plants themselves; Yapp
recognizes successional, communal and partial habitats
(qv). Svihla '32, Ecol. Monogr. 2:63. A definite type of
area characterized by easily recognized and relatively
constant features. Woodbury '33, Ecol. Monogr. 3:169.
The particular kind or type of area occupied including
recognition of the modifying factors. 3. J:169. The

geographic distribution or limits of a species; *see* range, station. *See* individual-H. isohabitum, mesohabitum, micro-H. 4. Newcombe '35. Ecol. 16:235 (Shelford). An area occupied by a community, the life of which is controlled by climate, soil, substratum, or water.

Habitat form. J:169 (Clements). The impress given to the plant by the habitat. fide Shelford '30. Forms characteristic of the habitat (trees, grass, shrubs, herb, forb, etc.), but not distinguishable for animals except through mores experiments. *See* biotype.

Habitat group. J:169. Applied to those organisms which have common habitats though not related, as halophytes, hydrophytes, etc.

Habitat races. J:169 (Magnus). Parasites which are adapted to respective species of hosts. *See* biotype.

Haematophagous. Chapman '31:160 (Handlirsch). Of/ organisms which suck another's blood, which does not as a rule kill the host.

Halarch. J:441. Saline conditions prevailing at the points of origin of a sere. *See* salt area communities, sere.

Half-culture community. Clements '16:264. (Krause '92). Communities owing their existence to the presence of man, such as the meadows of Germany, heaths, etc. *See* culture community.

Halic. Concerning saline soil or salt communities.

Halion. (Clements). Saline scrub climax.

Halobion. J:140 (Forel). A community of marine plants.

Halobios. Chapman '31:280 (Steuer). Life of ocean waters.

Halodrymium. J:170 (Diels). A mangrove community.

Halolimnetic. J:170 (Forel). Belonging to the sea or salt
lakes. *See* ocean.

Halonereid. (Warming). Marine plankton.

Halophyte. ESA 1934, List P-2. A plant which grows on
saline soil.

Haloplankton. Warming '09:160. Salt water plankton.

Halosere. (Clements). A hydrosere with salt water origin. Phillips '30, Jl. Ecol. 18:201. The sere commencing in saline water or upon saline soil.

Hamada desert. Hardy '25:205, *Geogr. of Plants.* Rocky
desert (Sahara).

Hammock. 1. Wright '32, Ecol. Monogr. 2:118. A large
or small .island in the swamp (Okefinokee swamps).
2. Thone '27, Bot. Gaz. 83:70. Any tree community
composed of Angiosperms, as distinguished from the
pinelands and swamps. Low H. are understood to be
swamp forests, high H., ravine forest of mixed hard-
woods, and oak H., evergreen oaks on dry sandy soil.

Hanger. Stork & Renouf '33:175, *Plant & Animal Ecology.* Woodland on the side of a steep hill.

Hapaxanthic. Warming '09:6 (Braun). Of/ plants which
reproduce but once during their life history. = monocarpic (deCandolle).

Hardpan. J:441. A hard substratum under the cultivated
soil which requires breaking up for the penetration of
roots.

Harmosis. Clements '05. Response of stimuli, comprising
both adjustment and adaptation. *See* epharmosis.

Hawaiian region. Lydekker '96:27. *See* appendix IX.

Heat. *See* temperature.

Heath. 1. Tansley '11:104, *Types of British Vegetation.*
A community, typically treeless, characterized by dwarf

shrubby Ericaceae, generally with linear ericoid or leathery leaves as the dominant plant forms. *Calluna vulgaris* is the usual dominant in Europe; a stable community usually on relatively coarse sandy soil with dark humus layers, generally with a thin layer of relatively pure dry acid peat, sometimes with a layer of ortstein. J:171. An expanse of peaty or sandy soil, with a predominance of Calluna. 2. Graebner '95 (in Clements '16:265). True heath is an open land with an important tree growth or a closed grass covering. *See* Cladina, moor, ericetal, ericilignosa, oxygon, sphagniopratum, sterric, xeropoium.

Hecistotherm. Raunkiaer '34:6 (A. deCandolle). Plants belonging to the cold regions, will grow where summer is short; able to endure a long and very dry winter; deCandolle included demands for moisture as well in this term.

Hedecaceous. J:172. Resembling the ivy habit. *See* liana.

Hedgerow. Hancock '11:432. A thicket of bushes between any two portions of land, often planted, but sometimes left after clearing wild land. *See* fencerow, culture community.

Hedium. Clements '05. A succession on a residuary soil.

Hekistothermic. (deCandolle) Warming '09:36. Of/ plants living beyond the limits of tree growth where the annual mean temperature sinks to below 0°C.; they often endure prolonged lack of light. Lundegardh '31:92, *Envt. & Pl. Develt.* The zone in which the temperature for most months of the year is below zero, and during the vegetative period does not rise above 5°C.

Helad. J:172. A marsh plant.

Helcotropism. J:172. Compulsory attraction of plants.

Heleoplankton. J:172 (Zimmer). The floating vegetation of marshes which overpowers the animal population; it differs from potamoplankton by less motion of the water.

Heliad. (Clements). A heliophyte or sun loving plant, adapted to full exposure.

Helic. Klugh '23, Ecol. 4:373. Of/ marsh communities.

Helio-. 1. Pertaining to the sun. 2.(Drude). Prefix denoting dependence on the sun for the vegetative period.

Heliophilous. Of/ organisms which select sunny habitats. syn: Photophilous.

Heliophobous. Of/ organisms which select shady habitats away from the bright sunlight. = Sciophilous.

Heliophytia. Clements '02. Sun plant communities.

Heliotropic angle. J:172. The angle of incident at which light has the most stimulating effect.

Helioxerophyll. J:173 (Vesque). The state of leaves capable of withstanding drought and strong sunshine.

Helium. Clements '02. A marsh community, sometimes used as a salt marsh community.

Helobios. Frederichs '30:233. Inhabitants of the shore zone of stagnant bodies of water.

Helobious. J:173. Living in marshes, paludal.

Helodium. J:173. A swampy open woodland.

Helodric. Klugh '23, Ecol. 4:373. Of/ a swamp thicket community.

Helodrium. J:173. A thicket community.

Helohylium. Clements '02. A swamp forest community.

Helohylophilous. Dwelling in wet forests.

Helolochium. J:173. A meadow thicket community.

Helolochmium. Clements '02. A meadow thicket community.

Helolochmophilus. Dwelling in meadow thickets.
Helophylium. J:173. A swamp forest community.
Helophyte. Warming '09:131. Marsh plants. *See* amphicryptophyte.
Heloplankton. J:173. The floating vegetation of a marsh.
Helorgadium. Clements '02. Swampy open woodland.
Helostadion. DelVillar '26, Proc. Int. Congr. Pl. Sci. 1: 560. Plants submerged at the base only.
Helotism. Warming '09:85. The relationship found between algae and fungi in forming lichens; a type of mutualism. *See* symbiosis.
Hemeranthy. J:173. Day flowering. *See* photoperiodism.
Hemerocology. Pearse '26:265. Ecology of areas modified by man. Harshberger '23, Ecol. 4:297. The ecology of cultivated fields, parks, and gardens. *See* culture community.
Hemerodiaphorous. J:441 (Linkola). Varied under cultivation. *See* ecad.
Hemerophilous. J:441 (Linkola). Readily cultivated.
Hemerophytes. J:173. Of/ plants introduced through the agency of man. *See* culture community, exotic, ruderal.
Hemiautophyte. J:173 (Boulger). Chlorophyll bearing parasites.
Hemichimonophilous. J:173 (Ludwig). Plant whose above ground development begins even during the prevalence of frost.
Hemicryptophyte. Raunkiaer '34:1. Plants with surviving buds or shoot apices situated in the soil surface. Braun-Blanquet & Pavillard '30. Phanerogams with vegetative buds at the level of the ground or substratum.
Hemicryptophyte climate. Raunkiaer '34 ('08):143. The

climate of the greater part of the cold temperate zone.

Hemicryptophytosynusium. J:441 (Gams). Community composed of life forms such as perennial plants with buds on the level of the soil but not related to each other.

Hemi-endophytic. J:174 (Salmon). Of/ a fungus parasite sometimes external and sometimes internal.

Hemi-epiphyte. Schimper '03:319. Epiphytes which germinate and pass through their earliest development on trees but subsequently become connected with the ground with their roots, so that regards their nutrition they are subject to the same conditions as are the terrestrial plants.

Hemiparasite. J:173. 1. Plants whose seeds germinate without a host plant, but whose after life is dependent on a host. 2. A facultative saprophyte, a parasite which can exist as a saprophyte.

Hemiplankton. Schimper '03:782. The mingled vegetation of shallow and deep water forms in land locked lakes.

Hemipsammic. J:174 (Thurmann). Of/ strata which give a moderately porous detritus, with the plants which select such habitats.

Hemisaprophyte. (Warming). A plant which appropriates humus although capable of self support; a facultative saprophyte.

Hemitropcial. J:175. 1. (McLeod) Of/ flowers which are restricted to certain insects for nectar gathering. 2. Of/ flowers of moderate adaptativeness to insect visitors. 3. (Loew) Of/ insects which visit such flowers as flies, short tongued bees, and most butterflies.

Hepedochae. Clements '05. A secondary succession or subsere.

Herarch. Cooper '13, Bot. Gaz. 55:11. Of successions originating in hydric habitats progressing towards mesic status.

Herbage. J:175. Herbs taken collectively; grasses and forbs.

Herbivorous. Chapman '31:160 (Handlirsch). Of/ organisms which eat on living plant parts.

Herblet. J:175. A small herb.

Herbosa. Rübel '30, *Pflgesel. der Erde*. 1. Herbaceous vegetation; communities of grasses and herbs; divided into Terriherbosa and Aquiherbosa. 2. ESA 1935. List P-3 (Rübel). A major life-form group including non-woody plant communities of grasses, herbs, cryptograms, etc., as prairies, plains, steppe, pampas, subalpine meadows, fens, marshes, etc.

Hercogamy. J:176. Applied to hermaphroditic flowers when some structural peculiarity prevents self pollenation; requiring insect visitation.

Hereditary symbiosis. J:176. The presence of mycobacteria in the tissues including seeds.

Hertzotropism. J:176 (Massart). Movement due to the influence of the Hertzian waves.

Heterochore. J:177. Species inhabiting two or more closely related communities. *See* fidelity.

Heterochromatism. J:339 (Lindman). Appearance of different colors in the flowers of the same inflorescence due to seasonal differences.

Heterodynamous. Shelford '29:160. Of/ forms in the same annual cycle exhibiting dissimilar biological activity. Uvarov '31:105. The annual cycle in such forms bears a more or less definite relation to the season and includes a resting stage usually coinciding with unfavorable seasonal conditions though not necessarily dependent upon them.

Heterogeophyte. J:442 (Gams). Saprophytes or parasitic cryptogam.

Heterohabitum. (Pearse). *See* mesohabitum.

Heteroecious. J:177. Forms which pass through their stages of development on different hosts. = metoecious.

Heteromorphic colony. Allee '31:23, 16. (Deegener). 1. A primary colony of essential union in which there is a differentiation between the members of the colony; = polymorphic. 2. A primary colony of accidental aggregations which are formed when divisions are unequal as in the Scyphozoa.

Heterophyte. 1. J:178. A parasitic plant destitute of chlorophyll. 2. (Warming) A plant which is a halosaprophyte or a parasite, unable to exist independantly. 3. (Brown) Species of wide range of habitats.

Heteroplanobios. Friederichs '30. Organisms passively transported in river floods.

Heterosymphylacia. Allee '31:30 (Deegener). Social unions giving increased protection for all individuals.

Heterosynepileium. Allee '31:30 (Deegener). Groups formed by more than one species of animal gaining greater hunting efficiency for the group.

Heterosynporia. Allee '31:31 (Deegener). Mixed migration societies.

Heterotroph. J:179 (Pfeffer). A distinct saprophyte.

Heterotrophic. J:179. Of/ plants found on soils apparently very diverse from their normal habitats.

Heterotrophy. J:179. 1. (Minks). The symbiotic habit of lichens. 2. (Keeble). Nutrition by ingestion.

Heterozone organisms. Böner '21, Art. Biol. Reich. L.v. Forstw. 10:413. Of/ organisms not restricted to a single habitat during their developmental stages. Cf. Hormozone.

Heterphaptomenon. J:442 (Gams). Life form of more or less parasitic plants.

Hibernacle. The place or habitat in which hibernation takes place.

Hibernacula. Needham & Lloyd '26:263. Overwintering buds of certain aquatic plants.

Hibernaculum. A winter residence.

Hibernation. Shelford '29:150. Overwintering in a state of inactivity without feeding; occasionally applied to eggs and other quiescent stages while passing the winter. fide Weese '35. A state of dormancy, usually during winter. See dormancy.

Hibernation. A state of dormancy, usually during winter. See aestivation, diapause.

Hidroplankton. J:180. Organisms which float by virtue of some secretion.

Hiemefruticeta. J:443. A scrub which sheds its leaves in dry seasons.

Hiemilignosa. Rübel '30, Pflgesel. der Erde. Vegetation in which leaves are shed during the hot dry summer; divided as Hiemisilvae: monsoon forests; and Hiemifruticeta: a mixture of tropical scrub and deciduous shrubs.

High moor. J:180. A moor arising from water, but emerging from it, and then dependent upon rain for water supply.

Highway. An area through which a migrating species may spread.

Hill. Hancock '11:432. A natural elevation of land arising above the common level of surrounding land, in height less than a mountain. *See* colinus, monadnock.

Histophytia. Clements '02. Parasitic communities.

Hizometer. Clements '05. An instrument for measuring gravitation water.

H-layer. *See* humus.

Hochmoor. *See* sphagniherbosa.

Höhengleider. (Braun-Blanquet). Altitudinal facies.

Holarctic realm. *See* appendix VII, IX.

Holard. Clements '05. The total water content of the soil.

Holde. *See* preferential species.

Holendobiotic. J:181. Of/ fungi which produce their spores in other organisms as Saprolegnia.

Holendophytes. Fungi confined to parasitic life within other plants.

Holendozoa. J:181. Fungi living within animals.

Holobiont. = homophyte.

Holocoen. Friederichs '30:233. An "organization" with its living and non-living components. = coen. (C. Heck). = Biocoenose plus Biotope.

Holoparasite. Warming '09:85. Organisms incapable of utilizing inorganic food material.

Holophytic. Pearse '26:72. Of/ plants that live on inorganic substances and carry on photosynthesis.

Holozoic. Pearse '26:72. Of/ animals that prey on other plants and animals. *See* predator, parasite.

Homalalochoric. J:182. Of/ a species confined to one community. *See* fidelity.

Home. Swynnerton '36, Trans. Roy. Ent. Soc. Lond. 84:

520. That portion of the organism's habitat used for both resting and breeding. *See* hotel.

Homeomorph. J:183. Similar organisms of different origin due to conditions of the environment. *See* biotype, ecad, growth form.

Homeoplasy. J:183. Normal growth composed of normal elements.

Homiothermal. Shelford '29:89. Of/ "warm blooded animals," those possessing a rapid acting heat regulatory mechanism.

Homobium. J:443 (Smith). An interdependent community of alga and fungus.

Homodynamic. Shelford '29:160. Of/ forms in which reproduction can continue indefinitely, generation after generation, without any resting period or "period of purification." Uvarov '31:105. Forms characterized by no definite annual life cycle, the number of generations per year depending on actual weather conditions.

Homogeneity. ESA 1934, List R-1. Refers to regularity in distribution of individuals of each species, especially of the dominant species, in a community or area. Kylin '26, Bot. Notiser. H. of vegetation depends upon the distance between individuals of the single species and the distance between the species. If the variation in distance between the individuals of a species and between the species is insignificant then the vegetation is homogeneous. As the variation increases the homogeneity decreases. The steeper the curve showing percentage of species to size of area (species area) the greater the homogeneity; the flatter the curve the lower the homogeneity. Measure of: ESA 1935. List P-3. A combined expression of constancy percent and total or average frequency percent, thus: 85^{90} would mean a constancy of 90% and total frequency of 85% based on 20 quadrats each in ten stands.

Homogeneous distribution. Braun-Blanquet & Pavillard '30. A plant population is more H. as the distribution of individuals is more regular, the sociability of each species is more uniform, the density of species in the population is less equal between themselves.

Homomorphic colonies. Allee '31:16,23. Primary colonies of accidental union which result when divisions are equal, and all members of the colony are similar, as in Salpa chains. 2. Colonies of essential aggregations, having all the individuals morphologically similar as may be found in sponges and at certain times among hydroids and bryozoa.

Homophyte. ESA 1933, List P-1. Plants growing in fissures or crevices in rock, and on ledges where rock debris has accumulated.

Homoplasy. *See* homeoplasy.

Homostatic period. J:184 (Tuzso). The period during which the present vegetation developed after the pliocene vegetation.

Homotypical association (aggregation). Allee '31:15 (Deegener). Consisting of members of the same species which have arisen either sexually or asexually, which have remained together because they are the offspring of the same parent, or which may have accidentally become associated together although of different parentage; the former are primary, the latter secondary.

Homotypical societies (aggregations). Allee '31:23 (Deegener). Societies composed of a single species.

Homozygosus. Of/ plants derived from the same group,

138

originally from the same strain of a pure line. Cf. clone.

Honey feeding. *See* melliphagous.

Hoogeveld. Hardy '25:240, *Geogr. of Plants.* Treeless areas caused by wind, drought, and soil; elevation 4000-5500 ft. (S. Africa).

Hopkins' Bioclimatic law. *See* bioclimatic law.

Horarius, horary. J:185. Lasting an hour or two. *See* periodism, ephemeral.

Hormozone organisms. Börner '21. Art. Biol. Reich. L.v. Forstw. 10:413. Of/ organisms whose larval forms are restricted to a single habitat as are the adults. Cf. heterozone.

Horological. J:185. Of/ flowers which open and close at stated hours. *See* photoperiodism.

Hortinus. = hornus, J:184. Pertaining to this year; the present year's growth.

Host. Henderson '29, *Dict. Sci. Terms.* Any organism in or on which another spends part or the whole of its existence, and from which it derives nourishment or protection.

Host-parasite relationships. *See* parasite.

Host selection principle. Chapman '31:162 (Craighead). When a species has been reared for several generations on one of several host plants, the progeny will tend to select the same host plant on which they were reared. (Hopkins). The progeny of any insect species that normally feeds on two or more hosts tends to breed on the host on which it was reared.

Hotel. Swynnerton, '36, Trans. Roy. Ent. Soc. Lond. 84: 520. That portion of an organism's habitat which can provide facilities to the organism for every purpose; resting, breeding, and feeding.

Hudsonian life zone. Includes the northern portion of the transcontinental coniferous forest of N. America, and the cold summits of the higher mountains; Chapman '31:221 (Merriam). The southern limit may be defined by the area having a mean normal temperature for the six hottest weeks of the year of 57.2°F. *See* appendix V, VI.

Humic water. Carpenter '28:68, *Life in inland waters.* Water strong in acids of vegetable origin, such as in peat moors.

Humicolous. Hancock '11:420. Of/ medium dry ground inhabiting species.

Humicular. = saprophytic.

Humidity, absolute. The amount of water vapor in suspension in the air.

Humidity, relative, USDA, Miscl. Pub. 70. The percentage of moisture in the air with reference to its capacity to hold moisture at the given temperature.

Humification. J:186 (Beyerinck). The reduction of dead plant substances by fungi.

Humus. Decomposing organic matter in the soil. ESA 1933 List P-1. The portion of the forest floor in which decomposition is so far advanced that its original form is not distinguishable; H. in a condition favorable to forest growth is said to be mild, neutral, or sweet; H. harmful to forest growth owing to an acid condition is said to be sour; incompletely decomposed H. is said to be raw. Romell & Heiburg. Ecol. 8:574. F-layer: Fermentation horizon or first decomposition layer; H-layer, humified horizon or heavily decomposed layer. *See* anthracriny, mor, muld, saprophile, sathro-.

Humus cover. Romell & Heidburg '31, Ecol. 12:567. A cover of unincorporated organic matter.

Humus lake. Carpenter '28:188, *Life in inland waters.* Dystrophic lakes, very rich in humic acids; little floating life.

Humus layer. ESA 1933, List P-1. The top layer of the soil, owing its characteristic features largely to the content of organic matter, if incorporated into the soil. *See* humus cover; humus, F-& H-layers.

Hunger cycle. Swynnerton '36, Trans. Roy. Ent. Soc. Lond. 84:520. The mean period elapsing between an organism's feeding times.

Huxley's zoological regions (1868). Lydekker '96:25. Notogaea and Arctogaea; division is based on the distribution of game birds; the former divided into Novo-Zelia, Australian, and Austro-Colombian regions, the latter of these being equivalent to the Neotropical of Sclater. *See* maps in appendix for synonymy.

Hybernacle. *See* hibernacle.

Hybrid. DuRietz '30a:390. A population intermediate between two or several different species, supposed to be originally formed by the crossing of biotypes belonging to different species.

Hydatophytia. J:187 (Diels). Submerged plant community.

Hydra. J:187 (Clements). The "wet form" of a species. *See* Ecad.

Hydrarch. Nichols '23, Ecol. 4:171. Of/ successions which originate in hydric habitats such as lakes and ponds and progress towards mesophytism or toward a developmentally more advanced condition.

Hydric. Cooper & Weese '26, Ecol. 7:390. Characterized

or pertaining to conditions of abundant moisture supply.

Hydrobios. Friederichs '30:233. Organisms of isolated ground water. *See* Edaphonekton.

Hydrocarpic. J:187. Of/ aquatic plants which are pollenated above the water but withdraw the fertilized flowers below the surface for development, as in Vallisneria. *See* pollenation.

Hydrochimous. J:187 (Drude). Of/ plants adapted to rainy weather.

Hydrochore. Clements '05. A plant distributed by water.

Hydrocleistogamous. J:187 (Knuth). Of/ flowers which do not open in consequence to emersion.

Hydrodynamic. J:187. Used for the action of tides and waves in distribution of species.

Hydroharmose. (Clements). Response to water stimuli.

Hydroid. (Clements). Watery.

Hydroid areas. (Clements). Algal climaxes in predevonian time.

Hydromegathermic. Warming '09:35 (deCandolle). Of/ plants making the greatest demands as regards heat and water; tropical.

Hydromorphosis. J:444 (Massart). Changes due to watery habitats.

Hydrophilous. 1. (Clements). Inhabiting wet land or water. 2. Pollenated by water.

Hydrophyte. Braun-Blanquet & Pavillard '30. A phanerogam, with reproductive organs under water. Braun-Blanquet '32:289. Water plants other than plankton; H. natanta: free floating; H. adnata; anchored to a substratum; H. radicanta: with roots. ESA 1934, List P-2. A plant which grows wholly or partly immersed in water.

Hydrophytia. Clements '02, *Engl. Bot. Jahrb.* :31. Water communities.

Hydrophytic (L. Braun '16). Of/ the type of forest in which the soil is saturated with puddles standing in all slight depressions during the spring and summer months—the growing season—and often dry at the surface during the late summer and fall.

Hydrophytium. J:188. A plant community of bog and swamp plants.

Hydroplankton. Braun-Blanquet '32:289. Micro-organisms floating in water.

Hydrosere. Phillips '30, Jl. Ecol. 18:201. A sere commencing in water or moist sites. ESA 1934, List P-2. Referring to all of the stages in a hydrarch succession.

Hydrospheric. J:444 (Adams). Of/ the agency of water in migration.

Hydrostatic. (Clements). Of/ a succession not prone to change towards greater moisture; completing succession under hydric conditions.

Hydrotherm figure. ESA 1935. List P-3. A graph of the annual course in temperature and precipitation used in study of climates. Raunkiaer, 1934.

Hydrotribium. Clements '02. A badland community.

Hydrotribophilus. Inhabiting badlands.

Hydrotrophy. J:188. 1. Unequal growth due to difference in the supply of moisture. 2. (Clements). Succession which tends towards mesophytism.

Hydrotropic. J:444 (Clements). Changing to a greater water content in a succession.

Hydrotropism. J:188. The phenomenon induced by the influence of moisture on growing organs.

Hyemal. = hiemal.

Hygrochastic. J:188 (Acherson). Plants in which the
bursting of the fruit and the dispersion of the spores is
caused by absorption of water.

Hygrocolous. Hancock '11:420. Of/ wet ground inhabiting species.

Hygrodrymium. J:444 (Diels). A rain forest.

Hygrometric. Clements '05. Measuring or absorbing
water.

Hygromorphism. J:188. 1. A form determined by moist
surroundings. 2. (Drude). The state of little water
absorption and equally little evaporation.

Hygropetrobios. Friederichs '30:233. Inhabitants of submerged rocks.

Hygrophilous. Schimper '03:2. Of/ the vegetation of
moist areas.

Hygrophorbium. J:189, 444 (Diels). Moist pasture,
fenlands, or low moor communities.

Hygrophytia. J:189 (Diels). Hygrophytic communities.

Hygrophytes. Raunkiaer '34:495. Hemicryptophytes and
Geophytes taken collectively.

Hygropoium. J:189 (Diels). A meadow community; evergreen meadows.

Hygrosphagnium. J:189 (Diels). High moor.

Hylacolous. Hancock '11:420. Of/ tree inhabiting species. *See* phytodyte.

Hylea. Hardy '25:136, *Geogr. of Plants*. (Humboldt).
Luxuriant floodforests of the Amazon. *See* appendix
VIII.

Hylium. Clements '02. Woodland, including a series of
forest communities.

Hylobios. Friederichs '30:233. Inhabitants of solid media.

Hylocola. J:444 (Diels). Forest dwelling.

Hylodium. Clements '02. Dry open woodland community.

Hylodophilus. Dwelling in dry open woodlands.

Hylophagus. Friederichs '30:Appendix. Of/ " 'stuff-eaters', not scavangers; eaters of stored products."

Hylophilous. Forest loving.

Hylophyte. Warming '09:135 (Pound & Clements). Woody plants (mesophytic).

Hymenolichen. J:189 (Mattirolo). A lichen symbiotically associated with a hymenomycetous fungus (i.e., one with spore mother cells exposed at maturity).

Hypactile. Klugh '23, Ecol. 4:371. Of/ the littoral zone uncovered by the tide for less than one quarter of the time.

Hyperbolic zero. Shelford '29:370. The zero of the equilateral hyperbola (α) to which the time-temperature curve conforms with the medial range of temperature; it is an imaginary threshold. See alpha, threshold.

Hyperdisperse. Braun-Blanquet '32:31, 36 (Schustler). Irregular mode of distribution of individuals resulting in crowding. Cf. hypodisperse.

Hyperparasites. Organisms which are parasitic upon parasites; also termed secondary parasites; as high as quaternary parasitism is recorded.

Hyphalmyroplankton. J:190 (Zimmermann). The floating organisms of salt water.

Hyphydrogamicae. J:190 (Knuth). Plants whose flowers are pollenated under water.

Hypnocyst. J:190. A dormant stage assumed when the conditions for growth are unfavorable.

Hypnoplasy. J:190. Arrested development due to various inhibiting reactions, which prevent the cells or tissues from attaining normal size. See dormancy.

Hypnosis. J:190 (Escombe). The state of dormant vitality shown by seeds while still retaining their power of growth and generation.

Hypobenthile. Klugh '23, Ecol. 4:371. Of/ the sea bottom below 1000 meters. = abyssal.

Hypoclysile. Klugh '23, Ecol. 4:372. Of/ low tide pools; those in which the water temperature does not rise more than 3°C above that of the sea.

Hypodisperse. Braun-Blanquet '32:31, 36 (Schustler). The regular mode of distribution of plant individuals. Cf. hyperdisperse.

Hypolimnile. Below the thermocline.

Hypolimnion. The portion of certain lakes below the thermocline which receives no heat from the sun, and no aeration by circulation.

Hypsiu. = hypsion. Clements '05. A succession caused by elevation.

Hytherograph. Shelford '29:18. A plotted diagram of mean monthly temperature and rainfall, a line surrounding the plotted points being a graphic expression of the climate of the area. First use: Taylor 1919. *See* climograph.

I

-ic. (Klugh). Suffix denoting association.

Ice. *See* snow.

Idiobiological unit. (DuRietz). *See* appendix II, species,

Idiobiology. J:444 (Turesson). Pertaining to the individual organism.

Idioecology. = autecology.

-ies. Suffix denoting consocies.

Igapu. *See* rebalsa.

Igarapis. Hardy '25:136, *Geogr. of Plants.* Sluggish channels choked with palm forests. *See* rebalsa.

-ile. (Klugh). Suffix denoting systase. (Clements). Suffix denoting society.

Imaginary threshold. *See* empirical threshold, hyperbolic zero, threshold.

Immobile. Clements '05. Without effective devises for migration.

Immunity. (Conn). The power of an organism to resist invasion by a parasite.

Imperfect succession. Clements '05. A succession in which one or more of the usual stages are omitted anywhere in the sere and a later stage appears before its usual turn. *See* xenodochae.

Incidental species. fide Shelford '35. Species occurring only in small numbers and probably of little ecological significance. = occasional species.

Inclination. ESA 1934, List R-1. The direction of a slope-facing; suggested to supplant aspect in this sense.

Incognita. (Watson). Plants whose origin or distribution are unknown. *See* exotic, endemic, ruderal.

Indeciduous. J:196 (Crozier). Evergreen or persisting foliage.

Indian zoological region. Lydekker '95:25 (Sclater). Includes India, SE.Asia, and part of the Malay archipelago. Renamed Oriental region by Wallace.

Indicators. (Clements). Species or climax or successional communities showing "factors, processes and practice." Tansley & Chipp '26:26. A given form of vegetation (community or species) as indicating the presence of certain conditions. *See* biometer, phytometer, zoometer.

Indifferent species. Braun-Blanquet & Pavillard '30.

Species growing more or less abundantly in many diverse communities. *See* vage, fidelity.

Indigenous. Of/ native species; not introduced. = endemic; cf. exotic.

Individual. DuRietz '30a:337. " . . . . the main criterion is physiological autonomy." See clone, sippe.

Individual habitat. Yapp '22, Jl. Ecol. 10:1. The H. of an individual organism whether solitary or forming a part of a community.

Individualism = individuation. J:196. 1. The state of being capable of separate existence. 2. Symbiosis in which the total aggregate result is wholly different from any of the symbionts.

Induced dormancy. (Breitenbecker) D. not normal for the life history but brought about by special environmental conditions.

Inferagarian zone. J:197 (Watson). The lowest portion of the cultivated land in Great Britain.

Influence. The effect of an influent on its habitat and associates. *See* dominance, influent.

Influences, geographic. For discussion on the use of this term, *see* Hubbard '32, Ohio Jl. Sci. 32:39.

Influent. Shelford '26, Ecol. 7:389. An organism which has important relations in the biotic balance and interaction. fide Shelford '30. . . . . has a primary effect upon the bodily well being of the sessile dominants by (*a*) destroying foliage or other parts, or (*b*) the number of individuals of motile organisms without changing the essential composition of the biotic community or markedly changing the rate of succession, or (*c*) affecting the dominants and subdominants through the planting of seeds, fertilizing the soil, etc. Woodbury '33, Ecol.

Monogr. 3:166. Suppressed forms that are usually effective in modifying the well being or numbers of the dominant groups or of other influents without changing the essential structure of the community; their roles are generally shown as benefactors, competitors, parasites, or predators. Their reactions may be shown by the planting of seeds, aerating the soil, competing for food, space, light, moisture, etc., destroying foliage, parasitizing hosts, or destroying entire individuals. The following degrees or rankings of influence or dominance are recognized: Dominant, Subdominant, Major influent, Influent, Subinfluent, Minor influent, Microdominant, Dominule, Subdominule (the latter three acting in microhabitats). *See* dominance; example of use of certain of these terms in appendix XI.

Inquiline. A guest, sometimes a commensual, in the nest, etc., of another.

Insectivorous. Organisms feeding on insects; predaceous.

Insect vector. An insect actively or passively responsible for the dissemination of a disease producing organism or parasite.

Insects, approved common names. *See* Jl. Ec. Ent. 24: 1273, 26:1169.

Insolation. Clements '05. Exposure to intense heat and light.

Instinct. Allee '31:10 (Wheeler). "The more or less complicated activity of an organism as a whole rather than as a part, as a representative of a species rather than an individual, without previous experience or modification of behavior caused by experience, and with an end or purpose of which it has no knowledge."

Intermediate. *See* crown class.

Interspecies group behavior. Warden, Jenkins & Warner '34:65. *Intro. Comp. Psychol.* Examples are parasitism, symbiosis, commensualism, and biotic community life.

Intertropic. J:200. Relating to the torrid zone, within the tropics.

Interzone. Swynnerton '36, Trans. Roy. Ent. Soc. Lond. 84:520 (Jackson). A narrow or wide strip separating two larger communities, and including species absent from either of them. (*See* ecotone).

Intradiel. Carpenter '34, Proc. Okla. Acad. 14:29. Pertaining to phenomena taking place within the confines of a single 24-hour day. *See* photoperiodism, day.

Intraspecies group behavior. Warden, Jenkins & Warner '34:65. *Intro. Comp. Psych.* Examples are aggregation, migration, leadership, domestic and familial relationships, play, etc.

Intrinsic factors. Uvarov '31:156 (Thompson & Parker). Of/ a highly efficient adjustment of the individual to environmental conditions; includes habit and structure peculiar to the species. *See* adaptation.

Inundatal. J:201 (Watson). Of/ plants which grow in places liable to inundation in wet weather, but dry in summer.

Inundatus. J:201. Flooded, sometimes under water, sometimes dry.

Invasion. Clements '16:29. The movement of plants from one area to another and their colonization in the latter; it is analysed into migration (the actual movement), ecesis (establishment), and competition.

-ion. Braun-Blanquet & Pavillard '30. Suffix to denote alliance.

Iron. *See* sidero-.

Irreciprocal colonies. Allee '31:24 (Deegener). Colonies in which all members do not contribute to the welfare of the whole. Cf. reciprocal colony.

Irreciprocal family. Allee '31:25 (Deegener). A group in which the social values rest only with the young.

Irreciprocal symporia. Allee '31:32 (Deegener). . . . . occur when one species attaches itself to the back of another without contributing aid to the animal on whose back it grows, or becoming parasitic.

-is. (Clements). Suffix to denote associes.

Isobiochore. = biochore.

Isocheim. J:203. The isotherm of the coldest months.

Isochimenal. J:445. Isophenes of winter temperature.

Isocies. 1. Braun-Blanquet '32:366 (Gams). Similar communities (Synusia) having similar characteristics on different parts of the globe; "homologous." (Pound & Clements). ESA 1935. List P-3 (DuRietz). An isocies is a group of synusiae more or less consistent physiognomically. Related layer communities. Habitat groups. *See* appendix I, II.

Isocoenosis. DuRietz '30b:493 (Gams). A physiographic group of phytocoenoses. ESA 1935. List P-3 (Gams). An isocoenosis is a group of phytocoenoses, physiognomically more or less consistent. *See* appendix I, II.

Isocoenosium. J:446. A community composed of Isocies.

Isocryma. J:446 (Setchell). A winter isotherm.

Isodems. Hartzell '31, Jl. Ec. Ent. 24:151. Isopracts surrounding areas of identical density of population.

Isofags. (Hartzell '31). Isopracts surrounding areas having the same degree of injury by insects or mammals.

Isogene einheit. (Lehmann). = species, biotype (Du-Rietz).

Isohabitu. Pearse '26:23. A continuous area where there is no important variation in any environmental factor.

Isohydrics. Hartzell '31. Jl. Ec. Ent. 24:151. Isopracts surrounding areas having similar hydrogen ion concentration.

Isohyet. An isopract delimiting equal rainfall over a given area.

Isohyp. Hartzell '31. Jl. Ec. Ent. 24:151. An isopract surrounding land areas of the same elevation; = contour line.

Isolaterality. J:446. Having both sides exposed to light.

Isolation. Clements '05. Separation by barriers. J:203 (Romanes). The prevention of intercrossing between a separated section of a species and the rest of that species or kind. See convivium.

Isonif. Hartzell '31. Jl. Ec. Ent. 24:151. An isopract surrounding areas having equal heights of snow.

Isophane. = isophene.

Isophene. Uvarov '31:183. Theoretical lines along which seasonal phenomena occur at the same date. Shelford '29:15 (Hopkins). An isophenal map: isopracts drawn through equivalent event dates at the same altitude; their positions and numbers correspond to latitude on the 100th meridian; the isophenal meridians are perpendicular to the isophenes and pass toward a pole in the region of Iceland for N. America. See Bioclimatic law.

Isophenous. J:204 (Johannsen). Of/ individuals which belong to the same phenotype.

Isophotic. Clements '05. Equally illuminated on all sides.

Isophyte. Hartzell '31, Jl. Ec. Ent. 24:151. An isopract surrounding areas having equal height of vegetation above the ground.

Isophytotonus. Clements '02. Of/ equal temperature requirements on the part of certain plants.

Isopleth. Hartzell '31, Jl. Ec. Ent. 24:151. An isopract surrounding areas having the same numbers of a given species or numbers of species.

Isopract. A line indicating the boundary of like frequency of expression of a given factor, as contour lines indicate similar areas of elevation. = isophene.

Isoreagent. (Raunkiaer). = Variety (DuRietz).

Isoterra. Pearse '26:23. An area which shows uniformity of habitat conditions over a considerable area.

-ium. (Clements '05), Res. Methods. Suffix denoting a formation.

J

Jarales. Warming '09:307. Maquis (shrub transition zones between steppe and forest) in the Iberian peninsula.

Jarovisation. ESA 1934, List R-1 (Lyssenke). The shortening of the vegetative period of plants by seed treatment. = vernalisation.

Jetsam. Flattely & Walton '22:53. The area of the beach where miscellaneous floating material is washed up and deposited or the material so deposited. = flotsam.

Jordanon (Lotsy). = variety (DuRietz '30a:350).

Juncaceous. J:205. Of/ rush like aspect.

Junin waste. See esteros.

K

Kalloplankton. J:207 (Forel). Organisms which float by being encased in gelatinous envelopes.

Kammenaia tundra. Haviland '26:149. Tundra of Siberia which is bisected by mountain ranges or raised into plateaux and hence become rocky or rugged.

Kar. J:205. Austrian geological term for hollows dug out by glaciers.

Kär. Warming '09:208. Communities transitional between heath and moor; characterized by a lack of raw humus.

Kar herbage. J:205. Plants occurring in hollows high in the mountains.

Kataklinotropism. Negative clinotropism.

Katharsbia. J:206. Organisms of clear water.

Kenapophytes. J:206 (Simmons). Plants which colonize on cleared land. *See* culture community, ruderal.

Kettle-trap. J:207. Applied to such flowers as those of Aristolochia which imprison insects until pollenation is effected.

Key industry. Elton '27:57, *Animal Ecology.* Animals which feed upon plants and which are so numerous as to have very large numbers of animals dependent upon them. *See* food chain, pyramid of numbers.

Khor. J:446. Stony desert waste.

Klasse. (Braun-Blanquet). *See* appendix I.

Klimax gebeit. (Braun-Blanquet & Pavillard '30). *See* climax complex.

Klinogeotropism. J:207 (Pfeffer). The drooping tendency of the free end of a climbing plant while nutating (nodding).

Klinotropism. = clinotropism.

Knephopelagile. Klugh '23, Ecol. 4:371. The middle pelagic area of the ocean; 30 meters to the extreme limit of light.

Knight-Darwin law. Darwin, Nature 58:630. The concept that nature abhors inbreeding.

Konspecies. (Reichenow). = subspecies (DuRietz "30a: 354).

Kopjes. Mesa-like structures in the S. African plateau.

Kopraphagous. Chapman '31:160 (Handlirsch). Of/ organisms which feed on animal excrement. = copraphagous.

Kormogene association (aggregation). Allee '31:15 (Deegener). Colonies in which the different individuals remain morphologically attached to each other.

Kormogene society. Allee '31:23 (Deegener). Homotypical societies (aggregations) having the different individuals composing them organically connected with each other.

Krautschicht. Braun-Blanquet & Pavillard '30. Herbaceous stratum. See stratification.

Kremastoplankton. J:208 (Forel). Floating organisms supplied with appendages which aid in floating, as cilia, etc.

Krogh's law. An increase in temperature results in a corresponding increase in the rate of a biological process.

$$V_{t2} = V_{t1} + (t_2 - t_1)k.$$

V:velocity

t:temperature

See Van't Hoff, Arrhenius.

Krummholz. Stunted growth form of trees in alpine regions; elfin wood.

L

Labile. Clements '05. Plastic, easily modified.

Lacus. Clements '02. A lake.

Lacuster. Clements '16:269 (Gadeceau). The central zone of a lake.

Lacustrine. ESA 1934, List P-2. Pertaining to, produced in, originating in, or inhabiting a lake.

Lag. The delay in the effectiveness or response with reference to a given factor or stimulus.

Lair herbage. ESA 1933, List P-1. Plants growing about the overmanured areas near Alpine dairy huts.

Lake. Hancock '11:430. A large body of water contained in a depression of the earth's surface and supplied from drainage of more or less extended area. Chapman '31: 304 recognizes the following classes: 1st order: definite thermal stratification or thermocline with the epilimnion of constant temperature or nearly so throughout the year. 2nd order: thermocline present, but bottom water temperature undergoes an annual fluctuation. 3rd order: without a thermocline, with little difference between top and bottom temperatures. *See* oligotrophic and eutrophic lakes (with regard to oxygen content); allotropic and autotropic (with regard to organic matter); chilile, pythic, lacuster, limnium, limnetic, ocean.

Lalang. Warming '09:298 (Pechuel-Loesche). A type of savannah vegetation in E. Asia.

Lamiation. Clements '36. Jl. Ecol. 24:276. A stratal or layer society of an association.

Lamies. Clements '36. Jl. Ecol. 24:276. A stratal or layer socies of an associes.

Laminarian zone. Shelford & Towler '25, Pub. Puget Sd.

Biol. Sta. 5:65 (of authors). A zone characterized by the group Laminariaceae which is, however, only seasonal and hence the permanent designation is not valid.

Latent development. Uvarov. '31:45. Metabolic activity toward advance in development during "quiescent" states. *See* dormancy.

Latent period. J:446 (Bose). The time between the incidence of a stimulus and the beginning of the response movement. *See* lag.

Lateral planation. Clements '16:311. Erosion of a stream along the sides of its course; "undercutting."

Laterite. (Tansley & Chipp '26). Tropical argillaceous soils under a heavy rainfall of at least 50 inches annually.

Laurifruticeta. J:446 (Rübel). Thickets with predominance of evergreens. Rübel '30, *Pflgesel. der Erde.* Laurel scrub of the Balkans, the Rhodendron bush of the Caucasus, and the Himalaya, and the Arbutus unedo areas of the oceanic Mediterranean region.

Laurilignosa. Rübel '30, *Pflgesel. der Erde.* Laurel vegetation. *See* lignosa.

Laurisilvae. Rübel '30, *Pflgesel. der Erde.* Laurel forests where the dominant trees are dicotyledons with glossy evergreen leaves and protected buds and conifers of the more mesic types; includes the temperate rain forests of Chili and New Zealand, the laurel forests of Macronesia, and the mesic conifer forests of N. America Pacific coast.

Laurophilus. Dwelling in sewers and drains.

Laurum. Clements '02. A sewer community; a drain community.

Layer society. Nichols '23, Ecol. 4:11. A community

within an Association which results from the tendency
of various species of smaller size than the dominant
life form to display their foliage at more or less definite
levels. Braun-Blanquet '32:40. Horizontal strata, the
product of a process of adaptation and selection in
which light is a dominant factor. Shelford '32, Ecol.
13:114. Composed of subordinate animals which do not
control the habitat. Trapnell '33, Jl. Ecol. 21:307. Recognizes the Ground (less than 10 cm.), Field (over 10
cm.) and Shrub (over 1 meter) layers in the vegetation.
See stratification, stratum, Synusium. suffix: -anum.

Layer transect. *See* bisect.

Leaf-size classes (of Raunkiaer) ESA 1935. List P-3.
More or less natural leaf size classes bearing a geomet-
rical relationship, leptophyll, nanophyll, microphyll,
mesophyll, macrophyll, and megaphyll.

Lebensgemeinschaft. = biotic community.

Leibig's law of the minimum. The determining factor in
the limitation of the distribution of the species is that
which is present in minimum amount. Shelford '18:48
(in Ward & Whipple, *Fresh Water Biology*) (Johnstone). "A plant requires a certain number of food-
stuffs if it is to continue to live and grow, and each of
these food substances must be present in a certain proportion; if only one of them is absent, the plant will
die; if one is present in the minimal proportion, the
growth will also be minimal." Taylor '34, Ecol. 15:
378. "When a multiplicity of factors is present and
only one is near the limits of toleration, this factor will
be the controlling one."

Leimocolous. J:447. Inhabiting moist grassland or meadows.

Lemurian realm. (Wallace). The island of Madagascar.
= Malagasy region.

Lenetic. Needham & Lloyd '16:315. Of/ still-water communities. *See* pond.

Lestobiosis. (Forel). = Synclopia.

Liana, Liane. Climbing and twining plants. *See* hedaca-
ceous.

Life form. 1. Tansley & Chipp '26:11. The characteristic
vegetative form of a plant species as trees, shrub, herb,
forb, grass, etc.; Shelford suggests using Mos (plural,
Mores) as the animal equivalent (except in cases of
fixed species). fide Shelford '30. Fixed hereditary
growth forms such as bivalve, sessile barnacle, snail,
etc. (DuRietz '26). An abstract plant type based on
physiognomy. 2. Nichols '23, Ecol. 4:13. All features
of form and structure by which a plant is adapted to
cope with various conditions of environment: size and
habit of growth, etc. Raunkiaer '34:112. Criteria for
the recognition of a life form: (*a*) the character must
be essential and represent something fundamental in
the plant's relationship to climate; (*b*) it must be fairly
easy to use, so that it can be easily seen in the field to
which life form a plant belongs; (*c*) it must represent
a single aspect of the plant, thus enabling a comparative
statistical treatment of the vegetation of different regions. *See* biological spectrum, phytoplankton, phytoedaphon, endophyte, therophyte, hydrophyte, geophyte,
hemicryptophyte, chamaephyte, phanerophyte, epiphyte.

Life-form dominance. ESA 1935. List P-3 (Adamson).
Where no one species, or even small number of species,
exerts strict dominance, but collectively several species

all of the same life-form dominate a plant community.

Life zone. (Merriam). *See* appendix V, VI.

Light requirement, relative. Braun-Blanquet '32:104. The relation of the light intensity of the habitat to full sunshine measured at the same time.

Lignicolous, Hancock '11:420. Of/ dead wood loving species. *See* geodyte.

Lignosa. Rübel '30, *Pflgesel. der Erde.* Woody vegetation; divided into Silvae and Fruticeta under Aciculignosa, Hiemilignosa, Aestilignosa, Ericilignosa, Durilignosa, Laurilignosa, Pluviilignosa.

Limestone. *See* gypso-.

Limnaen. J:447 (Rübel). Submersed wet meadows.

Limnetic. Pertaining to lakes. Klugh '23, Ecol. 4:372. The open water of lakes. *See* eulimnetic.

Limnicolous. J:447. Dwelling in lakes.

Limnium. Clements '02. A lake community.

Limnocryptophyte. Raunkiaer '34:1. A marsh plant with surviving buds buried below the surface. = helophyte.

Limnodic. Klugh '23, Ecol. 4:373. Of/ a salt marsh community.

Limnodium. Clements '02. A marsh community.

Limnodophilus. Dwelling in marshes.

Limnology. Strom '29, Jl. Ecol. 17:106. The study of everything connected with fresh waters, both stagnant and running . . . . the natural history of fresh waters in the broadest sense of the word.

Limnophilus. Clements '02. Of/ species inhabiting lakes.

Limnoplankton. Warming '09:160. Fresh water plankton.

Limonile. Klugh '23, Ecol. 4:373. Far beneath the surface of the ground.

Lineamentum. Clements '02. A line of stress.

Linneon. = species.

Lipalian. J:447 (Walcott). An era of marine deposit when pelagic life was adapted to littoral conditions, and the appearance of the species of the Cambrian.

Litharch. J:448 (Clements). Of/ a succession or adsere on hard rock.

Lithic. Concerning communities on rocks.

Lithophilous benthos. (Warming). The attached algae of the harbor bottom.

Lithosere. (Clements). A rocky adsere; seres having their origin on rock.

Litorideserta. Rübel '30, *Pflgesel. der Erde.* See shore "deserts" and open stands of halophytes.

Litter. ESA 1933, List P-1. The upper, but slightly decomposed portion of the forest floor.

Littoral. 1. Klugh '23, Ecol. 4:371. Of/ the seashore between the tide marks. Warming '09:172. Pertaining to intertidal areas. Shelford & Towler '25, Pub. Puget Sd. Biol. Sta. 5:62 (in sense of Appelöf '12 in Murray & Hjort). The zone down to 30-40 meters with no distinction between intertidal and subtidal zones. *See* actic. ESA 1935. List P-3. Pertaining to the shallower life zone near the shore of a body of water out to the usual limit of influence of wave action or tides and daylight on the bottom life.

Littoral belts. Johnson and Skutch '28, Ecol. 8:188, recognize the following divisions:
  —6 to + 2 ft.: sublittoral
   2 to   7 ft.: lower littoral

7 to 14 ft.: upper littoral. *See* Ecol. 8:327 for historical division of concept.

Litus. Clements '02. A strand community; a sandy seashore, or beach.

Livstype. (Danish). = biotype.

Llano. Warming '09:297. (Humbolt). Savannah of Venezuela having but few trees, and those frequently palm forests; in rain season often under water, but in dry seasons the vegetation assumes a xeric aspect.

Llano estacado. Hardy '25:93, *Geogr. of Plants*. Level, semi-arid shortgrass country of W. Texas.

Loam. A mixture of sand, silt, and clay soils.

Locality. Braun-Blanquet & Pavillard '30. The geographic position of an example of an association or other plant community. Waterman '22, Bot. Gaz. 74:7. The ground occupied by an individual community.

Lochmium. Clements '02. A thicket community.

Lochmodium. Clements '02. A dry thicket community.

Lochmodophilus. Dwelling in dry thickets.

Lochmophilus. Thicket loving.

Lociation. A local variant of an Association, varying in composition of the important subdominants and influents, as distinguished from Faciation, the local variant based on the presence of dominants.

Locies. The developmental equivalent of Lociation.

Loma. Warming '09:288 (Benrath). Grass steppes of Peru in which the growing season is the winter moist season.

Lophium. Clements '02. A hill crest community.

Lophophilus. Hill dwelling.

Lotic. Needham & Lloyd '16:315. Of/ rapid water communities living in waves and currents. Chapman '31:

347. Usually narrower and shallower than lenetic communities.

Lough. (Irish). A lake or pool.

Louisianian zone. (Seton). Humid Lower Sonoran Zone (Merriam) exclusive of Gulf Strip.

Low. *See* fen.

Lower beach. Flattely & Walton 122:35 (Davenport). The area which lies between low tide and mean high tide and is twice daily exposed to air and submergence.

Lows. Richards '29, Jl. Ecol. 29:139. Narrow valleys between the dune ridges corresponding to the slacks between the west coast dunes (of Britain).

Lucifuge. Carpenter '28:72, *Life in inland waters*. Of forms which do not inhabit light areas; photophobous; benthos forms.

Luciphile. = photophilous.

Lucus. Clements '02. A grove or park; a place grown with trees and grass. *See* savannah, parkland.

M

Macchia. (Italian). Shrubby mostly evergreen growth of the Mediterranean region. = maquis (SW S. Africa, Fynbosch (S & SW Australia), and Chaparral (California).

Macrophanerophyta. Braun-Blanquet '32:296. Trees.

Macrophyte. J:221 (Schimper). Marine algae of great length. (Warming). The non-microscopic pleuston or hydrocharid community.

Macrophytoplankton. J:221. Plants such as Ulothrix.

Macrosymbiont. J:221. The larger of two associated organisms in symbiosis.

Macrotherm. Schimper '03:209. Plants which are restricted to the tropics and which perish at the freezing point of water or even at some degrees above it. = megatherm.·

Macrothermophilus. Dwelling in the tropics.

Macrothermophytia. Clements '02. Tropical plant communities.

Magmaphilae. J:448 (Ivanoff). Algae which prefer warm and well lit waters, forming a colored mixture.

Major quadrat. 1. (Clements). A square of 4 meters. 2. Any designated sample area larger than one square meter.

Makroflora. J:222 (Levier & Sommier). The luxuriant vegetation of some of the valleys in the Caucasus.

Malagasy region. Lydekker '96:27. See appendix IX.

Malezales. Hardy '25:153, *Geogr. of Plants*. Deep swamps (Paraguay).

Mallee scrub. J:222. A shrub steppe largely composed of Eucalyptus about the height of a man.

Mangrove. Warming '09:234. Communities characteristic of flat muddy tropical shores where the water is relatively calm, as in lagoons, inlets, estuaries, etc.; the soil is flooded with water either at high tide or permanently; in many cases this type of vegetation extends far inland along rivers. Low forest or brushland; aerial roots abundant. *See* avicennietum, halodrymium, pluviifruticeta.

Maquis. Warming '09:288. Evergreen transition zone between steppe and forest in the Mediterranean region, the species being characteristic of the adjoining forest; mostly of taller scrubs. *See* macchia, Cistus maqui, espinal, Fynbosch, jarales, mesothamnium.

Maritime vegetation. Tansley & Chipp '26:204. Vegetation free floating, submerged; amphibious or subject to periodic inundation.

Marsh. Hancock "11:430. A tract of soft wet land, commonly covered wholly or partially with water. Needham & Lloyd '16:89. A meadow-like area overgrown with herbaceous aquatic plants, such as cattail, rushes, sedges. Sears '26, Ohio. Jl. Sci. 26:130. An herbaceous swamp, generally an extensive one; also used to designate a bog meadow. ESA 1934, List R-1. A swamp dominated by grasses or grass like vegetation. *See* ESA 1933, List P-1 for further definitions; emersiherbosa, fen, holophytia, helad, hele-, helic, heli-, helo-, hydro-, limnodic, mire, ·mose, bog, paludal, pontohalicolous, telmatium, travesias.

Mastigospore. Clements '05. A plant with ciliate or flagellate disseminules.

Mat geophytes. J:224. A closely intertwined vegetation of permanent spot bound plants, mostly monocots.

Math. J:224. Crop; aftermath. = second crop.

Mattae. J:449. (Clements). Mats of plants which form growths.

Matutinal. J:224. Pertaining to the morning; plants which flower early in the day.

Mbuga. Scott '34, Jl. Ecol. 22:197. Stage following upon hydroseral communities on alluvial soil which, if continuously protected from fire, give way to pioneer Acacias. Phillips '30, Jl. Ecol. 18:201. Periodically moist alluvial sunklands (Tanganyika Territory).

Mchaka. Phillips '30, Jl. Ecol. 18:201. Deciduous scrub (Tanganyika).

Mead. Clements '02. Wet meadow.

Meadow. Low prairie. Hancock '11:432. Lowland covered with coarse grass, composites or other herbage. Schimper '03:261. Hygrophilous or trophilous grassland. Warming '09:323. A community of tall long stemmed perennial herbs and especially of true grasses; the covering of vegetation is closely continuous and compact. *See* grassland, aquiprata, emersiprata, hygropoium, limnean, poium, poad.

Meadow moor. *See* fen.

Meadow thicket. Hancock '11:431. Lowland covered with thickly set trees and shrubs.

Mean sample tree. ESA 1934, List R-1. A tree of representative form which in diameter, height, and volume is an average of the trees in a group or stand.

Medanos. Hardy '25:155, *Geogr. of Plants.* Sand dunes on marsh or salt deserts. (W. Argentina).

Media. fide Vestal '33. Materials surrounding the organism.

Medial humidity. Shelford '29:368. The mean humidity accompanying mean temperatures under outdoor weather conditions.

Medial temperature. Shelford '29:368. The range of temperature within which the increase in rate of development under constant temperature is directly proportional to the rise in temperature.

Mediocolumbian zoological region. Lydekker '96:26, 146 (Blanford). America between 25° and 45° N. Latitude; = Sonoran zone (Lydekker).

Mediterraneus. J:223. 1. Inhabiting spots far from the sea. 2. Occurring in the Mediterranean region.

Megaphanerophyte. (Raunkiaer). Trees over 30 meters in height.

Megaplankton. = pleuston.

Megatherm. Raunkiaer '34:6 (A. deCandolle). Of/ plants demanding much heat, and growing only where temperature is high throughout the year; deCandolle included demands for moisture under this term as well as temperature.

Megecad. J:226. A group of several ecads of close affinity.

Megistrothermic. Warming '09:36 (deCandolle). Plants now extinct, which demanded uniformly high temperatures (above 30°C.).

Melangeophytia. Clements '02. Loam or alluvial communities.

Melittophilae. J:227 (Müller). Flowers which are adapted for pollenation by the larger bees.

Melliphagous. Chapman '31:161 (Handlirsch). Of/ organisms which feed on honey.

Meridian. Clements '05. = apparent noon.

Merism. J:449 (Janet). A primordial assemblage of cells.

Meroplankton. J:228 (Forel). Plankton found only at certain seasons of the year. *See* aspection.

Merriam's Life zones 1899, Smithsonian Report '91:365. Alpine, timber-line, hudsonian, Canadian, Yellow pine, pinon, and deserts were originally recognized; *see* appendix V, VI.

Mesa. Vestal '19; Bot. Gaz. 58:157. A table land capped by a more resistant stratum which keeps the top flat by retarding erosion except at the sides. *See* kopjes.

Mesad. (Clements). A mesophyte. *See* mesic.

Meseosere. (Clements). A mesophytic eosere; = gymneosere.

Mesic. Cooper & Weese '26, Ecol. 7:390. Characterized or pertaining to conditions of medium moisture supply.

Mesiophytia. Clements '05. Inland communities.

Meso-. Combining term meaning intermediate.

Mesobenthile. Klugh '23, Ecol. 4:371. Sea bottom, at depths of 200-1000 meters.

Mesochthonophytia. Clements '02. Inland communities.

Mesocline. (Clements). A moist cool slope; a mesic slope.

Mesohabitum. Pearse '26:23. A portion of an otherwise uniform habitat which differs from the remainder only in certain habitatic differences. See facies, locies.

Mesohydrophytic. J:229 (Whitford). Intermediate between mesophytic and hydrophytic; Of/ plants which incline to a damper habitat than the true mesophyte; = mesic.

Mesohylile. Klugh '23, Ecol. 4:373. Of/ moist forests. See woodland.

Mesolochmis. Klugh '23, Ecol. 4:373. Moist thicket associes.

Mesomorphous. J:229. Applied to plants not specially protected against desiccating influences.

Mesophanerophyte. (Raunkiaer). Trees 8-30 meters in height.

Mesophanerophytium J:229 (Vahl). A community of perennial plants 8-30 meters high.

Mesophilus. J:229. Dwelling in moist lands. = mesic.

Mesophorbium. J:229 (Diels). Alpine meadow; community. See montane.

Mesophyte. (Warming). Plants which are intermediate between hydrophyte and xerophyte; avoiding both extreme moisture and drought; moist land plants. *See* mesic.

Mesophythmile. Klugh '23, Ecol. 4:372. Of/ offshore lake bottoms at 6-25 meters.

Mesophytia. Clements '02. Moist land communities.

Mesophytic. 1. = mesic. 2. (Clements '16:288). Vegetation of the mesozoic.

Mesosaprobia. J:230. Organisms requiring a medium amount of impurity. *See* pollution.

Mesosaprobic. Alexander '25, Bull. Ill. Nat. Hist. Surv. 15: 441. Of/ the step in purification following the septic stage; corresponds to the pollutional and contaminate zone of Forbes & Richardson '13; characterized by variety of higher water plants and the increased amount of dissolved oxygen.

Mesosere. Clements '16:289. The eosere of the mesozoic period. = Gymneosere.

Mesostatic. (Clements). A sere completing a succession under mesic conditions.

Mesothamnium. J:230 (Diels). Maquis formed of hard leaved shrubs.

Mesothermophilus. Dwelling in the temperate zone.

Mesothermophytia. Clements '02. Temperate plant communities.

Mesotherms. 1. Warming '09:36 (deCandolle). Plants calling for an annual mean temperature of 15-20°C and at least during certain periods, abundant moisture. Raunkiaer '34:6. M. can endure a considerably lower temperature than megatherms during a longer or shorter period of the year; they can grow in the tropical and sub-tropical regions; but it is only in the sub-tropical regions that they can conquer competitors which demand a different degree of heat; deCandolle included demands for moisture as well in this term. 2. Schimper '03:209. Plants which, in their development, require alternating high and low temperatures.

Mesotrophic. J:230, 450 (Clements). Of/ a swamp moderately provided with nutrients; peat of transitional moors.

Mesotropic. Clements '05. Of/ a mesic succession which tends towards hydrophytism.

Mesoxerophytic. J:230 (Whitford). Midway between mesophytic and xerophytic; Of/ plants affecting a dryer habitat than pure mesophytes.

Metabiosis. J:230. Symbiosis, with one of the organisms preparing the way for the other.

Metabolometric scale. For discussion see Townsend '24, Ecol. 5:21.

Metagenesis. *See* alternation of generations.

Metanimic. Klugh. '23, Ecol. 4:372. Of/ a temporary stream.

Metoecious. = heteroecious.

Metrokoninia. Allee '31:32 (Deegener). "In ants, where the fertilized female of one species who has lost the ability to start a new colony joins herself with the fertilized female of another species that has retained this power, and is thus associated with a colony development which she would be unable to secure alone, and to which she contributes little or nothing."

Microclimate. Uvarov '31:128. The actual ecoclimate in which an individual lives.

Microcosm. A miniature universe. Forbes '87 (reprint '25, Ill. Nat. Hist. Surv. Bull. 15:537). A lake community "forms a little world in itself — a microcosm within which all the elemental factors are at work and the play of life goes on in full, but ·on so small a scale as to bring it easily within the mental grasp."

Microhabitat. fide Shelford '30. A small habitat within a recognized area covering a habitat, such as a dead animal, a dead tree or a fallen log, or a portion of a living plant with an aggregation of several species; forms here assume dominule and subdominule rank of microdominance or microsubdominance.

Micromelittophilae. J:233. Flowers whose pollenation is effected by small bees and similar insects; the attraction is not obvious.

Micromyiophilae. J:233. Flowers which are pollenated by small flies which are often imprisoned.

Microphagous. Pearse '26:73 (Folsom). Of/ feeders on sugars and salts (yeast and bacterias).

Microphanerophyte. (Raunkiaer). Trees of 2-8 meters in height.

Microphyte. J:234. 1. Bacteria. 2. (Schimper) the smaller algae, e.g., diatoms.

Microphytic community. J:234. A community composed exclusively of lichens or algae.

Microsymbiont. J:234. The smaller of two associated organisms.

Microtherm. 1. Warming '09:36 (deCandolle). Plants requiring an annual mean temperature of 0-20°C., little of the sun's heat, uniformly distributed atmospheric precipitations, and a period of rest caused by cold. Raunkiaer '34:6. Plants of temperate regions in respect to temperature; deCandolle included demands for moisture as well under this term. 2. Schimper '03:209. Plants which can support without injury frosty weather during the vegetative season and are able to complete their life cycle in a short time.

Microthermophilus. Dwelling in boreal regions.

Microthermophytia. Clements '02. Boreal forest communities.

Mictium. A heterogenous mixture of plants in an area as contrasted with zoned areas. Clements '16:140. When the dominant species of two or more dominant stages of a sere are present on somewhat of an equality a mictium may be said to result. *See* ecotone, alternation, alterne.

Midseral communities. fide Hefley '35. Developmental communities which are below the rank of subclimax communities, but above the rank of initial communities. *See* ptenophyta.

Migrant. Clements '05. A plant that is migrating or invading.

Migrarc. (Clements). A migration circle.

Migration. Gleason '23, Ann Am. Assn. Geog. 12:42. Any general movement by which the range of a species is changed. Clements '16:64. . . . . begins when a germule (or diseminule) leaves the parent area and ends when it reaches its final resting place; it may consist of a single movement or a number of movements.

Migrule. (Clements). The unit or agent of migration. *See* disseminule.

Mikrospecies. (Lotsy). = Variety (DuRietz '30a:350).

Mimicry. Pearse '26:311. The imitation in form, color, or behavior of a comparatively defenseless and edible species (mimic) of another species (model) which has qualities that cause it to be avoided by predatory enemies. Two kinds of mimicry are recognized by ESA

1934, List P-2. (*a*) The Batesian type in which an edible species obtains security by counterfeiting the appearance of an inedible species, and (*b*) that observed by Bates and Müller (Müllerian) in which both are inedible; Mimicry is often restricted to the former type. *See* Bates's theory, coloration.

Minimal area. Hanson & Love '30, Jl. Agr. Res. 41:557. The smallest area upon which the association reaches its definitive number of constants. Braun-Blanquet '32:52. The minimum area required by a plant community for its normal development.

Minimalraum. ESA 1935. List P-3 (Cain). The smallest area necessary for an association in a definite locality to exhibit its special species (its character and attendant species). A concept of the Swiss-French school of plant sociologists.

Minimiareal. ESA 1935. List P-3 (Cain, Rübel). It is the smallest sample area (one quadrat to the stand) which will show all or most of the constant species for the community type. A constant species is required variously to appear in more than half of the stands sampled, usually in 81 or 91% or more depending on whether a 5- or a 10-parted scale is used. It is a measure of the average individual distance of the constants of the community which stand farthest from one another.

Minimum, law of the. *See* Leibig's law.

Minimum effective temperature. = threshold of development.

Minimum Quadrat Area. ESA 1935. List P-3 (Hanson & Love, Cain). A quadrat of the size at which the species-area curve flattens strongly and above which (larger sample area) the accuracy or completeness of the data does not increase in proportion to the time and labor involved.

Miombo. Scott '34, Jl. Ecol. 22:220. = Berlinia globiflora woodland (Tanganyika).

Mire. J:236. A marsh or boggy place.

Mixed forest. ESA 1934, List R-1. Forest composed of trees if two or more species; usually a forest in which at least 20 percent are trees other than the leading species.

Mixotrophic. J:451 (Minchin). Fed by holophytic and saprophytic nutrition.

Mobilideserta. Rübel '30, *Pflges. der Erde.* Open communities maintained by an unstable substratum. *See* deserta.

Mobility. Clements '16:64. The ability of a species to move out of the parent area.

Modality. *See* bimodality, diacmic, diplobiont, aspection.

Moisture equivalent. Fuller '14, Bot. Gaz. 18:218.

$$\frac{ME}{1.8} = \text{wilting coefficient.}$$

Monadnock. Johnson '16, Geogr. Rev. 1:444. An erosion remnant left standing above a peneplane.

Monocarpic. Warming '09:6 (deCandolle). Of/ plants which produce flowers, fruits, or spores but once, then die. = hapaxanthic (Braun).

Monochronic. Clements '05. Arising but once.

Monoclimax. Phillips '34, Jl. Ecol. 22:566. A single climatic climax for all seres and successions; = climatic climax (Clements).

Monoclonal. J:451. Of/ populations derived asexually from a common ancestor; a single clone.

Monocormic. J:238 (Burtt). Of/ trees which have one main axis bearing lateral branches of bilateral structure.

Monogamy. Allee '31:26 (Deegener). Strict non-promiscuity, either seasonal or permanent.

Monogenesis. Clements '05. The origin of a new form at a single place or time.

Monogynopaedium. Allee '31 (Deegener). One female and her offspring which remain together for a period; if the young reproduce parthenogenetically such a complex group may be called a polygynopaedium.

Monophagous. Pearse '26:72. Of/ animals which are restricted to a single food; = stenopagous Monophylesis. Clements '05. Origin from a single ancestral type.

Monotocous. J:239. Fruiting once only, as annuals and biennials; monocarpic.

Monotopic. 1. Clements '05. Originating once only. 2. (Drude). Arising from a single center of dispersal.

Monotrophic. J:240. Nutrition confined to one host species.

Monotropic. J:240. Of/ bees which visit only one species of flower. *See* pollenation.

Monsoon forest. Schimper '03:260. Tropical deciduous forest subjected to heavy rainfall and a long dry season; more or less leafless during the latter; less lofty than the rain forest, rich in woody lianas, trophophilous in character, rich in herbaceous but poor in woody epiphytes. *See* Hiemilignosa.

Montane. *See* alpestrine, andean, alpine, cloudforest, mesophorbium, mountain-, petran, subalpine, timberline.

Montane region. Schimper '03:702. Regions with vegetation more hygrophilous and less thermophilous than
in the neighboring lowlands, resembling that of the lowlands of the higher latitudes.

Monte community. J:451 (Lorentz). Bushland of thorny
growth.

Moon. *See* lunar, seleno-.

Moor. Hancock '11:433. An extensive waste covered
with patches of heath and bearing a poor light soil;
sometimes marshy and abounding in peat. Clements
'16:268. (Schreiber). A habitat with at least 50 cm.
of peat soil of more or less decomposed plant remains;
types recognized: Reedswamp (flachmoor or nieder-
moor), reedmoss (reed swamp fossils below and sphagnum above), and low or hochmoor converted meadows
(meadow moss or meadow swamp). Warming '09:200.
An area underlaid by bog moss (Sphagnum) and arising on moist soil, but slightly permeable to water, does
not necessarily show open water though a very damp
air hangs over it. *See* ESA 1934, List R-1 for comment
on the usage of this term. *See* heath, moss, myr, sterrhium, hygrosphagnium, fen, marsh, bog.

Moss-schicht. Braun-Blanquet & Pavillard '30. = bodenschicht; ground or moss stratum; *see* stratification.

Mor. ESA 1933, List P-1. Comprises matted humus layers usually very high in organic matter and lying like
a carpet on top of mineral soil; may be more or less
tough or compact or both, not porous and friable like
mull. *See* duff, mull, muld, humus, litter.

Morass. Clements '16:271. (Fleroff). = swamp.

Mores. Shelford '12, Biol. Bull. 23:334. The index of
physiological conditions and constituting the dominant

phenomenon of a physiological life history. fide Shelford '30. The reactions common to all of the predominants of a community; groups of organisms in full agreement as to physiological life histories as shown by habitat preference, time of reproduction, reactions to physical factors of the environment; the organisms constituting a mores usually belong to a single species but may include more than one species. Singular: mos.

Mores index. fide Shelford '30. Reaction to some factor or factors such as the mean order of orientation of several species from different habitats in a decreasing water current velocity.

Mores ratio. fide Shelford '30. The ratio between different life habits which characterize the predominants of a community such as arboreal: fossorial forms; it corresponds to the vegetation form or landscape aspect of the plants.

Morphogeny. III Int. Bot. Congr. 1910:22 (Jaccard). The study of adaptations; the totality of the reactions (adaptations) of the plant to its habitat, from which its physiognomy results.

Morphosis. *See* morphogeny.

Mos. Shelford '12, Biol. Bull. 23:354. The term applied to animals having certain attributes. fide Shelford '30. The physiological equivalent of form used in taxonomy and applies to groups of individuals such as a species or subdivision of a species based upon the physiology of behavior, or two or more species which act together as one mos (such as mixed herds of African mammals). The term should be applied (whenever there is a change of habitat in the life history stages) to the different life history stages, or the selection of different habitats in different parts of the annual cycle. Plural: mores. *See* mores ratio.

Mosaic complex. DuRietz '30:339. A phytocoenosis-complex of proportionately small stands (Siedlungen) of definite Phytocoenoses; *see* appendix I, II. *See* association-complex, mictium.

Mose. Raunkiaer '24 ('09):264. = bog. *See* marsh.

Moss. J:240. A lowland moor.

Moss moor. J:240. Usually higher in the center with growth of Sphagnum.

Moss tundra. J:240. Flat or undulating tract, devoid of forest, in the north of Siberia.

Moth Flowers. J:241. Adapted for moths as pollenating visitors; usually white flowers.

Motile. Clements '15. Able to move by growth, by means of cilia, etc.

Motile colony. An associated group, not fixed to one place.

Mountain forest. Tansley & Chipp '26:206. Closed forest of high altitudes; generally subject to prevailing mist and clouds; temperature moderate.

Mountain meadow. Tansley & Chipp '26:206. Mountain grassland of high altitudes; dwarfed trees and shrubs are present if kept dwarfed by grazing or fire.

Muck. *See* gyttja.

Mud. *See* pelochthium.

Muld. = mull.

Mulga scrub. (Warming). A thicket composed chiefly of Acacia.

Mull. ESA 1933, List P-1. A porous, more or less friable humus layer of crumby or granular structure, with diffuse lower boundary, not or only slightly matted. =

mor, moar. Twin-, crumb-, grain-, and detritus- mull are recognized; *see* Romell & Heiburg '31, Ecol. 8:581.

Müllerian mimicry. Haviland '26:100. The possession of certain warning colors in common. *See* Bates' theory, mimicry, coloration.

Multivoltine. Uvarov '31:104. Of/ forms producing several generations a year; each generation taking only a short time for its development. Cf. univoltine.

Muskeg. Haviland '26:199. Moss bogs of the Canadian forest.

Mutable. Clements '05. Able to produce mutants.

Mutant. A form arising by mutation, the sudden appearance of new forms.

Mutualism. A form of symbiosis of benefit to both or all parties concerned; = commensualism. *See* symbiosis.

Mutualistic symbiosis. Of reciprocal advantage or mutual service to one another.

Mutuality. Yapp '25, Veroff. des Geobot. Inst., Rübel 44:701. Cases in which mutual benefit or mutual dependence arises from the proximity of plants to one another.

Mycetodomatia. J:244 (Frank). Fungus chambers which are formations of peculiar character found on the roots of plants sometimes regarded as possessed with the power of attracting fungi and ingesting them.

Mycetophagous. Of/ animals which eat fungi.

Mycorrhiza. Tansley & Chipp '26:158. Fungi found in symbiotic association with the roots of certain plants; the condition may be endo- or ectotrophic.

Myiophilae. J:244. Plants which are pollenated by diptera; the flowers are often dull and the odors disagreeable to man.

Myr. Warming '09:198. A general type of moor (Norway, Iceland).

Myrmecochorous. J:245. Dispersed by means of ants.

Myrmecodomatia. J:245. Shelters formed by plants in which the ants live.

Myrmecolous. Hancock '11:420. Inhabiting galleries of ants.

Myrmecophilous. J:245. Of/ plants which are inhabited by ants and offer specialized shelter or food for them.

Myrmecophily. Schimper '03:140. The plant condition of being adapted for attracting ants.

Myrmecophobic. J:245. Of/ plants which, by hairs, glands, etc., repel ants.

Myrmecophyte. Haviland '26:76. Plants living in symbiosis with certain insects, e.g., ants.

Myrmecotrophic. J:245. Of/ plants furnishing food to ants.

Myrmecoxenous. J:245. Of/ plants supplying both food and shelter to ants.

Myrmecrobromus. J:244 (Hansgirg). Of/ plants affording food to ants.

Myxotrophic. Pearse '26:72. Of/ chlorophyll bearing protista and alga containing animals that have two modes of nutrition in the same organism.

N

Namatium. Clements '02. A brook community.

Namatophilus. Of/ brook loving species. *See* stream.

Nanism. Raunkiaer '34:30. Dwarf growth, sometimes considered inherited.

Nannoplankton. 1. Chapman '31:325. Plankton taken in nets. 2. J:246. Floating organisms of extremely small size.

Nanophanerophyta. Braun-Blanquet '32:295. Shrubs. *See* phanerophytes. Not exceeding 2 meters in height.

Narcotropism. J:246. Movement due to a narcotic cause.

Nascence. Pound & Clements '98. The origin of a community upon a barren area (the commencement of a sere) as distinguished from the modification of existing communities.

Nastic movement. A movement caused by diffuse stimuli.

Natant. Floating, completely submerged.

Natio. = variety (DuRietz '30a:349).

Native. Indigenous, endemic. Cf. exotic, ruderal.

Natural area ESA '32 (U.S. For. Serv.). An area set aside with emphasis on the stationary elements of nature, hence is primarily floral.

Natural color. Moss '33, Jl. An. Ecol. 2:220. The maintenance of the population of a pest species by the action of natural factors at a certain numerical level whether this level is below the point where financially measurable loss to crops is produced or not.

Natural (native) pasture. Semple '24, USDA, Miscl. Pub. 194. Uncultivated lands wholly or mainly occupied by native or naturally introduced plants useful to grazing.

Natural plant. Kurz '28, Bot. Gaz. 85:86. A wild plant characteristic of relatively undisturbed areas. *See* native, ruderal, endemic, indigenous, exotic.

Nature reserve. *See* nature sanctuary.

Nature sanctuary. ESA '32. An area in which fluctuations in numbers of constituent organisms are allowed free play; 1st class: any area of natural vegetation containing all the animal species historically known to have primitively occupied the area in recent times except primitive man and thought to be of sufficient numbers to support themselves. 2nd class. (*a*) Second growth areas (of timber) approaching maturity but conforming to the 1st class requirements. (*b*) areas of original vegetation from which not more than two important species of animals are missing. 3rd class. Areas modified more than 2nd class.

Neap tide. The tide at low ebb.

Nearctic region. (Wallace, Lydekker). America as far south as Mexico. *See* appendix VII, IX.

Nebenstande. = coenosis (Klugh), society (authors).

Necrocoleopterophilous. J:246. Of/ plants pollenated by carrion beetles.

Necrogenous. J:247. Of/ fungoid parasites which hasten the decay of the plants on which they live.

Necron. J:452 (Sernander). Dead plants, not yet turned to humus. *See* duff, litter.

Necrophaga. Eaters of dead animals and plant bodies; sometimes applied to saprophytes.

Necrosis. J:247 (Escombe). The death of an organism, or part.

Necton. Organisms swimming at the surface of any body of water. *See* plankton.

Needle forest. *See* evergreen, coniferous, conilignosa.

Neidioplankton. J:247 (Forel). Plankton organisms possessing swimming apparatus.

Nekrophytophagous. Chapman '31:161 (Handlirsch). Of/ organisms feeding on dead plant substances. Also spelled necro-.

Nekton. = necton. Chapman '31:284. Organisms which swim with actively directed movement and are essentially independent of the bottom. Friederichs '30:233. Subnekton and supranekton are used to distinguish organisms swimming at the surface and below the surface of bodies of water.

Nemoralis. J:247. Inhabiting woods and groves. *See* woodland.

Nemus. Clements '02. Open woodland. *See* savannah, parkland.

Nemus paludosum. Clements '02. Swamp open woodland.

Neogaean. 1. Of/ the western hemisphere; the "new world." 2. Zoological region. *See* appendix IX. Lydekker. '96:25 (Sclater). Includes Nearctic and Neotropical regions. *See* appendix IX.

Neogeic. J:248 (Crampton). Occurring on recent geological formations.

Neophyte. J:248. A newly introduced plant. *See* ruderal, exotic.

Neophytic. Clements '16:288 (Saporta). Of/ the neozoic or tertiary geologic period.

Neotropical. 1. Of/ S. America. 2. Zoological region. The area embracing S. and Central America. *See* appendix IX.

Nereid community. Warming '09:169. A Community composed largely of algae.

Neritic. Of the coast or shore line; in shallow water.

Neritic plankton. ESA 1935. List P-3. That portion of the plankton which originates from the organisms of the bottom, e.g., free-swimming larvae, spores and seeds of aquatic plants, etc.

Nest epiphyte. Schimper '03:319. A species that by appropriate devices collects large quantities of humus and water for growth.

Netherveld. Hardy '25:248, *Geogr. of Plants.* A hilly district, transition between the brush steppe and tropical savannah; taller trees and grass than boschveld. (S. Africa).

Neuston. Carpenter '28:35, *Life in inland waters* (Naumann). Minute forms, such as bacteria and protista which float against the surface film; this concept may be extended to include the macroscopic forms also. *See* plankton.

New place effect. J:453 (Collins). Seed from a distant locality producing changed results in the new habitat.

Niche. Elton '27:63, *Animal Ecology.* The status of an animal in its community, indicating what it is doing; its place in the biotic environment; its relation to food and enemies. Woodbury '33, Ecol. Monogr. 3:169. The microhabitat or ultimate division of the habitat including the recognition of its modifying factors occupied by mores or species. *See* foodchain, pyramid of numbers.

Nipho. J:249 (Drude). Of/ snow.

Nitrophilous. J:249 (Schimper). Of/ alkali loving plants.

Nival flora. J:249. Flora above the snow line.

Niveal. Clements '02. Of/ snow.

Nomad. (Clements). A pasture plant.

Nomadic. J:250. Of/ certain steppe plants, blown from their original station.

Nomium. Clements '02. A non-wooded pasture community.

Nomophyllous. J:453 (Radlkofer). Of/ leaves normal for the genus or other group.

Nomophilus. Of/ species dwelling in pastures.

Non-pyric subsere. Wells-Shunk '31, Ecol. Monogr. 1:488. A subsere created by culture conditions other than fire.

Normal dispersion. Braun-Blanquet & Pavillard '30. Distribution of individuals according to the law of probability.

Normal specific assemblage. Braun-Blanquet & Pavillard '30. The floristic basis of the concrete study of association; it contains the usual floristic list of an example of an association which is found in nature; each example requires a certain minimum area in order to show the N.S.A. *See* specific assemblage.

Noterophilous. = mesophyte.

Notogaeic region. Lydekker '96:27. *See* appendix IX.

N.S. quotient. Braun-Blanquet '32:143 (Meyers). (Niederschlag und Sättigungsdefizit): the relationship of precipitation to saturation deficit.

Nudation. J:453 (Gams). The occurrence of bare areas due to various causes. = denudation.

Nutation. A rhythmical change in the position of growing organs in plants.

Nutricism. J:252. A form of symbiosis in which the fungus becomes the nurse and feeder of the other symbiont.

Nycanthes. J:252. Night flowering plants. *See* photoperiodism, day, periods.

Nyctigamous. J:252. Of/ flowers which close by day, but open at night and are often scented. *See* photoperiodism.

Nyctipelagic. J:252 (Forel). Of/ floating organisms which rise to the surface only at night.

Nyctitropism. J:252. Assuming the sleep position. *See* phototropism.

O

Obex. Clements '02. A barrier.

Obligate parasite. J:253. An organism in which parasitism is imperative in order to attain complete development.

Obligate symbiont. J:253. An organism which is dependent on another for its existence.

Occupation. (Clements). The possession of the ground by plants. *See* abyssal, bathile, benthos, dimersal, continental terrace, ellitoral, emerging belt, enhalid, epactile, epibenthile, eupelagic, halobios, halonereid, hololimnetic, knephopelagile, mesobenthile, mesopythmile, phaepelagile, phytobenthos, pontophilous, pythmic, skolopelagile, thalassium, trophosphere, vagil-benthon.

Oceanad. An ocean plant.

Oceanium. Clements '02. An ocean community.

Oceanophilus. Of/ ocean dwelling organisms.

Ochetium. Clements '05. A succession due to artificial drainage.

Ochthium. Clements '02. A bank community.

Octhophilus. Of/ bank loving species.

Oecology. = ecology.

Okefinokee swamp local names. Wright '32, Ecol. Monogr. 2:118. Bay, causeway, prairie, islets, run, crossing, strand, dreen, etc.

Oligohalile. Klugh '23, Ecol. 4:382. Of/ upper estuarine areas: the part of the estuary in which the total salt content is from 1-5 parts per mille.

Oligopelic. Clements '05. Of/ areas containing little clay.

Oligopetric. J:256 (Thurmann). Of/ plants which prefer rocks which yield a small amount of clayey detritus.

Oligophagous. Folsom '26:373. Of/ organisms feeding on several definitely fixed food plants.

Oligopsammic. 1. Clements '05. Of/ areas containing little sand. 2. J:256 (Thurmann). Of/ plants of certain dolomite and granite soils.

Oligorhizous. (Clements). Of/ marsh plants which form but few roots.

Oligosaprobic. ESA 1935. List P-3. A term applied to aquatic media that are high in oxygen content, very low in dissolved organic matter and with a minimum of decomposition of organic substances. *See* catarobic, Polysaprobic, Mesosaprobic.

Oligosaprobic zone. Alexander '25, Bull. Ill. Nat. Hist. Surv. 15:441. The zone of clear water. *See* septic.

Oligotropic. 1. (Warming). Of/ plants which grow in areas of poor soil with respect to the nutrient salts. 2. (Clements). Swamps poor in plant nutrients. 3. (Thienemann). Waters poor in humus, often rich in calcium with only a narrow zone of rooted forms because of rapidly deepening waters; no distinct oxygen stratification at any time. 4. Chapman '31:304. Of/ lakes which are rich in oxygen even to the bottom.

Oligotropic. J:256 (Loew). Of/ bees which visit a restricted range of plants.

Olisthion. = olisthium. Clements '05. A succession of land slips.

Ombratropism. Tropic responses of organisms to the stimulus of rain.

Ombrophile. J:256 (Weisner). A rain loving plant.

Ombrophilous. Schimper '03:2; Warming '09:32. Of/ plants which are rain loving; the leaves are capable of being wetted.

Ombrophyte. J:256 (Hansgirg). A shade loving plant.

Ombrotiphic. Klugh '23, Ecol. 4:373. Of/ temporary pools left by melting snow and temporary rains.

Omnicolous. J:453. Of/ lichens indifferent to their substrata. = ubiquitous.

Omnivorous. Of/ species not restricted in their food habit to a single type of food or host. *See* oligovorous, pleotrophic.

-on. Suffix denoting: 1. formation. 2. (Clements) family.

Oncospore. Clements '05. A plant with hooked disseminules.

Onomotologia. J:256. Rules to be observed in the construction of names. No such rules have ever been adopted in Ecology.

Open communities. 1. Communities in which competition is not severe and invasion is successful. Tansley & Chipp '26:368. The individual plants are scattered at intervals, and there is no reaction of species with species. (Clements). Communities in which the plants are scattered. Warming '09:137. Communities formed by shifting soil, extreme character of soil (e.g., rock), dryness of climate, or extreme cold. *See* sporadophytia. 2. Braun-Blanquet 32:371. Communities requiring competition for place to germinate and for food.

Open woodland. Tansley & Chipp '26:205. Parkland area with trees characteristically in groups but without a closed canopy; a general herbaceous ground covering, grass predominating.

Opium. Clements '02. A parasitic community.

Opophilus. Of/ sap loving species.

Optimal area. (Warming). The most favorable area for the development of a species or variety.

Optimum. Adams '15, Bull.Ill.St.Lab. 11:9. The complex of environmental factors which is the most favorable and the departure from which is in the direction of unfavorable conditions. (Blackman & Smith) When several factors are controlling a function, a small increase or decrease of the factor that is limiting, and of that factor only, will bring about an alternation of the magnitude of functional activity. J:258. The most advantageous degree of environmental conditions which best conduces to the vital activities of a given organism. (Schimper) The area of maximum numbers is the area of overlapping of the optima of various factors. Absolute O.: corresponds to the highest intensity of a function. *See* ecological optimum. Leibig's law of the minimum, pessimum.

Orchard. Hancock '11:431. An enclosure containing fruit trees; not usually applied to nut-bearing trees. *See* pomarium, dendrium.

Orchard country. Tansley & Chipp '26:205. Parkland with a typical orchard-like aspect with trees and often palms occurring singly and generally scattered throughout the grass. *See* savannah, parkland.

Order. Braun-Blanquet & Pavillard '30. A group of alliances related by floristic and sociological affinities. *See* appendix I.

Ordnung. (Braun-Blanquet). = order.

Ore. = Pasture (Danish).

Oread. J:259. A sunplant; heliophyte.

Orgadium. Clements '02. An open woodland community.

Orgadophilus. Dwelling in open woodland.

Orgya. J:259. Vegetation six feet in height. *See* shrub, scrub.

Oriental region. (Wallace). *See* appendix VII.

Ornithocoprophilous. J:454 (Sernander). Of/ lichens which benefit by the excreta of birds.

Ornithogaea. Lydekker '96:26 (Sclater). New Zealand and Polynesia.

Ornithophilous flowers. Schimper '03:120. Flowers which are adapted for pollenation by birds.

Orographic characters. Braun-Blanquet & Pavillard '30. Physiographic characters depending on the configuration of the surface of the earth (relief).

Orohylile. Klugh '23, Ecol. 4:372. Of/ subalpine forests.

Orolochmis. Klugh '23, Ecol. 4:373. Subalpine thicket associes.

Orophytia. Clements '02. Subalpine communities.

Orothamnic. Klugh '23, Ecol. 4:374. Of/ alpine heaths.

Orthogamy. J:454. The normal relations of male and female.

Orthoheliotropic. J:260. Movement directed toward the source of light, e.g., as in the linear leaves of grasses.

Orthophototropic. J:260. Movement due to the direct influence of light.

Orthotropic. J:260. Assuming a vertical position.

Ortstein. Clements '16:87. A stratum of soil which stops downward growth of roots and is the result of accumulation of humus at the contact of sand and a mineral salt solution.

Osmotropism. Tropism due to osmotic action.

Oued. J:261. A valley containing water in the rainy season (Arabic).

Outbreaks of pests. Uvarov '31:157. (Friederichs). Years leading up to outbreaks: (a) preparatory year, (b) predromal year, (c) eruption year or year of outbreak; terms not defined.

Overgrazing. USDA Dept. Bull. 790:160. Grazing which when continued for one or more years reduces the forage crop or results in an undesirable change in the type of vegetation.

Overstocked. ESA 1934, List R-1. The condition of a stand containing more trees or material of the species and age than the site is capable of supporting.

Overtopped. *See* crown class.

Overturn. ESA 1935. List P-3. Term applied to the thorough circulation that the wind brings about in deeper lakes when the top and bottom temperatures are sufficiently similar to eliminate the specific gravity difference that produces stratification of the water at other times of the year.

Oxbow lake. Needham & Lloyd '16:67. A lake resulting from the filling up of the ends of an abandoned channel with silt deposits.

Oxodic. Klugh'23,Ecol.4:373. Of/ a peat bog community.

Oxodium. Clements '05. A humus marsh community.

Oxygeophilus. Dwelling in humus.

Oxygeophytia. Clements '02. Humus plant communities.

Oxylic. Of/ sour or acid soil communities.

Oxylium. Clements '02. A humus marsh community.

Oxylophilus. Humus loving.

Oxyon. (Clements). A heath climax.

Oxypetrile. Klugh '23, Ecol. 4:274. Of/ acid rock communities.

Oxyphyte. (Clements). A plant which is an indicator of lack of oxygen in the soil; with low chreshard.

Oxysere (oxarch). Clements '16. Seres having their origin in acid aquatic media or acid soils.

Oxytropism. J:262. Movement caused by an excess of acid.

P

Pagium. Clements '04:138. A succession on glacial soil.

Pagophytia. Clements '02. Foothill communities.

Pajonales. Hardy '25:158. *Geogr. of Plants*. Reed thickets at the edges of Pampas streams.

Palaearctic region. (Wallace, Sclater). Europe, Africa, and Asia north of the Tropic of Cancer. *See* appendix III.

Palaeogaea. Lydekker '96:25 (Sclater '58). The region including Arctic Europe and the Ethiopian, Indian, and Australian zoological regions. Cf. Neogaea. *See* appendix IX.

Paleophytic. Clements '16:288 (Saporta). Of/ plants of the paleozoic era.

Paleosere. Clements '16:289. The eosere of the paleozoic period; = Pterosere.

Paludal. J:264 (Watson). Pertaining to marshes, wet all through the year.

Palus. Clements '02. Low ground near rivers; a marsh.

Paluster. Clements '16:269 (Gadeceau). The marginal zone of a lake.

Palustrine. J:264. Inhabiting boggy ground.

Pamir. Hardy '25:73, *Geogr. of Plants*. Alluvial mountain meadows (Tibet).

Pampas. Warming '09:286 (Brackebusch). Grass steppes of South America, "grass clothed, completely treeless, level plains." *See* grassland:

Pan. 1. J:264. A hard layer or substratum of earth impervious to plant roots; = hardpan. 2. Nichols '20, Bull. Torr. Bot. Club. 47:564 (Yapp & Johns). A shallow depression in meadows of the upper littoral zone. *See* lows.

Panclimax. Clements '36. Jl. Ecol. 24:270. Two or more related climaxes or formations of similar general climatic features, similar life form, and common genera of dominants; relationship is regarded as due to a common origin from an ancestral climax (eoclimax) of Tertiary or earlier time. *See* Eoclimax, appendix I.

Panformation. DuRietz '30:322. A Phytocoenosis composed of several independent and stable Formations in which one layer (the highest if not otherwise noted) is dominated by species of a distinct genus or family (i.e., consists of a distinct Panformion); only exceptionally do Formations exhibit common species; the other layers are often composed of entirely unrelated synusia.

Panformion. DuRietz '30:337. A stable Synusium of one or more Formions dominated by species of distinct genera or families, but only exceptionally are the same species present in different Formations. *See* appendix II.

Panne. Raunkiaer '34 ('08):149. A lagoon in the Danish West Indies separated from the sea, the edges of which bear luxuriant mangrove vegetation. *See* salt panne.

Panphotometric. J:264 (Weisner). Of/ leaves which adapt their position to both direct and diffuse light.

Pantachobryus. J:264. Growing in a circular manner.

Pantanos. Hardy '25:157, *Geogr. of Plants*. Brackish or fresh water marshes (Argentina).

Pantophagous. Chapman '31:160 (Handlirsch). Of/ organisms eating a great variety of food. = omnivorous.

Parachorium. Allee '31:32 (Deegener). The relationship where one animal lives within the body of another without being parasitic upon it. = raumparasitismus. *See* symbiosis.

Paraheliotropism. J:265. Diurnal sleep; the movements of "sleep" of leaves to avoid the effects of intense sunlight.

Parallelogeotropism. J:266. The tropic response of an organism directing itself axially towards the force of gravity. *See* orthotropism.

Paramutualism (Elenkin). Facultative symbiosis.

Parang. Clements '16:276 (Whitford). Second growth vegetation as a result of repeated cutting of bamboo (Phillipines).

Paranos. Hardy '25:125, *Geogr. of Plants.* Alpine meadows of the Andes.

Paraphagia. Allee '31:31 (Deegener). Societies composed of harmless companions of their host feeding commensually on fragments neglected by the host.

Paraphototropism. J:266. The tropic response resulting in the organism or organ being placed at right angles to the incident light. = diaphototropism.

Parasite. Chapman '31:160. An organism living on or in a living organism, or its body substances without killing immediately or at all, and staying in the most continually, a life time, or at least a long time in one stage. Young '27 Am. Jl. Bot. 14:481. An organism which lives in or attached to some other species of living organism from which it secures part or all of its food material in the form of living matter.

Parasitic saprophyte. J:266. A parasite which kills its host and then continues to feed upon it.

Parasitism. Allee '31:32 (Deegener). The phenomenon of one individual obtaining its nourishment from its host with whose continued existence the parasite is more or less closely bound. Pearse '26:349. An intimate association between two or more species in which one or more (hosts) are injured and others (parasites) benefit. *See* amentoecious, ectendotrophic, endophyte, endoxylophyte, endozoophyte, endotrophic, entophyte, euphytoid, haemotophagous, hemiautophyte, hemiparasite, heteroecious, heterphaptomenon, heterophyte, histophytia, holendophyte, holoparasite, hyperparasite, obligate P., perniciasm, symbiosis, phagocytosis, photobia, pleioxeny, pleophagous, plurivorous, root P., sekyotic, supercresence, superP., trixeny.

Parasitus spurius. = epiphyte.

Paratrophic. J:267 (C. Jones). Of/ organisms able to exist only in animals or plants.

Pardochoren. Friederichs '30:233. Organisms motile at one stage of their life history, and sessile at another, as Bryozoa, Hydrozoa, etc.

Parkland. Tansley & Chipp '26:204. Trees in groups or isolated, lianes generally absent, ground surface with a continuously or interrupted herbaceous cover. Cf. savannah. *See* boschveld, lucus, grove, enclave.

Paroecia. Allee '31:32 (Deegener). Neighborly groups in which the less conspicuous species finds protection from the other without occupying a part of its nest (e.g., ants, etc.).

Parorthotropism. J:268 (Archangeli). The movement of leaves placing themselves with the lamina vertical, but necessarily meridionally.

Parque. Hardy '25:148, *Geogr. of Plants*. Parkland of Acacia and narrow leaf grassland (Chaco, S. America).

Partial cutting. *See* selective cutting.

Partial habitat. Yapp '22, Jl. Ecol. 10:13. The habitat of an individual species during any period or stage of existence.

Partopaedium. Allee '31:25 (Deegener). A group in which the male remains with his offspring for a time. Cf. patrogynopaedium, gynopaedium, sympaedium.

Parvo-cariceta. J:268 (Warming). Communities of small species of Carex.

Pascual. J:269 (Watson). Of/ plants which grow in pastures and grassy commons, among less rank herbage than "pratal."

Pascuum. Clements '02. A pasture.

Pasture. Warming '09:326. Higher and dryer than a meadow; vegetation is shorter and more open. See nomad, culture community, nomium, pascual, pratal.

Patana. Warming '09:298 (Pearson). A xerophytic grassy slope somewhat akin to savannahs; a treeless area caused by the burning of forest (Ceylon).

Patrogynopaedium. Allee '31:19 (Deegener). A primary association (aggregation) in which both parents remain with their offspring in groups.

Peck-order, peck-right. Allee '31:344. "The peck order decides which birds may peck others without being pecked in return; hens are said to have the peck right over those submitting to the pecking."

Pediophytia. Clements '02. Upland communities.

Pedology. Soil science.

Pelagic. 1. Flattely & Walton '22:10. Of/ the seaward extension of the shallow sea, including surface waters to a depth of 100 fathoms. Klugh '23, Ecol. 4:371. Water of the ocean. 2. Warming '09:161. Of/ open water plankton and other organisms. Shelford & Eddy

'29, Ecol. 10:385. . . . . communities are motile and do not remain in any fixed position in relation to the bottom.

Pelagium. Clements '02. A surface sea community.

Pelagophilus. Clements '02. Living at the surface of the sea.

Pelochthium. Clements '02. A mud bank community.

Pelogenous. Clements '05. Producing clay.

Pelophile. J:271 (Thurmann). Occurring in clay.

Pelophyte. J:455 (Gadeceau). A plant growing in clayey or marshy places.

Pelopsammic. Clements '05. Composed of mixed clay and sand.

Pelopsammogenous. Clements '05. Producing clay and sand.

Pelosammic. J:271 (Thurmann). Yielding both clay and sand.

Peneplain. Fenneman '31:74, *Physiogr. of W. U. S.* A surface of low relief; "approximately a plain."

Peneplane. Johnson '16, Geogr. Rev. 1:444. The undulating erosion surface of moderate relief produced in the penultimate stage of any physiographic cycle. *See* peneplain.

Percurrent. J:272. Extending throughout the entire length.

Perdominant. Clements '36. Jl. Ecol. 24:258. A dominant species which is present in all or nearly all of the associations of a formation.

Perennate, perennating, perennial. J:272. Lasting throughout the entire year.

Perennation. J:272. Lasting; in a perennial state.

Perennial herb. J:272. A plant in which the above ground portion dies each year, the root persisting.

Perennial monocarp. J:272 (Möbius). A plant which lives long, but dies after once flowering.

Perfect succession. Clements '05. A sere passing in the usual succession from initial to ultimate conditions without interruption or omission.

Periodicity. Braun-Blanquet & Pavillard '30. The duration of each species and estimation of the intensity of competition during the course of the year; also permits the establishment of several seasonal aspects with their corresponding seasonal changes in the physiognomy of the community.

Periodism. *See* aspection, photoperiodism, horarius, diurnation.

Permanent communities. Braun-Blanquet & Pavillard '30. The communities of plants which remain unchanged for a long time and maintain their social individuality without corresponding to the climax of the region.

Permanent pasture. Semple, USDA, Miscl. Pub. 194. Grazing land occupied by perennial pasture plants or by self seeding annuals, usually both, which remains unplowed for long periods (5 years or more).

Permeant influent. fide Shelford '35. . . . . wander through most of the developmental stages; birds, mammals, and a few reptiles. (Cf. Ranging influent). Major P. I. include the large ungulates and carnivors; minor P. I. include animals down to and including the bobcats and foxes and includes the largest of the predatory birds.

Permobile. Clements '05. Extremely mobile.

Perniciasm. J:276 (Tubeuf). The killing of host cells by a parasite.

Perpelic. J:276 (Thurmann). 1. Of/ rocks which yield clay in pure and abundant quantities; 2. Of/ plants which inhabit such areas.

Perpsammic. J:277. Yielding an abundance of sandy detritus, with accompanying flora.

Perquadrat. Clements '05, Res. Methods. A quadrat of 16 square meters or more.

Perversum confusa. Allee '31:29 (Deegener). A group in which individuals of the same sex but of different species congregate during the breeding season.

Perversum simplex. Allee '31:27 (Deegener). A case where males attempt to mate each other, as observed for drones of the honey bee.

Pes-caprae community. A community of Ipomaea pes-caprae (Java).

Pessimum. Chapman '31:189. Used but not defined; presumably the most unfavorable conditions under which life may exist. Cf. optimum.

Petasospore. Clements '05. A plant with parachute-like disseminules.

Petran. (Clements). Pertaining to the Rocky Mountains (U.S.).

Petric. Klugh '23, Ecol. 4:374. Of/ rock slide communities.

Petricolous. Hancock '11:420. Of/ rock inhabiting species.

Petrium. Clements '02. A rock community.

Petrochthium. Clements '02. A rock bank community.

Petrodium. Clements '02. A boulder field or ravine community.

Petrodophilus. Dwelling in boulder fields.

Petrophilus. Inhabiting rock communities.

Petrosus. J:278. Growing among stones.

Pflanzenverein. (German). = Association.

pH. An inverse expression of the concentration of the Hydrogen ions, the figure used expressing the exponential power of 10 of the actual value derived from concentrations of H-ions per liter. Neutrality is pH 7; acidity is below pH 7; alkalinity is above pH 7. The scale extends from pH 0 to pH 14.

Phaenobiotic. J:278 (Knutze). Of/ the geologic period when plants made their appearance as evidenced by their fossil remains.

Phaeno-ecological spectrum. ESA 1935. List P-3 (Gams). A diagram combining the seasonal aspect (and duration) and life-form features of a plant community.

Phagocytosis. J:455 (Bernard). Intracelluler digestion.

Phagophilia. Allee '31:29 (Deegener). Heterotypical reciprocal societies wherein each species benefits, although at least one of the two receives its food through its association with the other; thus a passive species is freed of its parasites through the efforts of its associates, showing one variety of mutualism.

Phagoplankton. J:456 (Gams). Autotrophic algae.

Phanerophyte. Raunkiaer '34:1, 19. A plant with the surviving buds or shoot apices borne on negatively geotropic shoots which project into the air. Braun-Blanquet & Pavillard '30. A phanerogam with vegetative organs higher than 25-30 cm. above the soil.

Phanerophyte climate. Raunkiaer '34('08):143. Tropical zone where the precipitation is not deficient.

Phanerophytion. J:456 (Moss). A main isocies of phanerogamous plants.

Phanerozoic. Pearse '26:240 (Flattely & Walton). Of/ animals which live above the soil.

Phaopelagile. Klugh '23, Ecol. 4:371. Of/ the upper pelagic of ocean; the surface to 30 meters.

Phase. 1. Carpenter '34, Proc. Okla. Acad. 14:29. An intradiel sub-community; equivalent to the seasonal society in aspection. 2. Allee '31:321 (Uvarov). A diverse form of such species as migratory locusts of apparently related stock, but which is essentially a variant of a widely plastic and variable species. 3. Braun-Blanquet '32:321. A stage of development of an association. = seral stage, associes. 4. (Wells-Shunk '31, Ecol. Monogr. 1:478). = facies.

Phellium. Clements '02. A rock field community.

Phellophilus. Dwelling in rock fields.

Phenological isolation. J:279 (Jeffery). Isolation by a time of flowering earlier or later than the other species of the same genus. See aspection.

Phenology. Shelford '29:4. The study of the correlation between periodic phenomena such as the flowering of certain plants or the arrival of migratory game or important birds. ESA 1935. List P-3. The science that deals with the time of appearance of characteristic periodic events in the life cycles of organisms in nature, especially as those events are influenced by temperature, latitude, altitude, and other environmental factors. See aspection.

Phenomenology. = phenology.

Phenotype. J:456 (Turesson). "Reaction type."

Philotherm. J:279 (Baker). A plant which needs warmth to complete its life cycle.

-philous. Clements '05. Suffix denoting loving, dwelling in.

Phobic. J:280 (Massart). Of/ a repulsion or negative response due to a physiological reaction.

Phobotaxis. Wigglesworth & Gillett '34. Jl. Ex. Biol. 11:129 (Kühn). The "avoiding reaction" of animals which keeps them confined within the zone where stimuli are optimal.

Photeolic. J:280. Of/ the "sleep" of plants.

-photic. Clements '05. Of/ light.

Photic. J:280. Influenced by or adapted to the action of light; well illuminated as in the margins of pools, etc.

Photic region. Schimper '03:782. The region of aquatic environments in which the intensity of light is sufficient for the normal development of macrophytes.

Photic zone. That area of bodies of water (extending down 3000 feet) which is penetrated by sunlight.

Photism. J:280 (Massart). The emission of light under stimulus.

Photoaesthesia. J:280 (Czapek). The power of an organ to respond to the stimulus of light.

Photobia. J:280 (Tulasne). Ectoparasitic fungi.

Photocliny. J:280. Response to the direction of incident rays of light.

Photoharmose. Clements '05. Response to light stimuli.

Photokinetic. Having the power of movement due to light. Of/ the stimuli of light.

Photolepsy. J:281 (Weisner). Catching the light; = Lichtgenuss (German).

Photometric. J:281. 1. Of/ organisms which turn either end to the direction of the light rays. 2. (Weisner).

Of/ leaves which assume a definite position in light, to obtain most of it or to screen themselves from too much.

Photometry. J:281 (Oltmanns). The response to the amount of light stimulus.

Photoperiodic. J:456. Of/ reactions due to the relative length of day.

Photoperiodism. *See* day periods, equinoctial, hemeranthy, horological, matutinal, nycanthus, nyctigamous, phototonous, auroral, diel, vesperal, nocturnal.

Photophilous. Of/ organisms which select sunny and bright habitats. *See* sun.

Photophobism. J:281. The avoidance of light.

Photophygous. J:281. Of/ shade plants.

Photoplagiotrophy. J:281 (Goebel). A tendency to arrangement obliquely with reference to incident light.

Phototaxis. Orientation or movement of an organism with reference to light.

Phototonic. J:281. Of/ the increasing irritability by the influence of light.

Phototonus. J:281. The normal mobile condition resulting from the alternation of day and night.

Phototrophy. J:281 (Oltmanns). Unequal decrease on one side of an organ due to incidence of light in relation to the parent shoot.

Phototropism. Tropistic response to light.

Photrum. J:281 (Moore). The whole scale of illumination affecting photolysis, the arrangement of chlorophyll granules under stimulus of light.

Phreatophyte. Bryan '28, Ecol. 9:474. A plant which derives its water supply from ground water and is more or less independent of rainfall.

Phretium. Clements'02. A community of an artificial tank.

Phrygana. Prickly and stiff undershrubs.

Phycodomatia. J:282 (Lundstrom). Plant shelters inhabited by other plants.

Phyad. Clements '28:3, Pl. Succession & Indicators. Vegetation or growth form.

Phylktioplankton. J:280 (Forel). Plankton organisms supported by hydrostatic means.

-phyll. Clements '05. Suffix or prefix denoting leaf.

Phyllogenous. J:283. Growing upon leaves; epiphyllous.

Phyllophagic. J:283 (Boulger). Of/ plants which derive their sustenance by their leaves. =phyllophyte.

Phylocobia. Allee '31:29 (Deegener). The condition when two species occupy the same cavity, as many myrmecoles.

Physical drought. J:283. A condition in which soil contains very little available water.

Physiognomic classification of communities. *See* Tansley & Chipp '26:204-206 for a key to the types and subtypes.

Physiognomic dominance. Tansley & Chipp '26:368. Conditions where certain species provide the characteristic facies; in this usage, dominance has no necessary connection with frequency.

Physiognomic dominants. Raunkiaer '34:494. Species which dominate physiognomically in a given piece of vegetation; frequently dominants.

Physiognomy. Tansley & Chipp '26:11. The general outward appearance of a community is determined by the life form of the dominant species. Nichols '23, Ecol. 4: 12. The external morphology (so to speak) of a community. III Int. Bot. Congr. 1910:24. .... is determined by the various growth forms of which it is composed.

Physiographic climax. *See* edaphic climax.

Physiographic conditions. Nichols '23, Ecol. 4:21. Conditions not atmospheric; associated with the form, structure, and behavior of the earth's surface. *See* edaphic.

Physiographic factors. III Int. Bot. Congr. 1910:24. Altitude above sea level, exposure, slope, surface features, etc.

Physiographic formations. Nichols '23, Ecol. 4:164. A complex of Associations which are geographically linked with one another by physiography; may be a very heterogenous vegetational unit.

Physiography. Clements '16:36 (Salisbury '07). . . . . has to do primarily with the surface of the lithosphere and the relations of air and water to it; its field is the zone of contact of air and water with the land, and of air and water.

Physiological basis of classification of communities. Shelford '32, Ecol. 13:114. The use of physiological characters as criteria of community ranking; reactions of predominants to physical gradients. An example of the nomenclature is as "lithorheotactic community." This system is not at present used. The following equivalents may be used in using Shelford '13, *Animal Communities in Temperate America.*

Formation (sensu latu)	associes
Association (not climax)	associes
Subformation	associes
Stratum	Layer society or socies
Consocies	assembly
mores	mores

Physiologic drought. J:248. The condition in which soil contains a considerable amount of water but little of which is available for plant life.

Physiological life history. Shelford '29:151. The sequence of physiological states through which an organism passes from the sexually mature adult to the same state of the next generation. The life history of an organism as controlled by its physiological reactions, either spontaneous, or in responses to the environment.

Physiological races, species. Forms differing in physiological characters but not in morphological differences. *See* ecad.

Physiological response. *See* mores.

Physiological species. fide Shelford '30. Physiological or behavior types, not morphologically recognizable, nor named in taxonomy.

Physiological zero. The point at which development begins; usage vague. Uvarov '31:20 recommends that this term be used only for the temperature below which no metabolic processes can occur. *See* alpha, threshold.

-phyta. Suffix denoting the flora of an area.

Phytal zone. Pearse '26:210 (Muttkowski). Littoral area along lake shores which supports vegetation.

-phyte. Clements '05. Combining term denoting plant.

Phyteris. Clements '05. Plant competition and migration.

Phytium. Clements '05. Combining term for formation.

Phytobenthon. J:284 (Forel). Vegetation of the depths. *See* ocean plankton.

Phytobenthos. Chapman '31:335. That portion of the bottom which is covered with vegetation. *See* ocean.

Phytobiotic factors. DuRietz '26a: lists climatic (shadow, windshelter, increased humidity), edaphic (factors of the lithosphere and hydrosphere), vegetational (humus formation, increased soil humidity), and pyric (fire) factors of the actual non-anthropeic environment. *See* ecological factors.

Phytocoenose. = phytocoenosis.

Phytocoenosis. DuRietz '30:301. The total plant population of a given habitat (Standort) usually separable into two or more synusia which are more or less distinct; it may or may not be spatially divided into subcommunities. Such a population is composed of plants for the most part of unrelated species; however it is bound together at least in one layer by the definite high sociological affinity of its high ranking characteristic species (or at least of a series of closely related species groups). *See* appendix I, II.

Phytocoenosis-complex. DuRietz '30:76, Proc. V. Int. Congr. Pl. Sci. A vegetational unit consisting of phytocoenoses with little or no relationship to each other, but more or less alternating. '30:338. A continuous or discontinuous vegetation composed of stands of several often unrelated phytocoenoses combined with a certain regularity. Divided into Mosaic- and Zonation-complexes, Vegetation regions, and Vegetation-stufe.

Phytocoenosium. J:456 (Schroeter). = community.

Phytocoenostics. = Phytosociology.

Phytodytes. Hancock '11:420. Inhabitants of habitats above ground; divided into Gramnicolous, Compositicolous, Thamnocolous, Hylacolous.

Phytoedaphon. Braun-Blanquet '32:289. Microscopic soil flora.

Phytograph. ESA 1935. List P-3 (Lutz). A type of diagram devised to express the role a tree plays in the structure of the community. The four axes of the graph give data on dominant trees (10" d.b.h. or over) as follows: 1) abundance %, 2) frequency %, 3) size classes in which the species occurs, 4) basal area %.

Phytophagous. Chapman '31:160 (Handlirsch). Of/ organisms which eat substances of plant origin.

Phytoplankton. Braun-Blanquet & Pavillard '30. Floating microscopical plants.

Phytosociology. J:457. A branch of ecology devoted to the consideration of vegetation rather than habitat factors. *See* autecology, autochorology, autogenetics, synecology, synechorology, synegenetics.

Phytostrote. Clements '05. A species migrating by means of a plant body.

Phytosuccivorous. Chapman '31:161 (Handlirsch). Organisms which feed on plant saps.

Pinares. Warming '09:315. Pine forests of the Canary islands at from 1600 to 2000 meters.

Pine barrens. Hardy '25; *Geogr. of Plants.* Pine forests on the dry sandy gravelly soil of the low indented coastal shelf (E. U.S.).

Pinhiero. Warming '09:316. Forests of Brazil, composed of Araucaria; south of the tropics.

Pioneer. Woodbury '33, Ecol. Monogr. 3:168. A plant or animal which invades a primary bare area and persists upon it; usually a hardy species which can exist upon bare rock or whose food (except microscopic forms) comes from elsewhere. Clements '16:212 (Birger). A species which invades bare soil but does not build sharply delimited communities. *See* family (Clements), colony (Clements).

Pioneer stage. (Clements). The extreme condition of a

primary area with reference to a climax, as lichens in rock seres and submerged plants in hydroseres. *See* stage.

Piscine. Clements '02. A pond or pool community.

Place constant. J:287 (Shull). An invariable factor of plant life in a given locality.

Pladobole. Clements '05. A plant distributed by the action of moisture.

Pladopetric. Klugh '23, Ecol. 4:373. Of/ rocks moistened by dripping water.

Plain. *See* prairie.

Planation. J:458 (Clements). Stream erosion. *See* peneplane.

Plancton. Needham & Lloyd '16. That free floating assemblage of organisms in great water masses that is self sustaining and self maintaining and is independent of life on land. = plankton.

Plane. Johnson :16, Geogr. Rev. 1:444. The level erosion surface produced in the ultimate stage of any geologic cycle.

Planetons. J:458 (Balfour). A migratory species.

Plankt, plankter. Individual organisms comprising plankton.

Plankton. 1. Passively floating or weakly swimming organisms of bodies of water. 2. All small organisms near the surface of water. *See* anthoP, autopelagic, autopotamic, chimopelagic, desmoP, diacmic, encyonemetum, epiP, eulimnetic, eupelagic, eupotamic, eurycladous, false P., flos aquae, halonereid, heloP, hemiP, hidroP, hydroP, hyphalmyroP, kalloP, kremastoP, kryoP, limnoP, macrophyte, magmaphilae, megaP, meroP, microphytic, nannoP, necton, neidoP, nereid,

neuston, phagoP, phylktioP, phytostrote, plankt, planomenon, pleuston, potamoP, pseudoP, sadd, saproP,
scoticaP, seston, siraP, skaphoP, soleniaP, stagnoP,
stiliP, styliP, trichoP, triposP, tripton, tychcnoP, water
bloom.

Plankton. J:458. A constituent of plankton.

Plankton pulses. Chapman '31:283. Fluctuation in total
population of plankton which assumes rhythmic cycles.

Planktophyte. J:288 (Forel). A plant forming an integral part of plankton.

Planomenon. ESA 1935. List P-3. One of Gams' three
major divisions of life-forms referring to errant or
wandering types with the following life-form classes:
Plankton (passive movement in open water), Pleuston
(passive movement on the water surface), Kryo-plank-
ton (passive movement, preponderantly in and on snow
and ice), Edaphon (living in soil-water, passive movement), Tracheron (forms with active movement in water, air, and on land).

Plant association. Nichols '18, Trans. Conn. Acad. 22:
275. Any group or community of plants taken in its
entirety, which occupies a common habitat. *See* community, association.

Plant commune. J:288 (Schimper). Plants usually found
in the same community. *See* sociological affinity, coefficient of association.

Plant community. *See* community.

Plant cover. *See* vegetation cover.

Plant formation. 1. *See* formation. 2. J:288. An assemblage of plants living together in a community under
the same environment. = community.

Plant sociology. = phytosociology.

Plantae tristes. J:289. Evening flowering plants.

Plantesamfund. (Danish). = association.

Plasticity. Clements '05. The condition characterized by ready response to stimuli.

Plat. ESA 1934. List R-1. 1. A map or chart. 2. A piece of ground. *See* plot.

Playa (Spanish). = sea coast or beach; strand.

Pleiohalile. Lower estuarine; the portion of the estuary in which the total salt content is from 6 to 15 parts per mille.

Pleion. Clements '16:331. (Huntington [Arctowski]). A period of abundance the presence of which is determined by climatic factors which recur in cycles of 2.5 years.

Pleioxeny. J:288 (DeBary). The condition of a parasite invading several species of host.

Pleon. (DelVillar). = pleuston.

Pleophagous. J:291. Not restricted to one host.

Pleotrophic. J:291 (Jones). Feeding on various substances, not restricted to one.

Pleurotribal. J:291. Flowers whose stamens are adapted to deposit their pollen upon the sides of insect visitors. *See* pollenation adaptation.

Pleuston. 1. Warming '09:164. Free swimming vegetation often of shallow pools; often rootless. *See* tycholimnetic plankton. 2. (Forel). Plants which float by reason of their relative lightness. 3. Friederichs '30: 233. Organisms transported by floods.

Ploadostadion. DelVillar '26, Proc. Int. Congr. Pl. Sci. 1:560. Aquatic plants with upper parts above the water.

Plot. ESA 1933, List P-1. An accurately measured area

used for purposes of experimentation in which the entire yield, except for the possible exclusion of borders is used. *See* sample area, quadrat, sample plot, plat.

Plotophytes. (Clements). Floating plants, their functional stomata on the upper surface of their leaves. Klugh '23, Ecol. 4:372. Floating leaved vegetation.

Plucking. Malott, '28, Proc. Ind. Acad. 37:153. The process by which glacial ice withdraws rock fragments or blocks from surfaces by holding onto the surfaces or projecting parts. *See* appendix VII; fluviraption, erosion.

Plurannual. J:292 (Bailey). An annual plant which is so only by being killed by the cold at the end of the season. *See* annual.

Plurivorous. J:292 (Dietel). Of/ fungi which inhabit indifferently hosts belonging to widely different orders of plants. *See* parasite.

Pluvial. Moreau '33, Jl. Ecol. 21:428. The rain falling in a given catchment.

Pluviifruticeta. Rübel '30, *Pflgesel. der Erde.* Low tropic rain vegetation, as mangrove swamps, dwarf palm, and bamboo communities. J:292. A rain scrub.

Pluviilignosa. Rübel '30, *Pflgesel. der Erde.* Woody vegetation in the rain-tropics. J:292. Rain scrub and rain-forest combined.

Pluviisilvae. Rübel '30, *Pflgesel. der Erde.* Rain forests.

Pluvo-fluvial erosion. Malott '28, Proc. Ind. Acad. 37:153. Erosion by running water and wave erosion. *See* appendix XII; fluviraption.

Pnoium. Clements '05. A succession in an aeolian soil.

Poad. Clements '05. A meadow plant.

Podsol. J:459 (Vahl). Soils of a few inches of light powder below the humus layer.

Poecilothermic. = poikilothermic.

pOH. Hydroxyl ion concentration; as expressed by the logarithm of the reciprocal of the normality of OH ions. Cf. pH.

Poic. Klugh '23, Ecol. 4:373. Of/ grassland.

Poikilothermal, -ic. Shelford '29:89. Of/ "cold blooded animals"; organisms having no rapidly operating heat regulatory mechanism.

Poium. Clements '02. A meadow community.

Polar lakes. Pearse '26:202 (Whipple). Lakes whose temperature is never above 4°C.

Politropism. = polytropism.

Pollacanthic, pollachanthic. J:294. 1. Of/ plants which flower more than once; cf. hapaxanthic. 2. (Kjellman) perennial.

Pollard. J:294. A tree dwarfed by frequent cutting of its boughs a few feet from the ground, with a subsequent thick growth of shoots from the place where cut.

Pollakanthic. Warming '09:6 (Kjellman). Of/ plants which reproduce more than once in their life cycle. = polycarpic (deCandolle).

Pollenation adaptations. *See* allautogamia, dientophily, entomophilous, entomogamous, ephydrogamous, exotrophic, hercogamy, hydrocarpic, hydrophilous, hyphydrocarpous, hydrophilous, hyphydrogamicae, Knight-Darwin law, melittophilae, monotropic, myiophylae, microcoleopterophilous, ornithophilous, pleurotribal, polytropic, prehensile, prometatropic, proterandrous, protergynous, pseudodystrophy, psychrophilae, sapromyiophilae, sphingophilae, sternotribal, thermocleistogamy, trap, vexillary, wasp-flower, weel, xerocleistogamy, zoidiophilous, zoophilous.

Polluted. *See* septic.

Pollution, degrees of. Shelford '29:65 presents a comparison of the classifications of Richardson and Alexander with that of Kolkowitz:

Kolkowitz	Richardson
1. Polysaprobic	Septic or saprobic
2. Mesosaprobic,a	Pollutional, contaminated
3. Mesosaprobic,b	sub-pollutional
4. Oligosaprobic	clean water

Pollutional zone. *See* mesosaprobic.

Poloicous. J:459 (Lindberg). Having both fertile and sterile flowers on the same and different plants.

Polotropism. J:295. The tendency to direct proximal or distal extremities to the same point or pole.

Polsterpflanzenerien. Braun-Blanquet & Pavillard '30. Euchamaephytic seres.

Polyandry. Allee '31:26 (Deegener). The mating of several males with a single female, without the female being open to all males.

Polyanthous. Clements '05. Producing many flowers.

Polycarpic. Warming '09:6 (deCandolle). Of/ plants which produce fruit or spores more than one time before dying. = pollakanthic (Kjellman).

Polychronic. Clements '05. Arising at two or more times.

Polydemic. Clements '05. Dwelling in several regions.

Polygamy. *See* polygyny, polyandry.

Polygenesis. Clements '05. The origin of a new form at two or more places or times.

Polygynopaedium. *See* monogynopaedium.

Polygyny. Allee '31:26 (Deegener). The mating of one male with more than one female.

Polymorphic colony. *See* heteromorphic colony.

Polynesian region. Lydekker '96:27. *See* appendix IX.

Polyphylesis. Clements '05. The origin of a form, species, or genus from two or more ancestral types.

Polysaprobic. ESA 1935. List P-3. An adjective applied to aquatic media characterized by marked decomposition of organic materials and great scarcity or complete absence of free oxygen. *See* Catarobic, mesosaprobic, Oligosaprobic.

Polyspermatous. Clements '05. Producing many seeds in each flower.

Polytopic. Clements '05. Arising at two or more distinct places.

Polytrophic. J:298 (Jones). Obtaining food from a wide area of selection. *See* omnivorous.

Polytropic. J:298 (Loew). Of/ bees which visit a wide circle of flowers. *See* pollenation.

Polytropism. J:298 (Archangeli). The reaction of leaves which place their lamina vertically and meridionally, the two surfaces facing east and west.

Polyxeny. = pleioxeny.

Pomarium. Clements '02. An orchard.

Pomeridianus. J:298. Of/ the afternoon.

Pond. Carpenter '28:217, *Life in inland waters.* A stagnant body of water in which the littoral zone of floating vegetation extends to the center, and whose life greatly resembles that of the littoral zone of lakes. Hancock '11:430. A confined body of water of less extent than a lake; referred to sometimes as a basin.

See sink hole, solution pond, stasium, thinic, pool, buffalo wallow.

Pontium. Clements '02. A deep sea community. *See* ocean.

Pontohalicolous. J:460. Inhabiting a salt marsh.

Pontophilus. Clements '02. Dwelling in the deep sea.

Pool. Hancock '11:430. A small and rather deep body of fresh water. *See* pond, tide pool, ombrotiphic, buffalo wallow, piscine, tiphium.

Poophyte. Warming '09:135 (Pound & Clements). A mesic meadow plant.

Population. DuRietz '30:293. A general expression for all concrete plant communities large or small, homogenous or diverse, pure or with mixed composition. Friederichs '30:34. The sum total of the individuals of a species in a given area.

Population intensity. Diver '33, Jl. An. Ecol. 2:67. 1. Absolute intensity of a localized population (e.g., the number of grasshoppers per square yard irrespective of species). 2. The relative frequency of different species comprising such a population. 3. The degree to which a species occupies the available suitable loci.

Positive. J:299. The absolute or effective condition, opposed to negative, and prefixed for emphasis to such terms as geotropism, heliotropism, etc.

Post climax. 1. A relict of a former climax community remaining under favorable edaphic conditions in a region whose climate is no longer favorable for the development of the corresponding climax. 2. Clements '28:110, *Pl. Succession* & *Indicators*. A community existing under favorable edaphic conditions and indicating the character of the climax which would be developed as the result of a climatic change involving increase in available moisture.

Post clisere. (Clements). A sere proceeding from lower to higher climaxes, succeeding a clisere.

Potamic. Klugh '23,Ecol.4:372. Of/ a stream community.

Potamium. Clements '02. A river community.

Potamophilus. River loving.

Potamoplankton. Carpenter '28:172, *Life in inland waters*. Plankton of rivers. *See* automopotamous, tychopotomous, plankton.

Potential climax. Clements '16:107. The actual climax of an adjacent area which will replace the climax of the region concerned whenever the climate is changed.

Potometer. Clements '05. An instrument for measuring absorption.

Praefoliation. = estivation.

Prairie. (in N. America). 1. The grassland area dominated by the tall prairie grasses, as distinguished from the short grass plains. Hancock '11:432. An extensive tract of level or rolling land, destitute of trees, covered with coarse grass, and usually characterized by a deep fertile soil. Sears '26, Ohio. Jl. Sci. 26:128. " . . . . in early records meant a treeless area generally grassy but sometimes covered by low shrubs or brush; it might be wet or dry." 2. Wright '32, Ecol. Monogr. 2:119. (Okefinokee swamp region) a shallow open marsh or open water lily marsh.

Prairie pond. *See* buffalo wallow.

Pratal. J:301 (Watson). Of/ plants which grow in meadows or luxuriant herbage. *See* grassland.

Pratum. Clements '02. A meadow; a grassy field.

Precipitation rose. ESA 1935. List P-3 (Cain). A radial

diagram giving the monthly precipitation in amount or percent.

Preclimax. (Clements). The vegetation preceding the full development of a climax.

Preclisere. J:460 (Clements). A sere which proceeds from higher to lower climaxes, preceding a clisere.

Precocial. Of/ organisms which do not require parental care after birth.

Pre-community. ESA 1935. List P-3 (Daniker). In which the individuals are not regulated through mutual effects.

Preconnubia. Allee '31:27 (Deegener). Groups of animals collected before the mating season; both sexes may be present but mating does not occur.

Predator. ESA 1934, List P-2. An animal which is predatory.

Predatory. Chapman '31:160 (Handlirsch). Of/ organisms which prey on other forms and eat them either after being killed or while still living.

Predominant. Shelford '26, Ecol. 7:389. An organism of outstanding abundance or obvious importance. Shackleford '29, Ecol. 10:132. Animals of a community which are present abundantly during at least a portion of the year and active throughout the whole year. Woodbury '33, Ecol. Monogr. 3:165. Usually animals or parasitic plants of outstanding abundance or conspicuous influence which are effective (*a*) in giving aspect to the community, (*b*) altering the appearance of the habitat, or (*c*) conspicuously affecting, either temporarily or permanently, the community or the environment; they usually affect the dominants in a conspicuous way.

Predromal year. *See* outbreaks.

Preferendum. Uvarov '31:54 (Williams). The temperature preference apparently preferred by insects as shown by migration.

Preferential species. Braun-Blanquet & Pavillard '30. Species preferring one given community to others, though growing more or less abundantly in all. *See* fidelity.

Prehensile flowers. J:301 (Delpino). Flowers whose insect visitors grasp the style and stamens so as to cover their venters with pollen and so effect pollenation.

Preoviposition period. Shelford '29:155. A preparatory period of quiescence prior to oviposition; found in tiger beetle and codling moth.

Preparatory year. *See* outbreaks.

Prepupal period. Shelford '29:155. A preparatory period of quiescence prior to pupation; found in tiger beetle and codling moth.

Presence. Braun-Blanquet '32:52. The more or less persistent occurrence of a species in all the stands of a certain plant community. Braun-Blanquet & Pavillard '30. An expression of the presence or absence of a species in all the examples of a studied community.

Presence classes. *See* Dominance classes.

Presociation. Woodbury '33, Ecol. Monogr. 3:168. A morphological part of an association characterized by the presence of one or more predominants, usually of animals or parasitic plants (on land).

Presocies. Shackleford '29, Ecol. 10;131. A subordinate group of animals living among the dominant plants of an associes.

Prevernal. Clements '05. Pertaining to the early spring. *See* aspection, seasons.

Primary associations (aggregations). Allee '31:16 (Deegener). . . . . arise through sexual or asexual reproduction or when individuals descending from the same parents or parent remain near the place of origin and form an aggregation which varies from a loose to a firm integration.

Primary colonies (aggregations). 1. Allee '31:16 (Deegener). . . . . arise as the result of division in which the smaller pieces remain together, or as a result of budding in similar fashion. *See* homo- and heteromorphic colonies. Cf. concresence or secondary colonies. 2. Allee '31:23 (Deegener). Colonies having arisen from the same mother. *See* clone.

Primary community. Friederichs '30:34. A natural community of a region, not caused by the acts of man.

Primary succession. Clements '05. Successions arising on newly formed soils or upon surfaces exposed for the first time which have in consequence never borne vegetation before.

Primeval forest. Warming '09:339. A virgin forest that has preserved its original character because man has left it undisturbed in part or entirely. *See* natural area (ESA).

Primitive area. ESA '32 (U.S. For. Service). An area in which human transportation and conditions of living are kept primitive; some of the areas are to be cut over periodically. *See* natural area.

Prior. Clements '05. Earlier, used of Alpine aspects.

Priority. Yapp '25, Veroff. des Geobot. Inst. Rübel 44: 697. The relation in which one organism is so situated that it can intercept and retain all it is capable of using of a particular necessity before a second can procure any at all.

Prisere. Woodbury '33, Ecol. Monogr. 3:167. A sere beginning with pioneers on a primary bare area. Phillips '30, Jl. Ecol. 18:201. The natural regional succession upon sites undisturbed by man's agency, direct or indirect.

Pristine. = pioneer.

Proanthesis. J:302 (Pax). Flowering in advance of the normal period, as some flowers appearing in autumn in advance of the ensuing spring. *See* aspection.

Prochosium. Clements '05. A succession in an alluvial soil.

Proclimax areas. Clements '34, Jl. Ecol. 22:55. Used but not defined; relicts of original climaxes, somewhat modified by human agencies and introductions. *See* culture communities.

Procryptic coloration. Pearse '26:298 (Poulton). Protective coloration.

Prodophytium. Clements '05. An initial community. *See* pioneer.

Profile chart. Tansley & Chipp '26:65. The diagrammatic record of vertical relations of the vegetation. = bisect.

Progeoesthetic. J:303. Applied to the root tip when bending downward. *See* tropism.

Progrediens. J:303 Extending at one part, dying at the rear.

Prophydrotropism. J:303 (MacDougal). Turning towards a source of moisture.

Prole. (Engler). = subspecies (DuRietz).

Proletariat. J:304 (McLeod). Plants having only a small reserve, and self pollenated.

Prometatropic. (Pearson). Of/ obligate cross pollenation.

Promiscuity. Allee '31:27 (Deegener). The forming of communal connubia for apparent non-discriminate mating, with no demonstration of polyandry or polygyny.

Promunturium. Clements '02. A rocky sea-shore.

Proodophytia. Clements '02. Pioneer initial communities. *See* colony, family, pioneer, pristine.

Proschemotaxis. J:305. Attraction by certain substances shown by bacteria, antherozoids, etc.

Prosere. Polunin '35, Jl. Ecol. 23:196. . . . . constituted by ephemeral (migratory) communities that are not essential parts of the true successional series which is to follow (the "autogenic main sere" [Tansley]).

Prososmotaxis. J:305. The movement of motile organisms in consequence of the influence of fluids.

Prosperity. J:461. The extent to which a species completes its cycle of development in a given population.

Protanthesis. J:306. The normal initial flowering of an inflorescence.

Protaxis. Allee '31:46 (Wallin). The innate tendency of one organism or cell to react in a definite manner to another organism or cell.

Protective potential. Chapman '31:193. The potential ability of an organism to protect itself against the dynamic forces of the environment.

Protobenthon. J:461 (Church). The earliest bottom vegetation.

Protodoche. Clements '05. A primary succession. = prisere.

Protoepiphytes. Schimper '03:319. Species which are

compelled to acquire nourishment from the surface of the supporting structure and directly from atmospheric sources; strictly epiphytic.

Prototrophic. J:309 (C. Jones). Requiring no organic compounds for nourishment.

Prototrophy. J:309. A peculiar commensualism also styled "wet-nurse" relationship.

Protrophy. = prototrophy.

Provenance. ESA 1935. List P-3. The geographical source or place of origin of a lot of seed.

Province. 1. Braun-Blanquet '32:355. A subdivision of a region characterized by at least one climax community and by various edaphic communities. 2. Woodbury '33, Ecol. Monogr. 3:167. The geographic unit, usually including a group of associations. = formation or community-complex. J:309 (Crampton). An area in which climate tends to dominance, as of woodland or moorland. = climax association or formation.

Proximity. Clements '05. Nearness to the area invaded.

Psamathium. Clements '02. A strand community; on the sand of a seashore.

Psamathophilus. Strand loving. *See* beach.

Psammarch. (Clements). An adsere starting on sand.

Psammic. Concerning communities on sand or gravel.

Psammophile. J:309 (Lees). A plant of light sandy soils.

Psammophyte. J:309. A sand plant, confined to such areas.

Psammosere. (Clements). A loose sandy adsere; seres having their origin on sand.

Pseudaposematic colors. Pearse '26:299 (Poulton). Protective mimicry.

Pseudeposematic. Pearse '26:299 (Poulton). Of/ aggressive mimicry and alluring coloration.

Pseudoannual. J:309 (Bailey). An herbaceous plant which hibernates as a tuber or bulb.

Pseudodystrophy. J:310 (Loew). The condition of gaining access to nectar by secondary means as when certain bees bore into the nectaries instead of entering by the opening of the flower.

Pseudoephemer. J:310 (Hansgirg). A flower which lasts a little over a day and then finally closes. *See* aspection.

Pseudoepiphyte. J:310 (West). A plant whose stems die away at the base, the upper part deriving its nourishment from its own aerial roots.

Pseudomacchia. J:462. Xerophilous evergreen scrub-juniper and evergreen oak. Cf. laurifruticeta.

Pseudomaqui. = pseudomacchia.

Pseudophotometric. J:312 (Weisner). Leaves which do not conform to action of light.

Pseudoplankton. J:312 (Forel). Organisms accidentally floating.

Pseudosematic colors. Pearse '26:299 (Poulton). Of/ false warning and signal coloration.

Pseudoshrub. J:312. A growth form produced by the growth of suckers after cutting back. *See* pollard.

Pseudoxerophilous. J:313 (Lees). Of/ a subxerophilous condition, the plants exhibiting less sensitiveness to moisture.

Psilic. Of/ savannah communities.

Psilicolous. J:462. Prairie dwelling. *See* grassland.

Psilile. Klugh '23, Ecol. 4:374. Of/ prairie.

Psilium. Clements '02. A prairie community.

Psilophilus. Prairie loving.

Psychophilae. J:313. Plants which are pollenated by

diurnal lepidoptera, possessing brightly colored flowers, with nectar in the flower tube.

Psychric. Warming '09:136. Of/ cold soil communities.

Psychro-. J:313 (Drude). Prefix for frost.

Psychrokliny. J:313 (Voechting). The behavior of growing parts under the influence of low temperatures.

Psychrometer. Clements '05. An instrument that measures humidity by means of a fall in temperature.

Psychrophyte. J:313. An alpine plant on soil which hinders root action by its low temperature.

Ptenophyllophilus. Dwelling in deciduous forests.

Ptenophytia. Clements '02. Intermediate (between pioneer and climax) communities. See midseral.

Ptenothalium. Clements '02. A deciduous thicket community.

Ptenphyllium. Clements '02. A deciduous forest community.

Pterosere. Clements '16:289. The eosere of the Paleozoic period. = paleosere.

Pterospore. Clements '05. A plant with winged disseminules.

Ptenothalophilus. Dwelling in deciduous thickets.

Puna. Hardy '25:170, Geogr. of Plants. Rock and salt waste plateaux between the Cordilleras of the Andes. See montane.

Pure line. DuRietz '30a:338 (Johannsen). A population consisting of the individuals formed by strictly autogamous reproduction of one homozygous individual. See species, clone.

Puszta. Warming '09:282. Grass steppes of Hungary. See grassland.

Puteus ventosus. Clements '02. A blow out.

Pycnophytia. Clements '02. Closed communities.

Pyramid of numbers. Elton '27:69. *Animal Ecology*. "The animals at the base of a food chain are relatively abundant, while those at the end are relatively few in numbers and there is a progressive decrease in between the two extremes."

Pyrium. Clements '05. A burn succession.

Pyrophobe. J:463 (Gates). A plant liable to destruction in forest fires, and incapable of being replaced under the altered condition.

Pyrophyte. J:463 (Gates). A tree having a thick fire resisting bark, thus escaping permanent damage from forest fires.

Pythmic. Klugh '23, Ecol. 4:372. Of/ lake bottoms.

Q

Quadrat. Clements '05. A square meter of vegetation marked off for counting, mapping, etc. ESA 1934, List R-1. Either a plot or sample area, usually square in shape; ESA recommends plot or sample area. Dayton '31, USDA, Miscl. Pub. 110:29. A rectangular usually square sample plot used in ecological studies; especially a plot containing one sq. meter; a larger sample plot is often called a major quadrat. Clements '16:30 distinguishes List, Chart, Permanent, Denuded, and Aquatic quadrats, which may be modified into Line, Belt, Permanent, Denuded, and Layer transects varying in width and length. Perquadrat is considered usually as a sample area of 16 sq. meters: A major quadrat is usually a sample area of four sq. meters. *See also* plot, plat, sample area.

Quadrat, chart. J:317. A quadrat diagram with the position of each plant marked.

Quadrat, denuded. Quadrats with the original plants cleared off.

Quadrat, major. 1. A sample area of four square meters. 2. Any given area designated for intensive study.

Quadrat method. Clements '16:425. A method of enumerating or charting individuals of a community within a circumscribed area, disclosing as well as registering the changes in population structure which are the record of development.

Qualitative composition. Raunkiaer '34:307. The species composition and the adaptation to the environment of those species; adaptation here is in the sense of life form.

Quantitative composition. Raunkiaer 34:307. The total and proportional amounts of the constituent species of a community.

Quaquaversal. J:317. Directed or bending in every direction.

Quasiclimax. Gershbacher '32, Thesis, Univ. Ill. (Used but not defined). A pseudoclimax in an aquatic sere which is a true climax in the sense that it is relatively stable; it is not determined primarily by climate. *See* Shelford '32, Ecol. 13:108 for status of climax communities in fresh water.

Quetelet's law. Hancock '11. Individuals of a species represented by the mean measurements survive in the struggle for existence while those individuals which depart somewhat radically from this type, as represented by the maximum and minimum, are eliminated in the struggle for existence.

Quiescence. Shelford '29:150. All cases of suspended activity from dormancy to sleep. *See* hibernation, estivation, dormancy.

R

Race. Braun-Blanquet & Pavillard '30. The geographical variation of an Association. = faciation.

Rachion. Muttkowski, Trans. Wisc. Acad. 19:426. The breaker line in lakes marking the place where wave action and undertow cause the greatest turmoil. The bottom here is usually rocky with pebbles and shells.

Radicantia. Friederichs '30:233. Sessile organisms.

Rain. *See* ombra-, pluvii-.

Rain forest. Haviland '26:37. A low lying region, close to the equator, where the annual rainfall exceeds 80-90 inches, usually clothed with a dense growth of jungle. Tansley & Chipp '26:205. Closed forest with fresh ground water; low altitudes; temperature high and constant; dry season short, if any. Schimper '03:260. Evergreen, hygrophilous in character, at least 30 meters high, but usually much taller, rich in thick stemmed lianes, rich in herbaceous but poor in woody epiphytes.

Range. 1. Woodbury '33, Ecol. Monogr. 3:168. The geographic area of occurrence; the area included within the geographic exterior boundaries. J:320. The region over which a given form grows spontaneously. = distribution. 2. Semple, USDA, Miscl. Pub. 194. A very extensive natural pasture.

Rasenserien. Braun-Blanquet & Pavillard '30. Herbaceous seres.

Rasse. =race.

Rasse, geographische. (Rensch). = subspecies (Du-Rietz).

Ratoon. J:321 (Crozier). A shoot from a root of a plant which has been cut down; *See* pollard.

Raumparasit (German). An example of contingent symbiosis. *See* aulophyte.

Ravine. Hancock '11:431. A deep narrow hollow, usually worn by a stream or torrent of water.

Reaction. 1. Clements '16:79. The effect that a plant or a community exerts on its habitat. 2. J:321. Any alteration in organization or form consequent to stimulation. 3. Lillie '32, Am. Nat. 66:176. The specific performance of a living system.

Reaction level. (Clements). A space bisected by the soil surface, including a few inches above and below.

Reaction time. J:321. The period needed for an organism to show response to a stimulus.

Reaction type. (Johannsen). = phenotype.

Rebalsa. Hardy '25:136 (Spanish). Palm forest of the Amazon basin periodically flooded; trees feebly rooted, supporting each other, tied together by lianes. = igaqu, caa-gapu.

Reciprocal colony (Aggregation). Allee '31:23 (Deegener). A primary colony forming a kormogene society in which all of the individuals stand in reciprocal relationship to each other. Cf. irreciprocal colony.

Redivive. J:322. An herbaceous perennial which dies down each year, growing the following year from an underground bed.

Reeds. See arundineous.

Reed swamp. J:323. A community of tall usually monocotyledonous plants growing in standing water.

Reflorescence. J:323. A second blossoming. *See* diplobiont.

Reg desert. Hardy '25:205, *Geogr. of Plants.* Portions of the Sahara desert which are of clay or pebble stone surface; alluvial deserts. = areg.

Region. 1. Woodbury '33, Ecol. Monogr. 3:167. The primary division of the earth, whether marine, or terrestrial, usually including a group of provinces. III Int. Bot. Congr. 1910:28. Extensive stretches of country; "should not be used for the altitudinal belts on mountains." 2. Waterman '22, Bot. Gaz. 74:7. The ground occupied by a formation-complex. Braun-Blanquet '32:355. The most comprehensive unit of vegetation classification; characterized by numerous well-defined communities and many peculiar transition communities. 3. Schimper '03:209 (Grisebach). Climatic belts of mountains. 4. J:323. The area occupied by given species. = areg.

Regional climax. *See* climax.

Regional succession. J:323 (Cowles). Succession due to secular change.

Regional type of vegetation. Trapnell '33, Jl. Ecol. 21:307. The layer and structure and principal dominant or characteristic species of each layer which predominate through a complex or series of complexes of the same general region.

Regression. Clements '16:145. Reverse succession from a highly developed to a simple type. *See* retrogression.

Relative velocity of development. Shelford '29:192. The reciprocal of the time to complete a definite process.

Relic. J:323 (Crampton). Stable plant communities due to past climatic factors. (Warming). What is left of a former, but now suppressed vegetation.

Relict. Clements '05. A species properly belonging to an earlier vegetation type than that in which it is found. Clements '34, Jl. Ecol. 22:42. A community or fragment of one that has survived some important change, often to become in appearance an integral part of the existing vegetation.

Repeat (in bird banding). USDA, Miscl. Pub. 58. A short time return of a live bird at the original station used to indicate rediscoveries of banded birds that have apparently not been absent from the neighborhood since they were last handled.

Repium. Clements '05. A succession of plants on soils which have subsided.

Reprint. Torre-Bueno '31, Bull. Brooklyn Ent. Soc. 26: 229. Something printed again from an article or book already in existence; an entire book may be a reprint.

Reproductive potential. Chapman '31:190. The number of females of a species which are able to reproduce in a given period multiplied by the number of offspring which each female will produce.

Research preserve. ESA '32 (U.S. Park Service). A nature sanctuary to which admission is by permit only.

Residual stand. ESA 1934, List R-1. The smaller trees left behind after lumbering or the trees available for a second logging; = selectively selected logged stand.

Restant. J:325 (Crozier). Persistent.

Restibilis. J:325. Perennial.

Restinga. (Warming). A Brazilian forest, forming a transition from the littoral to xerophytic forest.

Restriction of food, habitat, etc. See oligo-, steno-.

Retama bushland. J:325. Shrub steppe in the south of Spain.

Return (in bird banding). USDA, Miscl. Pub. 58. 1. A recovery from the same or other station during or following a migratory period. 2. A banded bird meeting death at or near the station where banded.

Rheophilae. (Ivanoff). Forms inhabiting rapid running water.

Rheotaxix. Orientation of organisms with reference to currents of water. Cf. anemotaxis.

Rheotropism. J:327 (Jönsson). The reaction produced by the influence of a current of water.

Rhizanthous. J:327. Flowering from the root or seeming to do so.

Rhizobia. J:327. The organisms which cause root tubercles on the legumes. = mycorrhiza. See symbiosis.

Rhizocarpous. J:327. 1. (deCandolle). Of/ perennial herbs. 2. Producing subterranean flowers and fruit in addition to the aerial.

Rhizocollesy. J:327 (Morren). The union of the axes of two individuals of the same species solely by the roots.

Rhizoctonia. J:327. Hyphae twisted into strands like twine which fasten on the roots of trees.

Rhizumenon. Friederichs '30:233. = Radicantia.

Rhizumenon. ESA 1935. List P-3. One of Gam's three major life-form groups with classes as follows: Phanerophytes (tall, woody perennials), Chamaephytes (low perennials), Hemicryptophytes (perennating bud at the surface of the soil), Hydrocryptophytes (in water), Amphicryptophytes (amphibious), Eugeophytes and Zerogeophytes (perennating buds subterranean).

Rhoium. Clements '02. A creek community. See stream.

Rhoophilus. Creek loving.

Rhoptometer. Clements '05. An instrument to measure absorption of water by the soil.

Rhyacium. Clements '02. A torrent community; a stream that bursts forth; a mountain torrent. *See* stream.

Rhyacophilus. Torrent loving.

Rhysium. Clements '05. A succession due to volcanic action.

Ridge. Hancock '11:433. The upper part of a range of hills, or extended elevation between valleys.

Rill. Hancock '11:430. A very small brook. *See* stream.

Ripa. Clements '02. Bank; any rising ground; a dike.

Riparian, riparious. J:329. Growing by rivers or streams.

Rivalis. J:329. Growing by a brook side.

River. Hancock '11:430. A stream larger than a rivulet or brook. *See* stream.

Rivularis. J:329. Growing by water courses.

Rivus. Clements '02. A brook. *See* stream.

Rock communities. *See* calcipetrile, endolithophyte, endopetrion, endophyte, epilithophyte, eugeogenous, exolithophyte, lithic, oxypetric, petric, phellium, paldoletric, sax-.

Rookery. The breeding or nesting place of birds, seals, etc. For discussion *see* Nicholson '30, Jl. Ecol. 18:52.

Root parasitism. J:330. The condition of plants being partially parasitic, their roots penetrating the roots of other individuals.

Root sucker. ESA 1934, List R-1. A sprout from a root.

Rotation pasture. Semple '34, USDA, Miscl. Pub. 194. A field used for grazing which is seeded to perennials and /or self seeding annuals, but which forms a unit in crop rotation plan and is plowed within a five year or shorter interval.

Rubble. Small broken stone at the base of a rock slope. *See* talus.

Rubicolous. J:331. Parasitic on brambles.

Ruderal. A "weed": an introduced plant species growing under disturbed conditions. Kurz, '28, Bot. Gaz. 85: 86. Plants, native and introduced, of old fields, waysides, etc. (Thornber). Growing in waste places, or among rubbish. *See* aletophyte, chomophyte, viatical, waste communities, culture community, indigenous.

Rupestral. J:332 (Watson). Of/ walls and rocks.

Rupestrine. J:372 (Crozier). Growing among rocks.

S

Sabalian life zone (Merriam). The "gulf strip." (U.S.) *See* appendix V, VI.

Sabulicola. J:332. A plant growing on sandy places.

Sabuline, Sabulose. Sandy.

Saccospore. Clements '05. A plant with sack like disseminules.

Sadd. Clements '16:277 (Duerling). Floating matter and vegetation on the upper Nile. = sudd.

Saerhadd. Hardy '25:48, *Geogr. of Plants*. Elevated summer pastures (Persia).

Sal. Tansley & Chipp '26:28. A "fire sub-climax"; an area which is prevented from developing to the usual climax for the region by frequent fires.

Saline. J:333. Growing in salt marshes.

Salitrales. *See* esteros.

Salsuginous. J:333. Growing in places inundated by salt or brackish water.

Salt area communities. Chott,. drimium, enhalid, esteros, junin, salitrales, halarch, hal-, hyphalmyroplankton, litorilignosa, saline, salitrales, stenohaline, travesias.

Salt marsh. Hancock '11:430. Similar to fresh marsh, but land covered wholly or in part with saline water.

Salt panne. *See* panne.

Salt swamp. J:333. The swamps of still maritime inlets.

Saltings. J:333. Salt marshes, the grass overflowed at high water leaving numerous muddy channels.

Sample area. ESA 1934, List R-1. A portion or portions of the area of a sample plot.

Sample plot. ESA 1934, List R-1. An accurately measured area used for purpose of experimentation or of mensuration; may be either permanent or temporary.

Sampling methods for communities. ESA 1935. List P-3. The following types of sample methods are in wide use: 1) the quadrat (for abundance, density, cover, etc.), a) list quadrat (for species lists and frequency), b) chart quadrats (mapping for exact relationships and future comparisons): 2) the transect, including: a) line transect (listing contiguous species to the line to study ectones, etc.), b) strip transects (as above but giving greater information, and for timber cruising, etc.), bisect (vertical drawing of the species relationships.

Sand bar. Hancock '11:432. An extensive ridge of sand formed by currents in the water; usually submerged, but sometimes exposed by receding water.

Sand community. *See* aman-, psamm-, ammochthium, ripa arenosa, arenaceous, bleisand, cheradium, dune, enaulium, foredune, hemipsammic, medanos, sabulicola, syrtis, thinic.

Sand drift. Hancock '11:433. A tract of drifting sand.

Sandy shore. Hancock '11:431. The sandy land lying adjacent to the sea. *See* shore.

Sansouires. Clements '16:273 (Flahault & Combres). Moist alluvial soils clothed with Salicornia and Atriplex.

Sap coefficient. Uvarov '31:12 (Bachmetjew). Percentage of liquid in live weight of an insect.

Saprium. Clements '02. A saprophytic community.

Saprobia. J:334. Organisms growing in polluted water.

Saprobic. Of/ forms living in septic waters.

Saprogenic. J:334. Growing on decaying substances.

Sapromyiophilae. J:334. Plants pollenated by carrion or dung flies.

Saprophile. J:334. Growing on humus.

Saprophyte. A plant deriving all of its nourishment from the bodies of decaying organisms. *See* hemis, heterogeophyte, heterotroph, holos, humicular, hysterophyte, saprium, sathrophytia.

Saprophytophagous. Chapman '31:161 (Handlirsch). Of/ organisms feeding on decaying plants.

Saproplankton. Warming '09:160. Foul water plankton.

Saproxylobios. Friederichs '30:233. Inhabitants of dead wood.

Saprozoic. Pearse '26:73. Of/ organisms which absorb organic liquids, such as the tapeworm.

Sarcocaul. J:334 (J. Smith). A fleshy stemmed plant, as cactus and many Euphorbias.

Sarcophaga. Flesh eaters.

Sarcospore. Clements '05. A plant with fleshy disseminules.

Sarnian. J:335 (Watson). Of/ the islands of the English Channel.

Sathrophilous. (Pound & Clements). Of/ fungi which feed on "offal."

Sathrophyta. J:335. Humus plants.

Sathrophytia. Clements '02. Saprophytic communities.

Saties. Clements '36. Jl. Ecol. 24:276. A subdivision of a seasonal socies.

Sation. Clements '36. Jl. Ecol. 24:276. A subdivision of a seasonal society (sociation).

Saturation deficit. Braun-Blanquet '32:134. The figure obtained by subtracting the actual vapor pressure expressed in mm. of mercury from the maximum possible vapor pressure at the given temperature. USDA, Miscl. Pub. 70. The difference expressed in percent of total saturation between the amount of moisture present in a given medium and the amount of it can hold when saturated at the same temperature.

Saurochore. J:335 (Borzi). A plant disseminated by lizards or snakes.

Savana. Hardy '25:142, *Geogr. of Plants*. Plains with or without trees; campo vero. = savannah.

Savannah. 1. Schimper '03:260. Xerophilous grassland containing isolated trees. 2. Hancock '11:431. A tract of damp level land with a growth of grass or reeds (S. U.S.). 3. = parkland. *See* campine, campo, closed S, helodium, lalang, llano, psilic, tropodrymium, parkland.

Savannah forest (tropical). Schimper '03:260. More or less leafless during the dry season, rarely evergreen, xerophilous, usually less than 20 meters high, park like, very poor in underwood, lianas, and epiphytes, rich in terrestrial herbs, especially grasses.

Saxatile. J:335 (Crozier). Dwelling or growing among rocks.

Saxicolous. Growing among rocks.

Saxifragous. J:335. Rock breaking; growing in crevices.

Scandent. Clements '02. A climbing plant. *See* liana.

Scantentes. Clements '02. Climbers and twiners.

Scariose. J:336. A thorny scrub.

Schamm. = muck, gyttja.

Schichtenaufbau. (Braun-Blanquet & Pavillard '30). *See* stratification.

Sciophilous. Warming '09:18. Of/ shade loving organisms. = heliophobous, photophobous.

Schar. = cenosis (Klugh).

Sciad. Clements '02. A shade plant.

Sciophilous. Clements '05. Shade loving.

Sciophyte. Clements '05. A shade plant.

Sclater's zoological regions. Lydekker '96:25 (1858). *See* appendix IX; Palaearctic, Ethiopian, Indian, Australian, Nearctic, Neotropical divisions based on the distribution of the Passerine birds (1874); Arctogaea, Dendrogaea, Antarctogaea, and Ornithogaea divisions based on mammal distribution.

Scleric. Warming '09:136. Of/ communities of bush and forest.

Sclerocauly. J:337 (Schimper). The possession of dry hard stems as in Ephedra.

Sclerophyllous forest scrub. *See* Durifruticeta.

Sclerophyte. J:337. A shrub or bush having sclerophyllous leaves, usually evergreen and resistant to summer drought.

Scopulus. Clements '02. Of/ overhanging steep cliffs; crags.

Scoticaplankton. J:338. Floating masses of Ceratium.

Scotophilus. (Clements). Dwelling in darkness.

Scree. = Talus.

Screefing. J:465 (Watt). Weeding or thinning a forest.

Scroll gall. J:338 (Kerner). Malformations caused by insects on leaves which curl up on the side when attacked. See gall.

Scrub. J:465. Stunted or densely packed bushes; stunted growth due to want of water, with strong transpiration. See fruticeta, bush.

Scrub forest. Pearse '26:262 (Ruthven). Forest occurring in clumps on plains and on ridges with a little shade, little litter; two strata, arboreal and ground.

Sea. Hancock '11:430. One of the larger bodies of salt water, less than an ocean. See ocean.

Season, biotic. Shackleford '29, Ecol. 10:133. The period of duration of a seasonal society is called a biotic season; the duration of the seasonal group set limits to the biotic seasons at Urbana, Illinois (1926-27) as follows: Prevernal: March 15-April 12; Vernal: April 12-June 1; Estival: June 1-August 16; Autumnal: August 16-November 15; Hiemal: November 15-March 15.

Seasonal predominant. Woodbury '33, Ecol. Monogr. 3: 165. Predominants effective during the active open season only, including such forms as summer or winter residents, etc., if of sufficient importance. See influent, aspection.

Sebakhs. Warming '09:233. Depressions which contain salt water during the rainy season, but many of which are dry and covered by salt incrustations in the summer (N. Africa).

Secondary Associations (aggregations). Allee '31:20 (Deegener). Aggregations resulting from the coming together of free individuals rather than their merely remaining together.

Secondary colony. Allee '31:24 (Deegener). A society developing by concrescence.

Secondary communities. Communities arising through human interference.

Secondary edaphic communities. Nichols '17, Pl. World 20:343. Edaphic communities arising through human agencies, lumbering, cultivation, etc. *See* culture community.

Secondary forms. Newcombe '35, Ecol. 16:235 (Shelford). Influent forms of minor influence in the community; usually occupy a narrow range or a local habitat and occur in relatively small numbers.

Second growth. ESA 1934, List R-1. Forest growth which comes up naturally after cutting, fire, or other disturbing cause.

Secondary successions. 1. Any succession caused by man or human agency. 2. Clements '05. Successions on denuded soils.

Sector. Braun-Blanquet '32:355. An area without any peculiar climax of high rank.

Seed eating. Carpophagous.

Seed year. ESA 1934, List R-1. A year in which a given species bears seed more or less abundantly.

Segetalis. J:340. Growing in fields of grain. *See* culture community.

Seismotropism. J:341 (Pfeffer). The power of appreciating and responding to vibration.

Selagraph. Clements '05. An instrument for recording light values.

Selective species. Braun-Blanquet & Pavillard '30. Species found most frequently in a certain community but also though rarely in other communities. = feste.

Selenotropism. J:341 (Musset). Movement of plants caused by the light of the moon.

Selva (Portuguese). The low plain of the Amazon subject all year round to heavy equatorial rains, and in a damp cloudy atmosphere; flooded periodically. Hardy '25:138, *Geogr. of Plants*. Typically on firm ground, tall trees of larger size than caa-gapu (*see* rebalsa); poor in palms, rich in tree lianas and broad leaf epiphytes; rich in Brazil (para) nut trees; where these occur in dense stands, termed castanhal; after disturbance by man resulting in brush undergrowth, termed caapuera or capoeira. *See* hylea.

Sematic coloration. Pearse '26:299 (Poulton). Warning and signalling coloration.

Semiannual. *See* biferae, biflorous, aspection.

Semi-cultivated communities. Warming '09:143 (Krause). Communities which have changed but not in aspect through the agencies of man. *See* culture community.

Sempervirent. J:343. Evergreen, retaining leaves during the winter.

Sempervirentiherbosa. Rübel '30, *Pflgesel. der Erde.* Grasses and herbs (mostly evergreens) which depend upon cell turgor rather than mechanical tissue to maintain an upright position. *See* herbosa:

Sempervirentiprata. J:343. Meadow communities dominated by species mostly evergreens, in temperate climate where frequent rain enables them to grow during most of the year.

Separate. Torre-Bueno '31, Bull. Brooklyn Ent. Soc. 26: 229. An article separately printed, apart and distinct from a general publication.

Sepicola. J:343. An inhabitant of sedges.

Septic. Alexander '25, Bull. Ill. Nat. Hist. Surv. 15:440. Of/ the grossly polluted portions of a stream in which the decomposition of organic matters is progressing actively, producing an abundance of CO_2 and nitrogenous decomposition products to the more or less complete exclusion of the dissolved oxygen. For synonomy here *see* pollution (Shelford).

Sequence theory of parasite control. Thompson '23, Ann. Ent. Soc. Am. 16:115 (Fiske). No one parasite is capable of effecting the necessary amount of control of an insect of the character of the gypsy moth, and capable of similarly rapid rate of increase when unchecked by parasites; but a sequence of parasites, which will attack the insect in different stages of its development, and all of the component members of which will work together in harmony is absolutely necessary before the best results can be expected.

Seral. Phillips '30, Jl. Ecol. 18:201. Developmental, not fixed.

Seral stages. fide Shelford '30. The "larval" stages of a climax community not including the adult stage; these are termed associes.

Serclimax. Clements '36, Jl. Ecol. 24:264. A stage in a sere of more or less long duration which is "sub-climax"; frequently caused by standing water or imperfect drainage.

Sere. Phillips '30, Jl. Ecol. 18:201. A unit succession, comprising the development of a formation from the pioneer stage to the climax. (Tansley & Chipp). A concrete developmental series which can be traced. Braun-Blanquet & Pavillard '30. A chain of stages containing the initial stages, transitional stages, and a single final stage. ESA 1934, List P-2. The series of communities that follow one another on any given area of the earth's surface. Weaver & Clements '29:74, recognize the following sere types: Prisere and Subsere (on primary and denuded areas respectively), each being divided into Hydrosere, Halosere, Oxysere, Lithosere, Xerosere, and Psammosere according to their areas of origin. *See also* angeoS, autogenic mainS, cenoS, aquatoS, halarch, hepedochae, herarch, dydrarch, hydrotrophic, imperfect succession, proS, xenodoche, xerasium, xerarch, succession, colony, family.

Seriation. Clements '36. Jl. Ecol. 24:267. A series of communities produced by a graduated compensation across a valley and operating within a formation or an ecotone. Cf. ecocline.

Series. 1. (Cowles '01). Groups of communities based on physiographic aspects and development. 2.J:466 (Stout). A group of sister plants from the same parent, or same cross, in any one season. 3. (Vavilov). The phenomenon of variation; cycles, one or more.

Serotinal. Clements '05. Late in season, pertaining to autumn. *See* aspection.

Serrados. Hardy '25:142, *Geogr. of Plants*. Savannahs strewn with clumps of scattered trees (Brazil).

Sertao. Hardy '25:141, *Geogr. of Plants*. Half deserts covered with whitewoods or caatingas (NE Brazil).

Seston. 1. J:344. Plankton material retained by very fine meshed nets. 2. ESA 1935. List P-3. A collective term designating everything that floats or swims in the water, whether living (bioseston) or non-living (abioseston), produced locally (autochthonous seston) or transported in from elsewhere (allochthonous seston).

Settlement. Braun-Blanquet '32:25. Any small combination of individual plants without regard to taxonomic value or sociological status. *See* colony, family, community, assembly.

Shade communities. Dryad, ombra-, scio-, skio-, umbra-, phytophygous, heliophobous.

Shallow sea. Flattely & Walton '22:10. The zone extending from the low water mark of spring tides to the edge of the continental shelf.

Shelter parasite. *See* domatia, symbiosis, raumparasit, aulophyte.

Shingle. Oliver '12, New. Phytol. 11:74. Banks which arise on coasts when material such as flints are drifted together by littoral currents; recognized types: fringing, spit, bar, and apposition.

Shingle banks. Accumulations of rolled pebbles, due to tide or sea currents.

Shoot. *See* sprout.

Shore. Flattely & Walton '22:36. The line of contact between land and sea. *See* ocean, back shore, fore shore, beach, lower beach, litus, strand, shingle, neritic, playa, psamathium, sublittoral, submerged zone, supratidal, tidal, upper beach.

Shoshun. J:345 (Bose). The suction response of plants.

Shot. A hollow which accumulates water with salt; a salt spot (Algeria). = chott.

Shrub. J:346. A woody perennial of smaller structure than a tree. *See* frutice, nanophanerophyte, phrygana, subdumi, thamnium.

Shrubage. The vegetation which composes the shrub stratum or layer taken collectively. Cf. herbage.

Shrub steppe. Warming '09:274. Communities where vegetation is very scanty but nevertheless regular.

Shrub stratum. J:346. In mixed woodland from about 3-15 feet in height.

Shrubwood. Schimper '03:162. Woodland in which the shrubs constitute the chief feature.

Sibljak. Warming '09:288 (Adamovicz). Ecotone between steppe and forest; has arisen on deforested soil of Balkan peninsula; composed of species which are not characteristic of forest. *See* maqui.

Siccideserta. Rübel '30, *Pflgesel. der Erde.* All dry areas with open vegetation; subdivided as Steppe (more than half of the area covered with vegetation) and deserts (less than half of the area is covered). *See* deserta.

Siccissimideserta. J:436. Deserts on which less than half of the substratum is covered with vegetation.

Siccocolous. = xerophilous.

Siderophiles. J:466. Iron loving plants.

Siderotrophic water. Water with large amounts of dissolved iron compounds.

Siedlung. = settlement.

Sierra. A ridge of rugged mountains.

Sierran. (Clements). Vegetation of the Sierra Nevada Mountains (U.S.).

Siliceous, silicolous. J:346. Showing a preference for flint soils.

Silicion. J:466 (Moss). Sand-flinty soils.

Silva. Clements '02. A forest. *See* woodland.

Silva paludosa. Clements '02. Swamp forest.

Silvae. Rübel '30, *Pflgesel. der Erde.* Forests. *See* lignosa.

Silvester zone. Clements '16:269 (Gadeceau). The extra marginal zone of a lake.

Sink hole. Eddy '31, Bull. Ill. Nat. Hist. Surv. 19:449. "Water moving through limestone dissolves away a part of it so as to form underground chambers, the roofs of which settle and cause surface depressions that become filled with water draining from the surrounding lands." *See* solution ponds, ponds.

Sink Lakes. Needham & Lloyd '16:68. Lakes whose basins are produced by the dissolution of the limestone strata and the descent of the overlying soil.

Siotropism. J:347. Response to shaking, as with Mimosa.

Sippe. Rübel '27, Bot. Gaz. 84:432. "Not meaning the individual, but the abstract plant."

Siraplankton. J:348. Floating marine vegetation mainly composed of Thalassosira.

Site. ESA 1934, List R-1. An area considered as to its physical factors with reference to forest producing power, the combination of climatic and soil conditions of an area; use essentially similar to habitat, with reference to wood producing capacity.

Site Index. ESA 1934, List R-1. The basis for the classification of site quality commonly used is the height in feet of the average dominant and codominant trees in the stand, or the tree having the average basal area of all the dominants and codominants in the stand, at some standard age, usually 50 or 100 years.

Site index. Moss '32, Jl. Ecol. 20. 20:388. The average

height of the dominant trees in a stand at 50 years, or the height which would be reached by the dominant trees at 50 years (in Alberta, Canada).

Skaphoplankton. J:348 (Forel). Boat shaped organisms floating as a mass.

Skatobios. Friederichs '30:233. Inhabitants of detritus.

Skiophyte. J:348. A plant which is not adapted to full exposure, but prefers shade.

Skoliotropic. J:348. Curved. Cf. campylotropous.

Skotopelagile. Klugh '23, Ecol. 4:371. Of/ the lower pelagic area of the ocean, below the limit of light.

Slacks. J:348. Yorkshire name for shallow valleys due to glacial lakes in the Pleistocene. See lows.

Sleep (in plants). The changes in position of organs such as leaves due to the absence of light.

Slette (Danish). = plain.

Slope. USDA Bur. For., Bull. 61:21. The following are recognized: level: 0—5%(.0—3.0°), gentle: 5—15% (3.0—8.5°), moderate: 15—30%(8.5—16.5°), steep: 30—50%(16.5—26.5°), very steep: 50—100%(26.5 —45°), precipitous: over 100% (above 45°). See ecocline.

Slough. Hancock '11:431. A wet place of deep mud or mire. See oxbow, sluggish channel.

Sludge. Forbes & Richardson '13, Bull. Ill. St. Lab. 9: 510. The silt and other deposit accumulating on the bottom of a stream.

Snow. See chonium, niveum, niveal, cryophytic, nipho-.

Snow flushes. Dark patches of soil due to accumulated deposit from melting snow. See anthelietum.

Sociability. Braun-Blanquet & Pavillard '30:8. The manner in which the individuals of the same species are

disposed in relation to one another. Braun-Blanquet
'32:36. The predetermined degree of aggregation of individuals or shoots based on the manner of growth.
Social. Clements '05. Used of plants in which the individuals are compactly grouped; exclusive: excluding
individuals of other species; inclusive: permitting the
entrance of individuals of other species. Warming '09:
139. Dominant species whose individuals give the main
character to the vegetation. J:349. The condition of
individuals of the same species growing in company occupying a considerable extent of ground.
Sociales. III Int. Bot. Congr. 1910:25 (Drude). Dominant species (as an expression of frequency).
Sociation. DuRietz '30:307. A stable Phytocoenosis of
essentially uniform composition, at least with uniform
dominants in every layer. '30b:492. The elementary
unit of plant community; = Association of the Scandinavian school prior to 1928. See appendix I. 2. Clements '36. Jl. Ecol. 24:276. A seasonal society.
Socies. Clements '16:138. A seral society characteristic
of a developmental community (Associes) marked by
subdominance within a climatic dominance. Phillips
'30, Jl. Ecol. 18:201. A seral community with one subdominant or with several subdominants. Shackleford
'29, Ecol. 10:133. Each group of seasonals plus the
constantly present predominants make up a Socies.
Weaver & Clements '29:51. Societies of developmental
communities.
Société. = community.
Society. 1. Weaver & Clements '29:49. A community
characterized by one or more subordinants; aspect
(seasonal) and layer (stratal) S. are recognized. Phil-

lips '30, Jl. Ecol. 18:201. A climax community with one subdominant or with several subdominants. Vestal '14: 383. A representative of an Association distinguished by abundance of one or several secondary species. Shelford '32, Ecol. 13:118. Subordinate assemblages within association and associes; layer, seasonal, and local societies are recognized. = cenosis (Klugh). *See* allelarkean, autarkean, communis, complementary S, group, clan, colony, family, group S, layer S.

Layer Society. ESA 1934, List P-2. A plant community within an Association which results at more or less definite levels; such Societies are particularly characteristic of forest communities (e.g., small tree, tall shrub, low shrub, herbaceous layer; *see* stratification). A layer Society tends to be distributed more or less uniformly over the entire area occupied by a community. A Group is a community within an Association which results from the local aggregation to form more or less well defined clumps or masses of any species other than those which predominate in the Association as a whole (*see* Facies). 2. (Aggregational sense). Allee '31:35 (Wheeler). More closely integrated, more stable, and permanent systems primarily dependent on reactions of individuals to each other. Alverdes '27:4, *Social Life in An. World.* Genuine communities which exist in virtue of some particular social instinct in the animal concerned; an organic whole. Woodbury '33, Ecol. Monogr. 3:165. Communities held together by mutual attraction of the members (social instinct).

Sociological affinity. DuRietz '30:301. The tendency of two or more plant species to compose a mixed community. Species are said to have strong, weak, or no sociological affinity according to their respective tendencies to appear in mixed populations.

Sociological relevé. Braun-Blanquet & Pavillard '30. A floristic enumeration accompanied by coefficients or numbers corresponding with analytical or synthetical characters such as abundance and density, dominance, frequency, sociability, vitality, periodicity, and stratification.

Socion. DuRietz '30:334. A synusium which is limited to a definite Sociation and so exhibits at least the homogeneity of a Consocion. See appendix I, II.

Sociule. Clements '36. Jl. Ecol. 24:280. A seasonal socies of a microcommunity.

Soil. ESA 1933, List P-1. The stratum of earth lying between the upper soil and the bedrock. Tansley & Chipp '26:115. The layers inhabited by the root systems of vegetation. See chalic-, endodynamorphic, geodynamic, geo-, hardpan, podsol, rock, sand, etc.

Solar cycle. Clements '16:330. Equivalent to the sunspot cycle.

Solar plants. J:349 (Grew). Plants which twine with the sun, i.e., dextrorse.

Soleniaplankton. (Warming). Floating neritic vegetation characterised by abundance of Rhizoselenia.

Solfataras. (Schimper). Hot sulphur springs around which occurs characteristic xerophyll vegetation.

Solitary. Warming '09:139 (Drude). Of/ species whose individuals occur in extreme isolation. Cf. family, colony.

Solum. Clements '02. Soil.

Solution ponds. Eddy '31, Bull. Ill. Nat. Hist. Surv. 19: 449 (Cummings). Enlarged funnels produced by the penetration of surface waters into limestone. *See* ponds, sinkhole.

Somatropism, somatotropism. J:350 (VanTieghem). The directive influence of the substratum on the growth of the organism.

Sonoran life zone. *See* appendix V, VI.

Sorores. J:350 (Schröter). Physiological species.

Sparsae. III Int. Bot. Congr. 1910:25 (Drude). Species sparse or sporadic in frequency distribution. Warming '09:139 (Drude). Species having only isolated individuals.

Sparse. Clements '05. Scattered singly.

Specie mangiate/mangiata. Nicholson '33, Jl. An. Ecol. 3:148 (Volterra). The "eating" and the "eaten" species.

Specient. Clements '31, Yrbk., Carn. Inst. "A term to emphasize that each individual possesses a dual nature: as an individual and as (member of) a species or genus: the individual species."

Species. DuRietz '30a:357. The smallest natural population permanently separated from each other by a discontinuity in the series of biotypes; a population consisting either of one strictly asexual and vital biotype or a group of practically undistinguishable strictly asexual and vital biotypes, or of many sexually propagating biotypes forming a syngameon (intercrossing population) separated from all others by more or less complete sexual isolation or by comparatively small transitional populations. *See* ateliosis, ecad, ecospecies, ecotype, growth form, genospecies, hybrid, hydra, idiobiological unit, jordanon, konospecies, Linneaon, nanism, natio, mikroS, phenotype, prole, sippe, sorores, stock, symbasis, typiform, variad, variety, vegetation form.

Species constant. Raunkiaer '34:494. Characteristic species of a social unit; those species which must invariably be present in communities which belong to the same unit.

Species guild. Clements '05 (Drude). An invading community.

Speiranthy. J:352. The condition when a flower assumes a twisted form.

Spelaeobios. Friederichs '30:233. = Cavernicolous organisms.

Speleology. ESA 1935. List P-3. The science dealing with the natural conditions and biota of caves.

Spermatostrote. Clements '05. A plant migrating by means of seeds.

Sphacelate. J:353. Dark and withered as though dead.

Sphagnigerbosa. Rübel '30, *Pflgesel. der Erde*. Communities characterized by the presence and abundance of Sphagnum, by acid substrata, and the formation of peat. *See* herbosa.

Sphagniopratum. J:354. Moss moor; dependent upon rain rather than underground water.

Sphagnodyt. Friederichs '30:233. Inhabitants of water saturated moss.

Sphingophilae. J:354 (Mueller). Flowers pollenated by hawkmoths and nocturnal lepidoptera.

Sphyric. Klugh '23, Ecol. 4:374. Of/ rock slides.

Sphyrium. Clements '05. A plant succession on colluvial soils; talus, scree.

Spiladophilus. J:354. Dwelling in clay.

Spiladophytia. Clements '02. Clay plant communities.

Spirophototropous. J:355 (Drude). Of/ the majority of plants, those whose leaves so surround the axis that the light in turn falls upon all.

Spit. 1. A long narrow shoal extending from the shore. 2. A small peninsula.

Spongophyll. Clements '05. A leaf consisting of sponge tissue.

Sporadophytia. Clements '02. Open communities.

-spore. Clements '05. Combining term for migration contrivance.

Sporostrote. Clements '05. A plant migrating by means of spores.

Spring. 1. *See* vernal, prevernal, season, aspection. 2. Hancock '11:430. An issue of water from the earth. *See* crenium, fons, thermium, thermophytic.

Sprout. ESA 1934, List R-1. The young growth or shoot from a seed, root, or other plant part; a tree which has grown from a stump or root. *See* shoot, root sucker, coppice sprout, coppice shoot.

Spur top. *See* upland salient.

Stability. Clements '05. The condition in which the plant makes little or no response.

Stabilization. Clements '16:98. The increase of dominance, culminating in a stable climax; it is produced everywhere by progressive invasion typical of succession and is the mutual and progressive interaction of habitat and community by which extreme conditions yield to a climatic optimum and life forms with least requirements are replaced by those which make the greatest demands. J:467 (Clements). Equilibrium in plant growth; the final stage in development.

Stable. Tansley & Chipp '26:7. Of/ communities which

are able to maintain themselves unchanged for long periods of time.

Stade. = stage.

Stage. Braun-Blanquet '32:320. A single clearly marked
step in succession. Braun-Blanquet & Pavillard '30.
The result of every transformation of vegetation is
called a stage (= stadium, stade), if there is an appreciable change in the floristic composition or an evident extension of some species; three stages are recognized: pioneer, transition, final. *See* Associes.

Stagnophile. Carpenter '28:217, *Life in inland waters.*
A species appearing exclusively in stagnant water.

Stagnoplankton. J:467 (Ivanoff). Floating vegetation of
stagnant water.

Stand. ESA 1934, List R-1. An aggregation of plants,
more often trees, standing on a limited area, of more
or less uniformity of composition and conditions, or of
age. J:360. A pure Association (= Consociation).

Standard climate. Moreau '35, Jl. Ecol. 23:7. The climate recorded at a meteorological station by standard
methods of exposure. Swynnerton '36, Trans. Roy.
Ent. Soc. Lond. 84:523. The climate of a locality as
measured at the ordinary open meteorological station
by instruments in a Stevenson screen and outside it.

Standardized fertility. Hogben '31, Biol. Rev. 6:163. The
crude birth rate corrected by a statistical method in-
tended to make allowance for changes in age composition in the population.

Standard metabolism. Shelford '29:172 (Krogh). Metabolism of minimal functional activity which is taken
to be obtained when voluntary muscle movements are
eliminated and no food is being digested or absorbed.

Standard theoretical time. Shelford '29:369. The length of time of a given developmental stage in hours or days as calculated for average organisms from developmental units which take into account temperature and humidity only.

Standort. 1. DuRietz '30:301. The habitat of a plant or plant community. 2. (Kerner) = station. = Biotop. Any given local representative ("stand" in the forester's sense) of a given community.

Stase. Clements '16:291. A fossil plant deposit in which the plant remains stay in place; a definite series of layers formed by the remains of the associes and climax of a sere.

Stasis. (Clements). An arrest of growth.

Stasimorphy. J:360. A deviation from the normal, arising from arrest in development.

Stasium. Clements '05. A stagnant pool community.

Station. Braun-Blanquet '32:21. The exact place of occurrence of a species or individual within a given habitat. Braun-Blanquet & Pavillard '30. The normal habitat of any particular community; the community depends upon the habitat which partly determines the physiognomy of the community. = standort, habitat, biotope, stand. 2. III Int. Bot. Congr. 1910:8. A circumscribed area of any size representing a complete and definite ensemble of conditions of existence expressed by the uniformity of the vegetation.

Staurigamia. J:361 (Delpino). Cross fertilization.

Steganochamaephytium. J:361 (Vahl). A dwarf-shrub community under trees.

Steganocryptophytium. J:361 (Vahl). A community of hemicryptophytes and geophytes under an upper layer.

Stegmatomycosis. J:468. Fruits apparently sound, but damaged within due to punctures by plant feeding bugs.

Stenochoric. J:362 (Drude). Of/ a taxonomic group with a range of distribution over a narrow area of constant climate, and confined to one or very few plant communities.

Stenocoenose. J:468 (Gams). Of/ a species restricted in distribution.

Stenoecic. Limited to a narrow range of environmental conditions. Cf. Euryoecic.

Stenohaline. J:362 (Forel). Of/ organisms which can endure only 3-4% of salt in solution.

Stenomorph. J:468 (Bartsch). A diminutive form due to a cramped habitat.

Stenophagous. Pearse '26:72. Of/ animals having a narrow range of food diet.

Stenophotic. J:362. Requiring a constant amount of light within narrow variation.

Stenophyllous. J:362 (Beccari). Of/ plants on river banks, etc., with linear or very narrow leaves.

Stenosynusic. J:468 (Gams). Of/ plants restricted in distribution.

Stenothermal. J:468 (Setchell). Of/ species restricted to limited temperatures.

Stenothermic. Pearse '26:34. Of/ organisms which are limited to a narrow range of temperature changes. Cf. eurythermic.

Stenotherms. Carpenter '28:71. *Life in inland waters*. Species which can tolerate only a very narrow range of temperatures and are limited in distribution to areas where this limit is not exceeded.

Stenotope. Börner '21. Arb. Biol. Reich. L.v.Forstw. 10: 413. Of/ organisms restricted to a single habitat.

Stenotribal. J:362 (Delpino). Of/ flowers whose anthers are so arranged as to dust their pollen on the under part of the thorax of their insect visitors.

Stenotropic. J:468 (Solms). With narrow limits of adaptation to varied conditions.

Steppe. Haviland '26:120. A large tract of unforested and uncultivated or semicultivated territory, which has an unfrozen subsoil, and is covered with herbage for at least the greater part of the year. Schimper '03. A wide treeless plain of grassland. See grassland.

Stereotropism. (Loeb). Reaction to contact stimulus.

Sterrhium. Clements '02. A moor community.

Sterrhophilus. Moor loving.

Sterric. Klugh '23, Ecol. 4:374. Of/ heath, an upland community characterized by Ericaceous shrubs, xerophytic grasses and lichens.

Stesomy. J:362 (Morren). An arrest of metamorphosis. See stasis.

Stiliplankton. J:363. Floating marine vegetation chiefly of Rhizoselenia.

Stimulation. J:363. The act of being aroused by some exciting cause, such as heat or light.

Stimulus. J:363. The particular active agent which produces definite changes in the organism, such as moisture, light, etc. See reaction.

Stock. J:364. Race.

Stony community. See aigicolous, rock community.

Stool. J:365. 1. A plant from which offsets or layers are taken. 2. Several stems arising from the same root, as in wheat.

Strachey's formula for summing temperature. *See* Shelford '29:198.

Strand. 1. Clements '02. Sand of the seashore. Hancock '11:432. The shore, especially the beach of the sea; rarely, the margin of a navigable river. 2. Wright, '32, Ecol. Monogr. 2:119. Sphagnum bog communities of various sorts. 3. ESA 1935. List P-3. The area of bare beach above high water level subject to the action of wind and sand blasts. *See* Tidal zone.

Strand lakes. Needham & Lloyd '16:75. Lakes which are extremely temporary and are present only after heavy rains and vanish utterly between rainy seasons; *see* temporary ponds.

Strand vegetation. Tansley & Chipp '26:206. Vegetation where ground water brackish, not subject to emersion, but under constant maritime influence; open herbaceous vegetation.

Strange species. Braun-Blanquet '32:59. Species that are rare and accidental intruders from another plant community or relicts of a previous community (fremde).

Strangers. Braun-Blanquet & Pavillard '30. Species accidentally introduced into any given community. *See* relict, ruderal, exotic.

Strata. III Int. Bot. Congr. 1910:25. Different layers of many communities, including ground cover, herbaceous undergrowth, shrubs, and trees. Shelford '12, Biol. Bull. 23:355. Strata are groups of consocies occupying recognizable vertical divisions of a uniform area. Woodbury '33, Ecol. Monogr. 3:166. A group of organisms (individuals, mores, colonies) occupying a recognizable vertical division of a unit area; equivalent to the plant layer society. (Yapp) The differences in vegetation at different vertical levels. Friederichs '30:35-6. The vertical layers of plants and animals. The following layers are recognized: Edaphon (litter layer); the blanket layer ("gefilz," [Arndt '20] of moss and recumbent vines); herbs (grasses, herbs, ferns); shrubs; and tree crown (including lianas and epiphytes). *See* layer, synusium.

Stratal. Clements '16:291. A deposit of plant fossils where there has been a mixing of plant parts from various sources; a more or less definite fossil horizon with no fixed relation to development. Cf. stase.

Stratification. Braun-Blanquet & Pavillard '30. The natural division of vegetation into superposed strata (Schichtenaufbau); Ground or moss, Herb, Shrub, and Tree strata are recognized. Clayberg '20, Bot. Gaz. 69:37 classifies as follows: (*a*) Lower forest: soil stratum: roots; leaf stratum: thin crisp layer; herbage: includes seedlings. (*b*) Middle forest: sapling trunks and shrubs (the first really open stratum); death stratum: dead twigs below the sapling foliage; sapling synfolium stratum: sapling foliage. (*c*) Upper forest: tree trunk stratum (here ample light is first reached); upper synfolium: the broken zone of tree foliage.

Stratification of lakes. *See* thermocline, ocean, epilimnion, hypolimnion.

Stratobios. Friederichs '30:233. Inhabitants of the litter layer of a community.

Stratosphere. Lumby '34, Jl. Ecol. 22:316. The lower layer of high temperature of oceans.

Stratum. *See* strata.

Strauchschicht. Braun-Blanquet & Pavillard '30. Shrub stratum. *See* stratification.

Strauchserien. = phanerophytic series. *See* stratification.

Stream. Hancock '11:430. A flowing river or brook. *See* rhoium, fluvatile, rivus, argodromile, autopotamic, brook, creek, crenicolous, flumen, guts, metanimuc, namatium, potamic, rill, riparian, rhyacium, tachydromile, lotic.

Strophism, strophotaxis. J:366 (Czapek). A tendency to twist in response to some external stimulus.

-strote. Clements '05. Combining term for means of migration.

Structure. Tansley & Chipp '26:12. An expression of the life forms of a community together with their spatial relationships. *See* ecological structure.

Stufe. (Rübel). *See* vegetation-stufe (DuRietz). = belt. *See* appendix I.

Stygius. J:367. Of/ plants which grow in foul waters. *See* pollution.

Styliplankton. J:367. Situated almost on the ground level as a rhizome which is covered with leaves, but above the soil.

Subalpine. J:367. Of/ the vegetation zone below alpine.

Subaquatic climate. Shelford '29:3. Climatic conditions in water.

Subarctic. J:367. Of/ northern plants beyond the limit of arboreal vegetation (timber line).

Subassociation. Braun-Blanquet & Pavillard '31. A community distinguished from the Association (B-B) by net differences in floristic composition. Cf. Faciation.

Subclimax. Elton '27:21, *Animal Ecology*. Ecological succession may be held up by agencies other than climate and prevented from reaching its natural climax; the stage at which it stops is known as a sub-climax. Woodbury '33, Ecol. Monogr. 3:168. An approximately stable community in which factors other than climate are the stabilizing factors; edaphic (soil factors) and aquatic (water factors) are considered as controlling here. Phillips '30, Jl. Ecol. 18:201. A stage or several stages below the climax; a community simulating the climax because of its further development being inhibited by some disturbing factor, e.g., fire. Godwin '29, Jl. Ecol. 17:145. Communities existing under the influence of some external factor, such that removal of the factor at once initiates the succession towards the climax and its persistence entirely inhibits such succession. Tansley '29, Jl. Ecol. 17:146. "An apparent climax." Clements '16:107. . . . . subordinate to normal development or climatic climaxes and is below the climax; . . . . is subordinate fundamentally, though in dominance and persistence it may resemble a true climax. The subclimax stages of a sere usually resemble the climax in growth form of the dominants.

Subcopious. Clements '05. Scattered somewhat loosely.

Subdominant. Weaver & Clements '29:49. A species which is dominant over portions of an area already marked by the dominants of the Consociation or Association. Nichols '23, Ecol. 4:11. Of/ species belonging to life forms of subordinate rank. fide Shelford '30. . . . . have important influence in the control of the habitat but are usually present only a portion of the active or growing season. Woodbury '33, Ecol. Monogr. 3:166. Organisms which effect or dominate only in an appreciable part of their environment usually under the influence of the true dominants. 2. Nichols '23, Ecol. 4:13. Species belonging to life forms of subordinate rank.

Subdumi. Clements '02. Dwarf shrubs.

Subformation. DuRietz '30:318, '30b:492. Salient regional facies (Haupteile) of a Formation. *See* appendix I, II. Rees '35, Jl. Ecol. 23:81. A local difference in littoral communities due to differences in the substratum.

Subformion. *See* under Formion (DuRietz). *See* appendix II.

Subgeocolous. Hancock '11:420. Of/ underground inhabiting species.

Subgregarious. Clements '05. Arranged in loose groups.

Subinfluents. fide Shelford '30. Forms present during part of the year or especially a part of the growing season and others exercising a secondary influence. Woodbury '33, Ecol. Monogr. 3:166. Organisms of lesser effect or shorter period of influence than an influent. Cf. Vefluent.

Subitane development. Uvarov '31:45 (Heller). Development designated as active as distinguished from latent.

Sublittoral. 1. Near the seashore. 2. Warming '09:172. Of/ the area between the low tide mark and 20 fathoms (40 meters).

Submaritime. Viosca '35, Jl. Am. Iris Soc. (April). Of/ deltaic and lagoonal marshes and savannahs practically at sea level but preponderately of fresh water. 2. J:369. Plants characteristic of the seashore, but also occurring inland.

Submerged zone. Flattely & Walton '22:35 (Davenport). All that portion of the beach below low tide, but which may be exposed at the lowest spring tides.

Submersiherbosa. Rübel '30, *Pflgesel. der Erde.* Submerged aquatic communities of both fresh and salt water. *See* herbosa.

Subordinate association. Clements '16:135. (Moss). "The chief Associations of an area do not compose the whole of the vegetation of that district; the complete picture requires the details provided by the progressive or retrogressive Associations or, as they have been called, Subordinate Associations. (= Associes).

Subquadrat. Clements '05. A quadrat of 1-8 decimeters square.

Subsere. 1. (Tansley & Chipp) A secondary sere. Phillips '30, Jl. Ecol. 18:201. The succession upon areas disturbed specifically by man's agency, direct or indirect, e.g., through fire, grazing, agriculture, exploitation of forest, etc. Woodbury, '33, Ecol. Monogr. 3:167. A sere beginning in an area secondarily bare as a result of the removal of biotic cover; the beginning corresponds to some intermediate stage of prisere. 2. (Clements). The partial development of a climax of vegetation.

Subshrub. J:369. An undershrub, or small shrub which may have partially herbaceous stems.

Subsociation. 1. DuRietz '30:310. A complex of Synusia within a Sociation. 2. Woodbury, '33, Ecol. Monogr. 3:168. A morphological part of the Association characterized by the conspicuous presence of one or more subdominants under the general influence of the dominants; this is the equivalent of the term Society (Clements) but to be applied on a greater scale to the biotic field. = Society.

Subsocies. (Woodbury). A subsociation of an associes.

Subsoil. ESA 1934, List R-1. The stratum of soil lying between upper soil and bedrock occupied by few or no roots and essentially unmodified by plants.

Subspecies. DuRietz '30a:354. A population of several biotypes forming a more or less distinct regional facies of a species.

Substitute associations. = secondary communities.

Substitute community. (Smith). A community due to man or cattle, such as farmland and tree plantations; equivalent to Secondary Formations (Warming). *See* culture community.

Substitution quotient. Shelford '29:369. The sum total of modified and corrected temperatures at the time of completion of a stage.

Subsuccession. Clements '16 (Cooper '13). Early stages of equal development but in different subseres which early lead to a single series. Cooper '13, Bot. Gaz. 55:119. Minutic types of subseres; seres starting in rock surfaces, rock crevices, and rock pools.

Subxerophilous. J:370. Preferring dry situations, but not confined to them.

Succession. 1. Clements '16:4. The development of a climax . . . . may be analyzed into initiation, continuation, termination; a complete analyzing resolves these into basic processes (all but the first are functions of the vegetation): nudation, migration, ecesis, competition, reaction, stabilization. Tansley & Chipp '26:369. "It seems well to widen the concept to include physiographic succession as well." Braun-Blanquet & Pavillard '30. All transformations of the vegetation. Folsom '26:404 recognizes Ecological (a succession of mores over a given locality as environmental conditions change), Seasonal (a succession of species or stages in the life histories over a given locality due to the time of appearance of species living there [= aspection]) and Geological (Succession of species throughout periods of geologic time) successions. Nichols '23, Ecol. 4:167. The replacement of one community by another. Subdivided by Clements as Abrupt, Continuous, Imperfect, Intermittent, and Interpolated; by Cowles as Biotic, Polygenic, Regional, and Topographic; by Gams as Catastrophic, Local, and Secular. = sere. 2. J:370. Appearing in successive intervals on soils of differing character. = alternation. 3. Phillips ('34, Jl. Ecol., 22:568) suggests the following for different phenomena of succession: acceleration, retardation, deflection, interruption, postponement, termination.

Succession, deflected. Godwin '29, Jl. Ecol. 17:146. Normal succession turned to one side by an external factor which may result in a temporary subclimax. *See* discussion by Phillips in Jl. Ecol., 1934 et seq.

Successional habitat. Yapp '22, Jl. Ecol. 10:13. The changing habitat occupied by an allied group of plant communities which, as a rule, comprise the stages of normal succession or sere. = associes.

Succus. Clements '02. Sap tissue, juice of trees or other plants.

Sudd. *See* sadd.

Suffrutice. Warming '09:11. An undershrub which often has incompletely dignified or temporarily woody stems.

Suffruticosa. J:370. Somewhat shrubby.

Sulphuretum. J:469. A natural ecological community of sulphur bacteria.

Sulphur springs. *See* solfataras.

Summer wood, J:371. Wood formed during the middle of a growing season.

Sun, influences. Bronzing, helio-, photo-, solar, oread.

Sundarban. Hardy '25:136, *Geogr. of Plants.* Food forests at the mouths of the Ganges river.

Sunleaves. J:371. Leaves adapted to develop in full exposure to the sun.

Sun plants. J:371. (Willis). Plants which prefer full sunlight; their stems are often short, and their leaves have palisade cells well developed.

Sunscorch. J:469. The burning of foliage when the soil is parched.

Superagrarian. J:371 (Watson). Of/ the region of vegetation in Great Britain above the limits of cultivation.

Superarctic. J:371. Of/ plants which are confined to the highest zone in Great Britain, the most alpine of the flora of the islands.

Supercrescence. J:371 (Crozier). The state of parasitism.

Supercrescent. J:371. Growing above or on another body.

Supernatant. J:372. Floating on the surface.

Superparasite. A parasite upon a parasite; secondary parasitism.

Superparasitism. Salt '34, Proc. Roy. Soc. Lond. 114B: 456 (Fisk). The condition of any individual being attacked by two or more species of primary parasites, or by one species more than once. (Smith '16) That form of symbiosis occurring when there is a superabundance of parasites of a single socies attacking an individual host. = epiparasite (Haviland '22).

Superplant. J:372. A plant which grows upon another, either as an epiphyte or parasite.

Supersociety. (Allee '31:8). = Presociety (Smith).

Supporting plant. J:372 (Crozier). A plant upon or in which another grows; a host plant.

Suppressed forms. Woodbury '33, Ecol. Monogr. 3:166. All other organisms not included in the dominant group; those which are dominated.

Suprafolious. J:372. Growing on a leaf.

Supralittoral. (Warming). Of/ a coast region above the high water mark. *See* shore.

Supraterraneous. Above the ground; Cf. subterraneous.

Survival potential. Chapman '31:192. The degree of environmental resistance which an organism can endure.

Swale. Hancock '11:431. A tract of low and usually wet land; *see* fen. Sears '26, Ohio Jl. Sci. 26:130. Apparently (in old records) a small swamp.

Swamp. 1. Tansley & Chipp '26:231. An area in which the surface soil is waterlogged and where free water accumulates on the surface for some periods of the year. ESA 1933, List P-1. A flat wet area usually covered by standing water and supporting a growth of trees, shrubs, and grasses. Sears '26, Ohio Jl. Sci. 26:130. A habitat marked by standing water for most of the year, occupied by herbs (aquatics such as cattails or pickeral weed), shrubs (willows, alders, buttonbush) or trees (ash, elm, tamarack, elder). ESA 1934, List R-1. Any area where the ground is saturated with water throughout much of the year, but where at least most of the year the surface of the ground is not deeply submerged.

2. J:372. Local Yorkshire term for moorland bogs, particularly those in hollows.
See banados, bog, dreen, hydrophytia, marsh, malezale, morass.

Swamp forest. Hancock '11:431. A tract of land saturated with water and covered with trees that have never been cultivated.

Switch plant. J:373. A plant whose leaves are wanting or reduced, with green shoots acting in place of leaves.

Syke. J:373. 1. A stream which drains a bog. 2. The bog itself. (Yorkshire).

Syllestia. Allee '31:31 (Deegener). Societies (aggregations) containing robber guests which prey on the eggs or young of the species with which they are associated. = synechthren.

Sylvan. J:373. Of/ woods.

Sylvestral. J:373 (Watson). Of/ plants which grow in woods and shady places.

Sylvestrine. J:373 (Crozier). Growing in woods.

Sylvula. J:373. A plantation.

Symaedia. Allee '31:18 (Deegener). Primary associations (aggregations) in which the offspring from the same mother form the aggregation without the presence of either parent.

Symbion. J:373. An organism which lives in a state of symbiosis.

Symbiont. Pearse '26:352. An organism that lives in intimate association with another (host) which it benefits and from which it receives benefits.

Symbiophiles. J:469 (Rayner). Free mycorrhiza of hymenomycetous fungi, neither parasites or saprophytes.

Symbiosis. Pearse '26:349. An intimate association between two or more species which results beneficially to all concerned. Flattely & Walton '22:149. The close physiological association of two distinct organisms for mutual benefit. Dayton '31, USDA, Miscl. Pub. 110: 36. The living together of dissimilar organisms, especially (as opposed to parasitism) when the relationship is mutually beneficial. McDougall '18, Pl. World 21:254 classifies symbiosis (the living together of dissimilar organisms) as:

Disjunctive
social: epiphytes, etc.
nutritive:
  antagonistic: parasitism
  reciprocal: mycorrhiza,
    etc.

Conjunctive
social: communities
nutritive:
  antagonistic: feeding,
    etc.
  reciprocal: pollenating, etc.

See Antagonistic, commensualism, helotism, hereditary S, heterotrophy, homobium, individualism, inquiline, marcoS, metabiosis, microS, mutualism, mycorrhiza, myrmeco-, nutricism, obligate S, parachorium, paramutualism, paraphagia, parasitism, paratrophic, paroecia, phycodomatia, phycobiosis, prototrophy, thievery, zoodomatia. See Allee '31.

Symbiote. (Tubeuf). = symbiont.

Symbiotic saprophyte. J:334. A phanerogam which subsists by means of a mycorrhiza.

Symbiotrophic. J:373 (Kirchner). Deriving nourishment by symbiotic relationship.

Sympaigma. Allee '31:28 (Deegener). Groups of individuals brought together in order that they may engage in common play; certain authors believe this to be either protective or the response of a general environmental pattern.

Symphagia. Allee '31:21 (Deegener). Secondary associations (aggregations) about a favorable food supply.

Symphilia. Allee '31:30 (Deegener). Aggregations formed when one species receives food, protection and shelter from another, and in turn supplies excretions which are apparently narcotic in nature.

Symphotia. Allee '31:21 (Deegener). Secondary associations (aggregations) collected about a given source of light; Allee notes that if this category is to be accepted, it is equally valid to speak of synthermia, synthigmia, etc., as mass responses to environmental factors; he suggests syntropia.

Sympolyandria. Allee '31:21 (Deegener). Secondary associations (aggregations) which are accidental polyandric associations (aggr.) on a synchoric basis, as that of Alcippe, a barnacle which dwells on the deserted snail shells occupied by hermit crabs, forming an accidental heterotypical association (aggr.); but the barnacles considered alone form a sympolyandria.

Symporia. 1. Allee '31:28 (Deegener). Migration societies (aggregations). 2. Secondary associations (aggr.) which are migratory aggregations joined either because they originated in the same place or because they are going in the same direction.

Synandria. Allee '31:28 (Deegener). Groups of males which herd together.

Synanthesis. J:374. Simultaneous anthesis, stamen and pistils ripening at the same time. = synacmy.

Synaptospermy. (Murbeck). The condition in plants

whose seeds germinate near the parent plant instead of being dispersed at maturity.

Synarmophytus. J:375. Gynandrous.

Syncaryophyte. J:375. = sporophyte.

Syncheimadia. Allee '31:28 (Deegener). Combined over-wintering (aggregational) societies which may be illustrated by solitary beetles and coccinelid beetles.

Synchoria. Allee '31:21 (Deegener). Secondary associations (aggregations) which are locality aggregations formed primarily because of a limited expanse of particularly favorable locations for living.

Synchorologic. J:375 (Schröter). Relating to the distribution of plant communities and their conditioning factors.

Synchorology. Braun-Blanquet '32:2, 343. Geographic distribution of communities; the investigation of the arrangement of plant communities in space, their occurrence and distribution. The description of the occurrence and distribution of plant communities, the delimiting of their areas, and the grouping of them into natural areas. = Synecology. 2. J:469. Plant distribution in time, as fossil species and their duration during geological periods.

Synchoropaedia. Allee '31:19 (Deegener). Primary associations (aggregations) in which eggs laid by different females in a favorable place hatch out and the larvae remain together from the very first, not as separated families, but freely mixed into a common aggregation.

Synclopia. Allee '31:31 (Deegener). Thieving aggregational societies in which one species feeds on the stored food of the other. = cleptobiosis, and lestobiosis.

Syncollesia. Allee '31:32 (Deegener). Cemented aggregational societies in which one animal cements its own covering or case to that of another species without killing the latter.

Synechorology. = synchorology.

Synechthren. (Wheeler). = syllestia.

Synecology. (Turesson). The ecology of communities = Ecology. (Rübel). The relation between the community and its habitat. Braun-Blanquet '32:2. The study of the dependence of communities upon one another and upon the environment. III Int. Bot. Congr. 1910. The study of conditions of the environment and adaptation of species taken in association. Cf. autecology, phytosociology, ecology, synchorology, geobotany.

Synepileia. Allee '31:28 (Deegener). Marauding (aggregational) societies or hunting bands.

Synfolium. Clayberg '20, Bot. Gaz. 69:37. The foliage layer in a stratified forest community. *See* stratification.

Syngenesis. Braun-Blanquet & Pavillard '30. The genesis of plant communities, i.e., their natural evolution tends towards the final climatic community or climax. *See* sere, succession.

Syngenetic geobotany. J:469 (Shröter). The ecologic investigation of plant communities. = ecology.

Syngenetics. J:457 (Rübel). The change of communities. Braun-Blanquet '32:2. The development of communities, closely related to synecology, the discovery of the laws of the rise, development, and decline of communities. = successional ecology.

Syngenia. Allee '31:17 (Deegener). Primary associations (aggregations) which arise by means of asexual reproduction.

Syngynia. Allee '31:28 (Deegener). Groups of females which herd together.

Synhesia. Allee '31:21. Secondary associations (aggregations) which are swarming aggregations under the influence of the breeding season, such as those of the palolo worm.

Synhesma. Allee '31:27 (Deegener). Swarming societies which collect under the influence of reproductive drives; androsynhesmia (male), gynsynhesmia (female), and amphoterosynhesmia (mixed swarms) are recognized.

Synoecium. Allee '31:31 (Deegener). The association (aggregation) between certain animals and the nests of other animals.

Synoporia. Allee '31:22 (Deegener). Secondary associations (aggregations) due to unfavorable conditions as exemplified by beetles which are collected by the wind and deposited as beetle-drifts in the same way as snow is drifted.

Synsitia. Allee '31:29 (Deegener). Symbiotic societies (aggregations) in which one of the associates lives on the shell or outer covering of the other without being parasitic and without the type of relationship of a Phagophilium.

Syntropia. Allee '31:21-22. Aggregations resulting from mass response to a given environmental factor; *see* note under symphotia.

Synusiologic. = ecologic.

Synusium. A stratal society. Braun-Blanquet '32:302. A natural community of species belonging to the same

life form groups and with uniform ecological requirements. Braun-Blanquet & Pavillard '30. An assemblage of plant individuals belonging to the same category of life forms. DuRietz '30b:496. The elementary
one-layered unit vegetation. DuRietz '30:326. A plant
population either continuous or divided into spatially
separated partial populations not further divisible into
distinct layers, and often occupying only a portion of its
habitat (Standort). It is composed mostly of a series
of systematically unrelated species but is held together
by a species group characterised by the definite sociological affinity of its principal members or at least by
a series of systematically closely related species groups.
J:470. (Gams). Life forms associated in growth and
habitat, but distinct as to affinity. *See* appendix I, II.

Synzoic. J:376 (Sernander). Of/ intentional dispersal
by means of animals.

Synzoochory. J:376. Dispersion by animals.

Syrphetobios. Friederichs '30:233. Organisms of mull
or compost heaps.

Syrtidophilus. Dwelling on dry sand bars.

Syrtis. Clements '02. A dry sand bar community.

Sysgenia. Allee '31:20 (Deegener). Secondary associations (aggregations), arising from the secondary fusion
of two or more syngenia, consisting of fused "children
families" and arise when one sympaedium meets another.

Systasis. Klugh '23, Ecol. 4:369. "If two or more communities exhibit a constant difference, but not a difference of sufficient magnitude to give them rank as separate communities, each may be termed a systasis:
those standing together." Cf. Facies.

Sysympaedia. Allee '31:20 (Deegener). Secondary associations (aggregations).

T

Tachydromile. Klugh '23, Ecol. 4:372. Of/ swift flowing streams.

Tachysporous. J:377 (Ulbrich). Of/ plants which quickly disperse their seeds.

Taiga. Haviland '26:197. Flat marshy forests; the area between tundra and steppe (Russia).

Talus. (Warming). An accumulation of loose fragments at the base of rocks. *See* rubble, scree.

Tame pasture. Semple '34, USDA, Miscl. Pub. 194:5. Lands once cultivated that have been seeded with and are now occupied by domestic pasture plants and used chiefly or entirely for grazing livestock.

Tank epiphytes. Schimper '03:319. Species in which the root system is developed only as an anchoring device, or is entirely suppressed, so that the entire process of nutrition is carried on by the leaves.

Tapestry. J:470. Forest growth on steep slopes, forming an unbroken arboreous mantle.

Tapestry forest. MacCaughey '20, Bot. Gaz. 70:137. Groves which maintain themselves on precipitous slopes of Hawaii; although the trees are of small stature, the area is closely occupied forming an unbroken aborescent mantle.

Taphrium. Clements '02. A ditch community.

Taphrophilus. Ditch dwelling.

Tarn. A small mountain lake or pool.

Taungya. Tansley & Chipp '26:248. Deserted cleared
areas of Burma which return but slowly if at all to the
native forest. *See* caingin.

Taxis. J:378 (Czapek). The reaction of free organisms
in response to external stimuli by movement. *See* geoT,
phoboT, photoT, proschemoT, prosomoT, strophoT,
thermoT, thigmoT, tonoT, topophotoT, topoT, trophoT.
Cf. tropism.

Tegmen. Clements '02. Vegetative covering.

Tegulicolous. J:470 (A. L. Smith). Of/ lichens living
upon tiles.

Telianthus. J:379. Hermaphroditic.

Telmathium. Clements '02. A wet meadow community.
(Ganong). A wet marsh.

Telmatophilus. Clements '02. Dwelling in wet meadows.

Telmicolous. J:470. Dwelling in fresh water marshes.

Telotaxis. *See* topotaxis.

Temperate lakes. Pearse '31:202 (Whipple). Lakes
whose temperatures vary above and below 4°C.

Temperate life zone. (Merriam). *See* appendix V, VI.

Temperature. *See* frigifuge, hecistotherm, homiothermic,
isocheim, isochimenal, isocryma, nacrotherm, megatherm, magistotherm, microtherm, philotherm, poikilothermic, psychrotherm, stenthermal, thermo-, trophosphere, xeromorphosis, xero-.

Temperature summing. *See* aliquote, Stracy's formula,
Thermal constant.

Temporary pond. Mozley '32, Am. Nat. 66:235. A
small depression in which water from melting snows
collects and persists through the months of April and
June; such ponds are characterized by having a relatively short period of submersion followed by progres-

sively drier conditions and are subject to low temperatures in the winter. *See* pond, pool.

Terrace. Hancock '11:433. A level plain usually with abrupt front, bordering a river, lake, or sea.

Terrestrial. Of/ dry ground.

Terricolous. J:380. Living on the ground. Hancock '11: 420 recognizes the following types: hygrogeocolous, humicolous, ammoclous, petricolous, lignicolous, subcorticolous, geosylvacolous, subgeocolous, troglocolous, brotiocolous, myrmecolous.

Terriherbosa. Rübel '30, *Pflgesel. der Erde.* Herbaceous communities of dry land; subdivided into Duriherbosa, Sempervirentiherbosa, and Altherbosa. *See* herbosa.

Terriprata. J:380. A class of plant community developed upon substrata· not influenced by ground water, and consisting of grasses, herbs, and bryophytes.

Thalassium. Clements '02. A sea community. *See* ocean.

Thalassophilus. Clements '02. Sea loving.

Thalleosere. = proteosere (Clements).

Thalloid climax. J:470 (Clements), Climaxes of the predevonian period of bryophytes.

Thallostrote. Clements '05. A species migrating by means of offshoots.

Thamnium. J:83. The bushy thallus of certain lichens.

Thamnocolous. Hancock '11:420. Shrub inhabiting species. *See* phyodytes.

Thelytonic. = parthenogenetic.

Therium. Clements '05. A succession due to animals.

Thermal constant. Uvarov '31:22. "Completion of a given stage in development requires an accumulation of heat energy; the theoretical truth of this assumption can scarcely be disputed but in practice it has proved

to be impossible to measure actually the amount of heat
energy which should be measured as calories."

Thermal emission. Watson '33, Ohio Jl. Sci. 33:435.
Radiation and conduction of heat into air.

Thermesotherm. J:384. With summer heat of 12-20°C.

Thermium. Clements '02. A warm or hot spring community.

Thermocleistogamy. J:470 (Knuth). The self-pollena-
tion of unexpanded flowers, due to low temperature.

Thermocline. (Birge '97), See epilimnion, hypolimnion.

Thermogenic. J:470. Heat producing, as in the case of
certain bacteria.

Thermopegic. Klugh '23, Ecol. 4:372. Of/ hot springs.

Thermophilus. Clements '02. Dwelling in warm waters.

Thermosis. J:384. A change in an organism due to heat.

Thermotactic. J:471. Of/ tactic reaction to heat.

Thermotaxis. J:384. Movement induced by heat, moving
towards its source.

Thermotonus. J:384. The relation between temperature
and the manifestation or irritability.

Thermotoxy. J:384 (Balls). Death caused by excesses
of heat; especially if the plant is short of water.

Thermotropic. Tropistic reaction to heat.

Therodrymium. J:384 (Diels). A leafy forest community.

Theromegatherm. J:384. Having a high summer temperature of 20°C. and above.

Therophyllous. J:384. Producing leaves in summer; deciduous leaved plants.

Therophyte. Braun-Blanquet '32:289. Annuals; plants
which complete their life cycle from germination to ripe
seeds within a single vegetative period. Raunkiaer

'34:1. Annual plants which die at the approach of the unfavorable vegetative season through which they pass in the form of seeds.

Therophyte climate. Raunkiaer '34:143. The climate of regions of the subtropical zone with winter rain.

Thicket. Hancock '11:431. A wood or collection of trees, shrubs, etc., closely set. *See* carpolochmis, forest edge, driodium, dumetum, enclave, forewold, glade, heloloch-mium, lochmodium, mesolochmis, mulga, ptenothallium, virgulata, coppice.

Thievery. Pearse '26:359 (Wheeler). Spoken of small animals which live in the walls of ant nests and prey on the food stores or brood of the ants. *See* symbiosis.

Thigmomorphosis. J:384. Change in the original struct-ure due to contact.

Thigmotaxis. Taxic response to mechanical stimulus.

Thigmotropism. Tropic response to mechanical stimulus.

Thigmotropism. A tropic response of an organism to con-tact.

Thinic. Klugh '23, Ecol. 4:374. Of/ a dune community.

Thinicolous. (Warming). Dwelling on shifting sand dunes.

Thinium. Clements '02. A dune community.

Thinophilus. Dune loving.

Thorn country. Tansley & Chipp '26:206. Parkland of low thorn bearing trees singly or in thickets with spiny shrubs; grass rarely forming continuous ground cover; generally in clumps or tufts; dry season prolonged; range of temperature great.

Thorn forest. Schimper '03:261. Resembles the tropical savannah forest as regards foliage and average height but is more xerophilous, is very rich in underwood and in slender stemmed lianes, poor in terrestrial herbs, especially in grasses, and usually has no epiphytes. = caa tinga.

Thorn woodland. Schimper '03:492. An edaphic community in tropical rain forest districts; and in grassland districts on dry, sandy soil; in Argentina a forest type in the east, a scrub type in the west.

Threshold. The point of a series of graded stimulations above which response begins to be perceptible. Lillie '32, Am. Nat. 66:176. The quantity of stimulus necessary for occurrence of reaction. Shelford '29:192. That intensity or amount of any factor immediately above which development begins to be perceptible in amount.

Tidal forest. = mangrove.

Tidal zone. Flattely & Walton '22:9. The narrow strip of territory between high and low water marks of spring tides; also termed strand zone.

Tide. *See* actic, hypactile, littoral.

Tide pools. *See* clysotremic, epiclysile, hypoclysile.

Till. J:471. The product of glaciation; ground moraine. A soil of mixed clay and pebbles.

Tiller. J:385. A sucker or branch from the bottom of a stem.

Tillow. = tiller.

Till plain. A plain whose soil is derived from glacier deposited clay and pebbles.

Tilth. The depth of the soil to which cultivation may be carried and to which the surface roots may penetrate.

Timberline. The upper limit of tree vegetation in mountains.

Tiphic. Klugh '23, Ecol. 4:373. Of/ a pond community.

Tiphicolous. J:471. Pond dwelling.

Tiphium. Clements '02. A pond community.

Tiphophilus. Clements '02. Pond loving.

Tirium. Clements '05. A badland community.

Tjemoro. (Warming). Aphyllous forest formed chiefly of Casvarina in Java and Sunda islands.

Tocotropism. Tropic responses of organisms in giving birth to young.

Toleration, law of. fide Weese '35. The geographic or local range of any species is limited by the fluctuation of a single factor (or factors) beyond the limit tolerated by that species. See Leibig's law of the minimum.

Tombolo. Fenneman '10:29. (Italian). A bar which connects islands with a mainland.

Tomillares. Thyme covered areas in the south and east of the New Castile (Spain) table land. Warming '09: 304. Sclerophytic suffrutescent vegetation of regions where the air is very dry and the rainfall small.

Tonisis. J:386. Changes in turgescence due to intercellular osmotic force.

Tonobole. Clements '05. A plant whose seeds are scattered by projection from calyx or involucre.

Tonotaxis. J:386 (Beyerinck). Response to osmotic variation.

Topical. J:386. Local, confined to a limited area.

Topochemotaxis. = strophic chemotaxis.

Topographic. J:386. I. Of/ place changes due to water, wind, gravity, etc. 2. (Crampton). Used of stable plant communities where the prevailing factors are physiographic and edaphic.

Topophototaxis. J:386. Movement towards the origin of light.

Topotaxis. Wigglesworth & Gillett '34, Jl. Ex. Biol.

11:129 (Kühn). Movements in which the organism is truly oriented with reference to stimuli; two types are recognized: tropotaxis: bilateral tropistic effect (Loeb's idea), and telotaxis: a reaction to one stimulus to the exclusion of all others; chiefly of visual stimuli.

Topotropism. J:386. A turning towards a place from which a stimulus comes.

Torfaceous. J:386. Growing in bogs.

Torrent. Hancock '11:430. A stream suddenly rising and running rapidly, as down a precipitous slope.

Torrential. ESA 1934, List R-1. Of/ organisms living in swift streams.

Touradon. Schimper '03:187. Sandy hillocks in sand areas about which collect sand and gradually humus.

Traject. Myers '33, Jl. Ecol. 21:335. A reconnaissance or trip through a region.

Transect. Clements '05. A cross section of vegetation. '16:430. Essentially an elongated quadrat; in its simplest form it is merely a line through a community or series of communities on which are indicated the individuals of the species observed.

Transgressive strata. Braun-Blanquet & Pavillard '30:10. Inferior strata of certain communities which are also found in other communities.

Transition stage. *See* stage, ecotone.

Transition life zone (Merriam). *See* appendix V, VI.

Transverse tropism. *See* diatropism.

Trap flowers. J:389. Prison flowers, which confine insect visitors until pollenation has taken place.

Trap day (trap night, etc.). Shelford '29:41 (Grinnell). A unit for expressing density of population of a species: one trap for one day set by a skilled trapper; hence 20 traps set for 8 days would constitute 160 trap days.

Travesias. Hardy '25:155, *Geogr. of Plants.* Marsh or salt deserts (W. Argentina).

Trechometer. Clements '05. An instrument for measuring runoff.

Tree-grass-steppe. Schimper '03:369 (Engler). Consists chiefly of various species of Acacia; a true savannah in sense of Schimper (Africa).

Treue. (Braun-Blanquet). = exclusive species.

Tribium. Clements '05. A succession in an eroded soil.

Trichoplankton. J:390 (Cleve). Floating marine vegetation composed of Thalassiothrix.

Triduus. J:391. Lasting three days.

Trimonoecium. J:392. Having male, female, and perfect flowers on the same plant.

Triposplankton. J:393 (Cleve). Floating marine vegetation made up chiefly of *Ceratium tripos.*

Tripton. Chapman '31:325 (Wilhelmi). Detritus taken in plankton samples.

Tristes plantae. J:289. Evening flowering plants. *See* day, period.

Trixeny. J:393 (DeBary). The condition of a parasite which passes its career in three hosts.

Troglocolous. Hancock '11:420. Cave dwelling.

Tropelagic. J:393 (Archangeli). Collecting food material for the plant.

Trophallaxis. Allee '31:388 (Wheeler). Mutual feeding in which (for example) the mother may feed on secretions from the larvae who in turn are fed by the mother.

Trophobia. Allee '31:30 (Deegener). . . . . exist when one species feeds on the excretions or wastes of another, and in turn furnishes protection for the weaker species.

Trophophyte. Schimper '03:21. Vegetation of areas whose climate is alternately damp and dry or cold.

Trophosphere. Lumby '34, Jl. Ecol. 22:316. The upper layer of high temperature in the oceans.

Trophotaxis. J:394 (Stahl). Phenomena induced in a growing organ by the chemical nature of its environment.

Tropical lakes. Pearse '26:202 (Whipple). Lakes whose temperatures are always above 4°C.

Tropical life zone (Merriam). Chapman '31:221. The northern limit is defined by the sum of the normal mean daily temperature above 43°F. for the six hottest weeks, 26,000°F. See appendix V, VI.

Tropism. Movement in response to a stimulus on the part of attached organisms (most plants), coelenterates, certain protozoa, etc. J: 394 (Copeland). A curvature which results from a response to some stimulus; the disposition to respond by turning or bending. See alkaliT, anemoT, aphaptoT, aphelioT, aphercoT, aphoto-T, autonyctiT, autoorthoT, baroT, clinoT, cryoT, cyto-T, diaphotoT, diaT, dromoT, edaphoT, epigeoT, geodiaT, helioT, hertzoT, hydroT, kataklinoT, klinoT, klinogeoT, narcoT, nyctiT, ombraT, orthoT, ortho-, osmoT, ozyT, panphotometric, parahelioT, parallel geo-T, paraphotoT, parorthoT, photoT, polyT, progeoesthetic, prohydroT, rheoT, seismoT, selenoT, sioT, somaT, stenoT, stereoT, teloT, topoT, thermoT, thigmoT, tocoT, topochemoT, torsion, transverse T, zenoT, taxis.

Tropo-. J:394 (Drude). Prefix to denote climates alternating between torrential rain and sunny drought. See trophophyte.

Tropodrymium. J:394 (Diels). A savannah forest community.

Tropotaxis. *See* topotaxis.

Tuitans. J:396. Of/ leaves assuming the sleep position, appearing to guard the stem.

Tumble weed. J:395. Certain weeds which break adrift when dry, and are blown to a distance scattering their seeds as they go.

Tumulus. Clements '02. Of/ a dune.

Tundra. Warming '09:205. A large flat or gently undulating tract, devoid of trees; arctic fell fields, with mosses dominant. Schimper '03:685. Dwarfed growth, a distinctly xerophilous character, predominance of mosses and lichens, the incomplete covering of ground are everywhere characteristic of the tundra. *See* crymic, kammenaia.

Turbarian. J:395. Of/ a stage in the formation of peat, characterized by the presence of dwarf willows.

Turfaceous. Pertaining to bogs.

Tussock. J:396. A tuft of grass or grasslike plants.

Twin Communities. ESA 1935. List P-3 (Gams). Such biocoenoses which conform only in one or two of the communities (synusiae, layers) composing them while others change. Hult used "twin formations" referring to all strata. The changing communities are called "alternating communities." = consociations.

Tycholimnetic. Warming '09:150. Of/ false plankton: fresh water forms which are at first fixed, but later break loose and float. J:396. Of/ floating vegetation which at times is at the surface and at others is attached to plants and rocks at the bottom.

Tychopotamic, -ous. J:396 (Zimmer). Of/ the floating

organisms of pools and river overflows. Carpenter '28: 171 (Schröter). Of/ species indigenous to ponds.

Typiform. J:396. (Kuntze). A constant form arising either by natural selection or by animal adaptations; its existence is frequently dependent upon animals.

U

Ubiquist. J:396 (Thurmann). A plant which occurs on any kind of soil.

Ubiquitous associates. III Int. Bot. Congr. 1910:25 (Brockman). Species occurring constantly in several communities.

-ule. (Clements). Suffix for socies.

Umbraticolous. J:397. Growing in shady places.

Umbrosus. J:397. Growing in shady places.

Undergrowth. ESA 1934, List R-1. Underbrush, seedlings, shoot, small saplings, and all herbaceous growth in a forest.

Undershrub. J:398. 1. Any low shrub. 2. A partially herbaceous plant, the ends of the branches dying during the unfavorable season.

Uneven aged. ESA 1934. List R-1. Applied to a stand of forest in which considerable differences in age of trees occur, differences varying with the average of stand or forest Univoltine. Uvarov '31:104. Producing but one generation a year.

Unstable. Tansley & Chipp '26:7. Of/ transient communities, those which are not able to maintain themselves for any length of time without change.

Upland. Nichols '23, Ecol. 4:156. All types of topography other than depressions occupied by lakes, swamps, or in close proximity to rivers, streams, or seas.

Upland salient. Vestal '18, Trans. Ill. Acad. 11:123. The tops of spurs of small upland areas consisting of "ends" and "corners" which are too small or narrow for cultivation.

Upper beach. Flattely & Walton '22:36 (Davenport). The area reached only by extremely high tides.

Urophile. J:400 (Chodat). Of/ algae growing on soil containing ammonia.

V

Vadal. Chapman '31:280 (Steuer). Floating near the shore (cf. pelagic, floating at the surface).

Vage. Braun-Blanquet '32:59. Indifferent species with reference to limitation to habitat.

Vagil-benthon. J:47 (Forel). Wandering organisms of the ocean bottom.

Valency. ESA 1935. List P-3. Synonymous with degree of frequency and with frequency index.

Van't Hoff's formula. Uvarov '31:29. The velocity of a reaction increases with the temperature and the coefficient Q_{10} (expressing the rate of increase per 10°C.) has a value between 2 and 3 for each 10° interval.

Variad. *See* Clements '25, Carn. Inst. Yrbk. 24:312.

Variant. Trapnell '33, Jl. Ecol. 21:307. Any sample of a complex taken under a uniform set of external factors; often mixed in character.

Variation. Clements '05. The origin of new forms by the action of selection of minute differences.

Variety. DuRietz '30a:348. A population of one or several biotypes, forming a more or less distinct local facies of a species.

Varzea. J:402. A partially submerged forest (Brazil).

Vector. *See* insect vector.

Vedomin. Shelford '35. Ecol. Monogr. 5:259 (Clements). A small domin: the rôle of minute planktons. *See* domin.

Vefluent. Clements '36. Jl. Ecol. 24:271. A microscopic influent of little significance in a community.

Vegetation. ESA 1934, List P-2. Plants in general, or the total aggregation of plants. *See* herbosa, shrubage, herbosa, lignosa.

Vegetation belt. DuRietz '30 Proc. Int. Congr. Pl. Sci. 1:76. Vegetation regions homologous in their altitudinal position; more local altitudinal divisions within one vegetation belt are called vegetation horizons. = vegetation-stufe.

Vegetation form. A characteristic growth form, as tree, shrub, forb, etc. *See* life form.

Vegetation region. DuRietz '30:244. A phytocoenosis extending over a large area, composed for the most part of an extremely variable mosaic, often of large stands of definite Phytocoenoses. *See* appendix I, II.

Vegetation stage. *See* associes, vegetation-stufe (DuRietz).

Vegetation-stufe. (DuRietz) '30:352. A phytocoenosis consisting of a series of vegetation regions of whatever rank, homologous in altitude, and mostly exhibiting a clearly recognizable floristic relatioaship; less frequently of a single vegetation region including a definite altitude. *See* vegetation belt.

Vegetational type. Aldous & Shantz '24, Jl. Agr. Res. 28:99. A plant community of any size, rank, or stage of development; = plant community.

Vegetations-typus. (Drude). *See* appendix I.

Vegetationsfleck. Braun-Blanquet '32:25. = settlement.

Veld, veldt. J:403. The tree steppe or savannah of S. Africa. Warming '298 (Gibbs). Rhodesion tree steppe. 2. J:472 (Evans). All native vegetation from rich forest on the SE coast of S. Africa to desert in interior Karoo.

Velocity of development. Shelford '29:192. The number of developmental units per hour under any combination of conditions.

Verband. Braun-Blanquet & Pavillard '30. = Alliance. *See* appendix I.

Verein. = synusium.

Vermuth steppe. J:404 (Warming). Extensive plains on which the dominant plant is Artemesia.

Vernal. Clements '05. Of/ spring.

Vernalization. The process of shortening the vegetative period of plants by seed treatment.

Vesperal. Carpenter '34, Proc. Okla. Acad. 14:29. Of/ the evening crepuscular period; the complement of auroral.

Vespertine. J:405. Of/ the evening.

Vexillary. J:405 (Plateau). Of/ the giving (by a flower) of an attractive signal to insects.

Viatical. J:405. Of/ plants which grow by the roadside or path.

Vicarious. J:405 (Crozier). Supplying the place or function of some other thing. *See* substitute.

Vicine. Clements '05. Invading from adjacent communities.

Vicinism. J.405 (DeVries). Variation due to growth of other plants in close proximity.

Vigilae florum. J:406. Periods during which certain plants open and close their flowers. *See* photoperiodism.

Virgin forest. ESA 1934, List R-1. Applies to mature or overmature forest essentially uninfluenced by human activity.

Virgulata. Clements '02. A thicket or coppice.

Vitality. Braun-Blanquet & Pavillard '30:9. An expression of vigor and prosperity attained by different species.

Vixigregarious. Clements '05. Arranged in small or indistinct groups; sparse.

Volcanic. *See* rhysium.

Voltine. Pertaining to the number of generations per year. *See* univoltine.

W

Wady. J:407 (Arabic). A valley containing water only in the wet season. = wed, oued.

Waldserriesm. Braun-Blanquet & Pavillard '30. Tree seres.

Wallace's life zones '76. Californian, Rocky Mountain, Alleghany, and Canadian.

Wallace's rule for mimicry. Folsom '26:203. The imitative species should occur in the same area and occupy the same station as the imitated; the imitators are always the more defenceless; the imitators are always less numerous in individuals; the imitators differ from the bulk of their allies; the imitation is external and visible, never extending to internal characters or to those as do not affect the personal appearance. *See* mimicry, coloration.

Wallace's Zoogeographical regions. *See* appendix VI.

Warning coloration. *See* aposematic coloration.

Wasp flowers. J:407. Flowers adapted to wasp visitors, but also visited by other insects and pollenated by them.

Waste. Hancock '11:432. Unproductive and unused land. *See* chersium, chledium, ruderal, chomophyte.

Waterbloom. J:407. A sudden development of certain algae in lakes, also known as the "breaking of the meres."

Water capacity. *See* absolute water capacity, full water capacity, available soil moisture.

Water content. Clements '05. The water of the soil or habitat; Physiological WC: the available soil water; Physical: the total amount of soil water. *See* echard, cheshard, holard, full water capacity, physical drought, physiological drought.

Water table. J:488. The level of saturation of soil by ground water.

Watten (= wadden). The shallows separating certain of the Friesian islands.

Webber's law. Shelford '29:189. A formula having to do with the shape of the developmental curve near the threshold.

Wed. *See* wady.

Weed. J:408. Any useless or troublesome plant which occurs without intentional cultivation. *See* ruderal.

Weel. J:408 (Ogla). A term borrowed from a wicker eel trap for an arrangement of hairs which keeps out unbidden insect visitors from flowers.

Weeping tree. Raunkiaer '34:19. Trees with branches hanging downwards, especially towards their apices; Passively WT caused by the weight of the branches arching them to the ground.

Wet meadow. Hancock '11:430. Lowland covered with coarse grass or rank herbage.

Wiesner's law. J:473. Leaves are usually placed so as to receive the maximum illumination from a source of light.

Wilting coefficient. The amount of water contained in the soil at the time of permanent wilting of a standard plant; = echard. *See* moisture equivalent.

Wind. *See* anemo-. aura.

Winter. *See* hiemal.

Winter-annual. J:408. A plant which germinates in autumn, lives through the winter, fruits and dies.

Wold. = woodland.

Woodland. Schimper '03:162. Areas whose vegetation is composed essentially of woody plants. *See* forest, bushwood, shrubwood, bush, carpohylile, coppice, copse, forest, helophylium, silva, savannah, parkland, helorgadium, hylium, mesohylile, mixed forest, nemoralis, nemus, orgadium, sylvestr-, therodrymium, xerodrymium, xerohylium, xylium, thicket.

Woodland climate. Schimper '03:171. Climate having a warm vegetative season, continually moist subsoil, damp and calm air especially in winter.

Wood-meadow. Warming '09:335. Park-like forests of Sweden, probably caused by man. *See* parkland, savannah.

Wuchsort. = locality. (Braun-Blanquet & Pavillard).

Wuchsstelle. = locality.

Wurzelort. = station.

X

Xenodoche. Clements '05. An anomalous succession.

Xerarch. Cooper '13, Bot. Gaz. 55:11. Of/ successions which, having their origins in xeric habitats, become more and more mesic in their successive stages. Nichols '23, Ecol. 4:171. Of/ successions which originate in xeric habitats such as rock shores, beaches, and cliffs and which become more mesic in their successive stages.

Xerasium. Clements '05. A succession due to drainage or drought.

Xeric. Cooper & Weese '26, Ecol. 7:390. Characterized by or pertaining to conditions of scanty moisture supply.

Xeriobole. Clements '05. A plant whose seeds are scattered by dehiscence due to dryness.

Xerochastic. J:410 (Ascherson). Of/ plants whose fruits burst by desiccation and whose seeds or spores are thus scattered.

Xerocleistogamy. J:473. (Hansgirg). Pollenation in closed flowers because of insufficient moisture.

Xerocline. (Clements). A dry, warm slope.

Xerocolons. = xerophilous.

Xerodrymium. J:410 (Diels). A xeric forest community.

Xerogeophytes. J:473 (Massart). Plants whose inactive period is in the dry season.

Xerohylium. Clements '02. A dry forest community.

Xeromorphosis. (Herbst). Change induced by action of drought.

Xerophile. J:410. A plant which grows in a dry situation.

Xerophilous. Warming '09:36. Of/ plants calling for much heat, but making the most modest demands for water. *See* Thoday '33, Jl. Ecol. 21:4.

Xerophorbium. J:411 (Diels). Garide, tundra and dunes.

Xerophylophilous. Dwelling in dry forests.

Xerophyte. J:411. A plant which can subsist with a small amount of moisture, as a desert plant. *See* dissophyte.

Xerophytia. Clements '02. Dry land communities.

Xerophytism, xeroplastic. Thoday '33, Jl. Ecol. 21:1. The habit of plants characteristic of dry habitats, irrespective of modes of adaptation of these habitats.

Xeropoium. J:411 (Diels). Steppe. (Cooper) Dry steppe. Clements '02, heath community.

Xeropoophilous. Heath loving.

Xerosere. Phillips '30, Jl. Ecol. 18:201. A sere commencing on dry sites (rocks, dry soil) and characterized by a scarcity of water content. *See* lithosere, psammosere. ESA 1934, List P-2. A collective term referring to all stages of a xerarch succession.

Xerosion, xerosium. Clements '05. A plant succession on drained and dried up soil.

Xerostatic. J:411 (Clements). Of/ successions completed under xeric conditions.

Xerotactic. J:473 (Clements). Of/ successions not greatly changed by dry conditions. Cf. xerotropic.

Xerothamnium. J:411 (Diels). A spiny shrub community.

Xerotherm. J:411. Capable of withstanding drought and heat.

Xerotropism. J:411 (Borzi). The tendency of plants or parts thereof to alter their position to protect themselves from desiccation.

Xylium. Clements '02. A wood community (saprophytic, epiphytic).

Xylophagous. Chapman '31:161 (Handlirsch). Of/ organisms which feed on woody plant parts.

Xylophilous. Clements '02. Wood loving.

Y

Ygapo. J:412 (Trail). A forest wholly submersed for two months of a year (Brazil).

Yield. ESA 1934, List R-1. The timber or wood value that is actually or can be normally produced by a stand of a given composition at a given age under given site conditions and treatment—the actual or normal product of the stand; involves the ideas of futurity, hence for a statement of actual material on hand the terms stock or growing stock are preferable.

Young growth. ESA 1934, List R-1. Forest growth which comes up naturally after cutting, fire or other disturbing cause; *see* residual stand, second growth.

Z

Zenotropism. J:412 (Fayod). Negative geotropism.

Zero point. (Schimper). The extremes of high and low temperature which plants can endure without being killed.

Zoidiophilous. J:412. Pollenated through the agency of some animal.

Zoidogamae. J:412 (Kirchner). Plants in which pollenation is effected by animal agency.

Zoidospore. J:473 (Clements). A plant whose seeds are dispersed by animals.

Zonal. J:412 (McMillan). Plant communities which exhibit well marked radial symmetry as though spreading from a single center. Clements '05. The condition in which plant groups or communities appear in belts or zones. Braun-Blanquet '32:345. A girdle or belt-like arrangement of the units of vegetation, whether on a large or on a small scale and caused by similarly arranged differences of important factors of the habitat. Braun-Blanquet & Pavillard '30. The climatic and edaphic conditions and the configuration of the surface relief give place to more or less distinct zonation in the vegetation. *See* belt, ceinture, mictium, azonal, girdle, ectone, alterne, shore.

Zonation complex. DuRietz '30:343. A Phytocoenosis-complex composed of distinct Phytocoenoses or Mosaic-complexes more or less zonally arranged.

Zone. III Int. Bot. Congr. 1910:28. The great climatic belts of the earth; should not be used either for altitudinal belts on mountains, for a zone like arrangement within a Formation (zonation of Clements), nor for the subdivisions of a territory (Engler). Klugh '23, Ecol. 4:369. Communities which exhibit a well marked concentric or parallel arrangement, as peat bogs, some lake margins, and mountains. Tansley & Chipp '26:202. Types of vegetation superimposed in height (mountainous) or depth (marine). Clements '05. A belt of more or less uniform vegetation. *See* Intertidal Zone, Tidal Zone.

Zoobiotic. J:412. A fungus whose host is an animal.

Zoocecida. J:412 (Tubeuf). Plant galls produced by animals.

Zoochore. Clements '05. A plant distributed by animals.

Zoodomatia. J:413. Shelters formed by a plant for those animals which are of benefit to it.

Zoolapton. Friederichs '30:233. Organisms transported on the exterior of animals. = Zoochore.

Zoometer. Shelford '29:62. Biometers which indicate conditions through the abundance or number of individuals.

Zoomorphosis. J:413. Changes produced in plants by the action of animals, the formation of galls caused by animals.

Zoophagous. Chapman '31:160 (Handlirsch). Organisms eating substances of animal source.

Zoophilous. Pollenated by animals.

Zoophobous. J:413. Of/ plants which protect themselves against animals, such as ants, by hairs, secretions, etc.

Zoosuccivorous. Chapman '31:160 (Handlirsch). Of/ organisms which eat on decaying animals.

Zoosaporphagous. Chapman '31:160 (Handlirsch). Of/ organisms which feed on liquid secretions of other animals such as spittle, honeydew, etc. *See* tropholaxis.

Zufällige. Braun-Blanquet & Pavillard '30. Accidental species.

LITERATURE CITED IN GLOSSARY

Allee, W. C. 1931. Animal aggregations. Univ. Chicago Press.

Braun-Blanquet, J. 1932. Plant sociology; the study of communities. Translated, edited, and revised by G. D. Fuller & H. S. Conard. McGraw-Hill.

Braun-Blanquet, J., and J. Pavillard 1930. Vocabulary of plant sociology. Translated by F. R. Bharucha. Imprim. de la Charité, Pierre-Rouge, Montpellier.

Chapman, R. N. 1931. Animal ecology, with reference to the insects. McGraw-Hill.

Clements, F. E. 1902. A system of nomenclature for phytogeography. Engler's Botanische Jahrbuch 31, b.70.

———— 1904. The development and structure of vegetation. Bot. Surv. Nebraska, Lincoln.

———— 1905. Research methods in ecology. Univ. Pub. Co., Lincoln.

———— 1916. Plant succession: an analysis of the development of vegetation. Carn. Inst. Wash. pub. 242.

Committee on Nomenclature, Ecological Society of America. 1933-4. Tentative glossary of Ecological terms. Preliminary lists 1 and 2, revised list 1, mimeographed.

Dayton, W. A. 1934. Glossary of botanical terms commonly used in range research. U.S.D.A. Miscl. Pub. 110.

DuRietz, G. E. 1930. Vegetationsforschung auf soziationsanalytischer Grundlage. Handbuch der Biol Arbeitsmeth. (Abderhalden). Lief. 320, Abt. 11, teil 5, heft 2.

———— 1930a. Fundamental units of biological taxonomy. Sv. Bot. Tidskr. 24:333-428.

———— 1930b. Classification and nomenclature of vegetation. Sv. Bot. Tidskr. 24:489-503.

ESA 1932. Committee for the study of plant and animal communities, Ecological Society of America. 1932. Memorandum on nature sanctuaries or nature reserves. (mimeographed).

ESA 1933, List P-1; 1934, List P-2; 1934, List R-2; 1935, List P-3. See Committee on nomenclature, Ecol. Soc. Am.

Flahault, Ch., and C. Schröter. 1910. Phytogeographical nomenclature, reports and propositions. III International Botanical Congress, Brussels. Zurich.

Flattely, F. W., and C. L. Walton 1922. The biology of the sea shore. Macmillan.

Folsom, J. W. 1926. Entomology with reference to its biological and economic aspects. 3rd edition, Blakiston.

Friederichs, Karl. 1930. Die Grundfragen und Gesetzmäsugheiten der Land—und Forstwirtschaftlichen Zoologie. I Band: Ökologischer Teil. Berlin.

Haviland, M. D. 1926. Forest steppe and tundra. Cambridge.

III Int. Bot. Congr. 1910. See Flahault and Schröter, 1910.

"J" See Jackson, 1928.

Jackson, B. D. 1928. A glossary of botanic terms with their derivation and accent. London, Duckworth.

Needham, J. G. and J. T. Lloyd. 1916. The life of inland waters. Comstock, Ithaca.

Pearse, A. S. 1926. Animal ecology. McGraw-Hill.

Raunkiaer, C. 1934. The life forms of plants and statistical plant geography (collected papers). Oxford.

Schimper, A. F. W. 1903. Plant geography on a physiological basis. Translated by W. R. Fisher. Oxford.

Shelford, V. E. 1929. Laboratory and Field ecology. Williams & Wilkins, Baltimore.

Tansley, A. G., and T. F. Chipp. 1926. Aims and methods in the study of vegetation. London.

III Int. Bot. Congr. 1910. *See* Falhault and Schröter, 1910.

U.S.D.A. 1905. Terms used in forestry and logging, U.S. Dept. Bur. Forestry Bull. 61.

U.S. Forest Service. 1930. Glossary of terms used in fire control. U.S.D.A., Miscl. Pub. 7.

Uvarov, B. P. 1931. Insects and climate. Trans. Ent. Soc. London 79:1-247.

Warden, C. J., T. N. Jenkins, and L. H. Warner 1934. Introduction to comparative psychology. Ronald.

Warming, E. 1909. Oecology of plants. Oxford.

Weaver, J. E. and F. E. Clements 1929. Plant ecology. McGraw-Hill.

HISTORICAL BIBLIOGRAPHY

1895. Warming, E. 1895. Plantesamfund; Grundträk auf den okologiske plantegeografi. Kjoenhavn. German transl. by Knoblauch, 1896. Lehrbuch der oekologischen Pflanzengeographie. English transl. by Percy Groom, 1909. Oecology of Plants, Oxford.

1898. Schimper, A. F. W. Planzengeographie auf physiologischer Grundlage. English transl. by W. R. Fisher, 1903. Plant geography on a physiological basis, Oxford.

1899. Warburg, O. Einfuhrung einer gleichmässigen Nomenklatur in der Pflanzen-Geographie. Verhandlungen des Siebenten Int. Geogr. Kongr., Berlin. 1:51-52; 2:443-448. reprinted in Engler's Bot. Jahrb. 29(3/4), b.66:23.

1900. Flahault, Ch. Projet de nomenclature phytogeographique. Congr. Intern. Bot. Paris. English transl. 1901. A project for phytogeographic nomenclature. Bull. Torrey Bot. Club 28:391-409.

1901. Flahault, Ch. Premier essai de nomenclature phytogeographique. Bull.Soc.languedocienne Geogr.

1902. Clements, F. E. A system of nomenclature for phytogeography. Engler's Bot. Jahrb. 31, b.70.
——Greek and Latin in biological nomenclature. Univ. Nebr. Stud. 3:1.

1904. ——The development and structure of vegetation. Bot. Surv. Nebr., Lincoln.

1905. —— Research methods in Ecology. Univ. Pub. Co., Lincoln.

Harshberger, J. W. Suggestions toward a phytogeographic nomenclature. Science 21:789-790.

Olsson-Seffer, P. The principles of phytogeographic nomenclature. Bot. Gaz. 39:179-193.

1907. Clements, F. E. Plant physiology and ecology. Holt, New York.

1910. Farlow, W. G., & G. F. Atkinson. The botanical congress at Brussels. Bot. Gaz. 50:220.

Flahault, Ch., & C. Schröter. Phytogeographische Nomenklatur; Berichte und Vorschläge von der Kommission für Phytogeographische Nomenklatur, IIIe Congr. Int. Bot., Bruxelles, 1910. Zurich. English transl. 1910, Phytogeographical nomenclature, etc. Zurich.

Moss, C. E. The fundamental units of vegetation. New Phytol. 9:18-53.

1912. Brockman-Jerosch, H. & E. Rübel. Die Einteilung der Pflanzengesellschaften nach ökologisch-physiognomischen Gesichtspunkten. Leipzig.

Pavillard, J. Essai de nomenclature phytogeographique. Bull. Soc. Lang. Geogr. 35.

1913. Braun, J. & E. Furrer. Sur l'étude des associations. Bull. Soc. Lang. Geogr. 36.

Shelford, V. E. Animal communities in temperate America. Bull. Geogr. Soc. Chi. 5.

1916. Clements, F. E. Plant succession: an analysis of the development of vegetation. Carn. Inst. Wash. pub. 242. (Reprinted, H. W. Wilson Co., 1928.)

Samuelsson, G. Om den ekologiska växtgeografiens enheter. Sv. Bot. Tidskr. 10.

AN ECOLOGICAL GLOSSARY   303

1917.   Gleason, H. A. The structure and development of
        the plant association. Bull. Torrey Bot. Club
        44:463.
        Nichols, G. E. The interpretation and application
        of certain terms and concepts in the ecological
        classification of plant communities. Pl. World
        20:305-319; 341-353.
1918.   DuRietz, G. E., Th. C. E. Fries, & T. A. Teng-
        wall. Vorschlag zur Nomenklatur der soziolo-
        gischen Pflanzengeographie. Sv. Bot. Tidskr.
        12:145-170.
        McDougall, W. B. Classification of symbiotic
        phenomena. Pl. World 21:250.
        Pearsall, W. H. On the classification of aquatic
        plant communities. Jl. Ecol. 6:75-84.
1919.   Pavillard, J. Remarques sur la nomenclature phy-
        togeographique. Montpellier.
1920.   Clements, F. E. Plant indicators: the relation of
        plant communities to process and practice. Carn.
        Inst. Wash. pub. 315. (Reprinted, H. W. Wil-
        son Co., 1928)
1921.   Hansen, A. A. The terminology of the ultimate
        vegetation. Ecology 2:125.
1923.   Klugh, A. B. A common system of classification
        in plant and animal ecology. Ecology 4:366-377.
        Nichols, G. E. A working basis for the ecological
        classification of plant communities. Ecology
        4:11-23, 154-177.
1925.   Yapp, R. H. The interrelation of plants in vegeta-
        tion and the concept of "association." Festschr.
        Carl Schröter, heft 3.

1926. Cooper, W. S. The fundamentals of vegetational change. Ecology 7:392-413.

DelVillar, M. Sur la method et la nomenclature de geobotanique, etc. Proc. Int. Congr. Pl. Sci. 1:560.

DuRietz, G. E. Fundamental units of vegetation. Proc. Int. Congr. Pl. Sci. 1:623-627.

Nichols, G. E. Plant associations and their classification. Proc. Int. Congr. Pl. Sci. 1:629.

Pearse, A. S. Animal Ecology. McGraw-Hill.

Shelford, V. E. Terms and concepts in animal ecology. Ecology 7:389.

———(editor). Naturalist's guide to the Americas. Baltimore, Williams & Wilkins.

Tansley, A. G. Succession: the concept and its values. Proc. Int. Congr. Pl. Sci. 1:677-686.

——— & T. F. Chipp. Aims and methods in the study of vegetation. London.

1927. Soo, R. von. Zur nomenclature und methodologie der pflanzensoziologie. Gragger-Gedenkbuch, Berlin.

Taylor, W. P. Ecology or bioecology. Ecology 8:280.

1928. Braun-Blanquet, J. Pflanzensoziologie. Berlin. English transl. by G. D. Fuller & H. S. Conard, 1932. Plant sociology, the study of communities. McGraw-Hill.

1929. Weaver, J. E. & F. E. Clements. Plant ecology. McGraw-Hill.

1930. Tansley, A. G. The classification of vegetation and the concept of development. Jl. Ecol. 8:118.

Braun-Blanquet, J. & J. Pavillard. Vocabulary

of Plant Sociology, transl. by F. R. Bharucha. Montpellier.

DuRietz, G. E. Vegetationsfurschung auf soziationsanalytischer Grundlage. Handb. der biol. Arbeitsmeth. (Abderhalden) Lief. 320, Abt. 11, teil 5, heft 2.

———Fundamental units of biological taxonomy. Sv. Bot. Tidskr. 24:333-428.

——— Classification and nomenclature of vegetation. Sv. Bot. Tidskr. 24:489-503.

Stefanoff, B. A parallel classification of climates and vegetational types. Sbornik. Balg. Akad. Nauk. 26. (*see* Jl. Ecol. 22:211 for review.)

1931. Phillips, J. The biotic community. Jl. Ecol. 19: 1-24.

Shelford, V. E. Some concepts of bioecology. Ecology 12:455-467.

Beklemischev, W. N. Ueber die Anwendung einiger Grundbegriffe der Biocönologie auf tierische Komponente der Festlandbiocönosen. Bulletin of Plant Protection 1:278-358 (in Russian, German summary).

1932. Shelford, V. E. Basic principles in the classification of communities and habitats and the use of terms. Ecology 13:105-120.

1933. Committee on nomenclature, Ecological Society of America. Tentative glossary of ecological nomenclature, preliminary list No. 1 (mimeographed).

1934. ——— *Ibid.* Preliminary list No. 2 (mimeographed).

——— *Ibid.* Revised list No. 1 (mimeographed).

Phillips, John. Succession, development, the climax, and the complex organism: an analysis of concepts, part I. Jl. Ecol. 22:554-571.

1935.   Pavillard, J. The present status of the plant association. Botanical Review 1:210-232.

Phillips, John. Succession, etc., part II. Jl. Ecol. 23:210-246.

————— Succession, etc., part III. Jl. Ecol. 23:488.

APPENDIX

Comparison of Plant-sociological Terminology, Terms by DuRietz[30]

Examples	G. E. DuRietz 1928-1930	H. Gams	E. Rübel	H. L. Shantz	G. E. Nichols	L. Cockayne	F. E. Clements	A. G. Tansley	J. Braun-Blanquet	O. Drude	A. K. Cajander	G. E. DuRietz 1917-1927
The *Cetraria islandica*-layer of the alpine *Vaccinium uliginosum*-*Cetraria islandica*-heath of Middle Europe	Socion (Synusia)	Synusia	Synusia	Society	Society	Colony	Society	Society	—	—	Bestand	Bestand (1918) Boden-schicht-typus
The alpine *Vaccinium uliginosum*-*Cetraria islandica*-heath of Middle Europe	Sociation		Sociation	—	—	—	—	—	Part of a Facies	Elementar-associationen mit floristischer Facies	Facies	Association
The alpine *Vaccinium uliginosum*-heath of Middle Europe (with variable bottom-layer)	Consociation		Consociation	—	Consociation	Sub-association	Con-sociation	Con-sociation	—	—	Association	
The alpine *Empetrum-Vaccinium uliginosum*-heath of Middle Europe (Braun-Blanquet's *Empetreto-Vaccinietum*)	Association	Phytocoenoses	Association	Association	Association	Association	—	—	Association	Association		
The alpine *Loiseleuria-Empetrum-Vaccinium uliginosum*-heath of Middle Europe (Braun-Blanquet's *Loiseleurieto-Vaccinion*)	Federation		(Association-) Verband	—	—	Groups of associations	—	—	(Association-) Verband	—		
The Middle-European ericaceous heath (Braun-Blanquet's *Rhodoreto-Vaccinietalia* in somewhat widened sense)	Sub-formation		Formation	—	—	—	Association	Association	(Association-) Ordnung	Hauptassociation (earlier formation)		

Right-side bracket labels: *Phytocoenoses* (spanning H. Gams and E. Rübel group); *Association-classes* (A. K. Cajander); *Association-groups* (G. E. DuRietz 1917-1927).

APPENDIX I (Continued)

The boral ericaceous heath	For-mation	—	—	Formation	—	(Minor) Formation	Formation (Climax)	—	(Associations-) Klasse	Associations-gruppe	—	Formation
The boreal, tropical-subalpine, and austral ericaceous heaths, scrubs, and dwarf-forests	Pan-formation	—	—	(World) formation group	—	(Major) Formation	Pan-climax	—	—	Vegetations-typus	—	—
The physiognomic group of lichenous dwarf-shrub heaths	Isocoenoses	Isocoenoses	—	—	—	—	—	—	—	—	—	—
The physiognomic group of all dwarf-shrub heaths			Formation group	—	Association-type	—	—	—	Homologous Formations	Formation (earlier Formations-klasse)	—	Formation group
The deflation-complex of the low-alpine morain-ridges	Mosaic-complex	—		—	Association-complex (physiographic formation)			(Physiographic) Formation	Association Complex	Komplex von Elementar-assoziationen	Siedlungs-komplex	Association complex
The *Loiseleuria-Empetrum-Vaccinium uliginosum*-region of the low-alpine belt of the Alps	Vegetation-region	Gebiet	Vegetations-stufe	Formation	Climatic formation	—	Formation with its seral (ontogenetic) stages	(Climatic) Formation	Klimax-gebiet	Vegetations-region	Formation	Vegetation-region

Spanning labels: "Phytocoenose-complexes" and "Isocoenoses"

APPENDIX I (Continued)

CHANGES TO "UNITS AMONG THE SYNUSIA"
Presented by G. E. DuRietz
at the Amsterdam Botanical Congress, 1935

DuRietz, 1930	DuRietz and Gams, '35	Gams, 1932-'33	Hippmaa	DeVries
Consocion	Society	Society Sociotype	Facies	Association
Associon	Union		Einschichts Association	
Federion	Federation	Federation (Verband)	Associations Gattung	

APPENDIX II

COMPARISON OF SOCIOLOGICAL UNITS,
AFTER DuRIETZ '3C

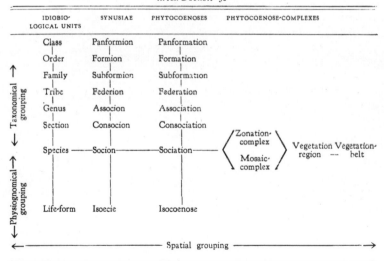

COMMUNITY CLASSIFICATION, AFTER SHELFORD '32

CLIMAX COMMUNITIES		ON LAND		SEA BENTHIC	
		Magnitude of area covered	Condition	Magnitude of area covered	Condition
1.	Biome or biotic formation	1,000,000 sq. mi.	Usually continuous	10,000 sq. mi.	Usually continuous
2.	Association	100,000 sq. mi.	Usually broken by 7	5,000 sq. mi.	Continuous
3.	Consociation	100 sq. mi.	Continuous	100 sq. mi.	Continuous or fragmented
4.	Faciation	10,000 sq. mi.	Broken by 7 or 8	100 sq. mi.	Broken
5.	Lociation	1 sq. mi.	Continuous	2 sq. yd.	Continuous
6.	Clan	4 sq. yd.	Continuous	0.5 sq. yd.	Continuous

DEVELOPMENTAL COMMUNITIES		TERRESTRIAL XERIC		TERRESTRIAL HYDRIC	
		Size	Condition	Size	Condition
7.	Associes	10,000 sq. mi.	Continuous	100 sq. mi.	Fragmented
8.	Consocies	100 sq. mi.	Continuous	Small	Fragmented
9.	Facies	1,000 sq. mi.	Continuous	10 sq. mi.	Fragmented
10.	Locies	1 sq. mi.	Continuous	1 sq. mi.	Fragmented

APPENDIX IIIA

SUBDIVISIONS OF THE BIOTIC FORMATION, AFTER J. RICHARD CARPENTER

DURATION	CLIMAX UNITS	(PLANTS)*		(ANIMALS)*		SERAL UNITS
		Dominants	Subdominants	Predominants Major Infl.	Sub-Influents Minor Infl.	
Per-annual	Association complex		x	x	x	Locality-complex[5]
	Association[1] Presociation	a, b, c		x		Associes[1] {Pre-associes[2] Pre-associes complexes[2]}
	Faciation[1]	a, b, c + d a, b − c				Facies[1]
	Consociation[1] Lociation	a	x			Consocies[1] Locies
Seasonal	Society[3]		x		x	Socies[3]
	Presociety[3]				x	Presocies[3]
Intradiel	Phase[4]			x	x	Phase[4]

1. Distribution of dominant species (plant on land) (a, b. & c) may result in one dominant (c dropping out, thus causing a Faciation (composed of a and b) to be recognized, or all save one may drop out, leaving a " pure stand," or Consociation (of a). A Faciation may also be formed by the addition of another dominant (d) (thus forming a Faciation of a, b, c + d).

2. Only rarely will predominants, etc., be restricted to a single seral stage; hence the designations of Pioneer (or Initial), Midseral, and Subclimax Pre-associes-complexes of seral stages may be applied. Such predominants are termed Ranging or Permanent influents.

3. Classed as Prevernal, Vernal, Estival Serotinal, Autumnal, and Hiemal or Hibernal Societies or Socies.

4. Classed as Auroral, Diurnal, Vesperal, and Nocturnal Phases (see Carpenter '35, Ecology 16 (2) 203 (April).

5. The Locality complex may be considered as including both the climax and seral stages of a given region bound together by ranging influents and predominants.

* Plants are usually considered as the dominant on land, and animals in marine and deep fresh-water communities.

APPENDIX IV

Biotic Areas in North America, after Shelford '26

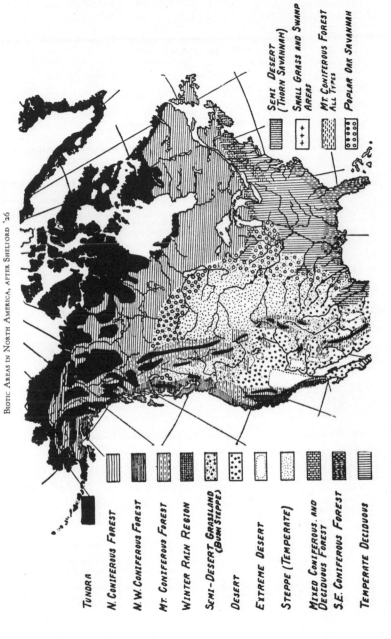

SEMI DESERT
(THORN SAVANNAH)

SMALL GRASS AND SWAMP
AREAS

MT. CONIFEROUS FOREST
ALL TYPES

POPLAR OAK SAVANNAH

TUNDRA

N. CONIFEROUS FOREST

N.W. CONIFEROUS FOREST

MT. CONIFEROUS FOREST

WINTER RAIN REGION

SEMI-DESERT GRASSLAND
(BURN STEPPE)

DESERT

EXTREME DESERT

STEPPE (TEMPERATE)

MIXED CONIFEROUS. AND
DECIDUOUS FOREST

S.E. CONIFEROUS FOREST

TEMPERATE DECIDUOUS

APPENDIX V

Life Zones and Biotic Communities in America North of the Amazon, after Shelford, Jones, and Goldberg '26

VEGETATION TYPE	COMPOSITION	MERRIAM'S LIFE ZONE
I. Tundra and Alpine Summits		
A. Arctic Tundra	Lichens and herbs	Arctic-Alpine Zone
B. Paramos or Alpine Meadow	Sedges, grasses and herbs, dwarf willows	
II. Coniferous Forest		
A. Northern Coniferous Forest	Red, black and white spruces, balsam fir	Hudsonian and Canadian
B. Mountain Coniferous Forest		
1. Rocky Mountain Forest Sub-alpine	Engelmann spruce and alpine fir	Hudsonian and upper Canadian
2. Sierran Sub-alpine Forest	Mountain hemlock, firs white-bark pine	Hudsonian and upper Canadian
3. Rocky Mountain Montane Forest	Western yellow pine, Douglas fir, white fir, lodgepole pine	Canadian and upper Transition
4. Sierran Montane Forest	Sugar pine, western yellow pine, incense cedar, white fir, Douglas fir	Canadian and Transition
5. Larch-Pine Forest of Northwest	Western white pine, western larch, western hemlock, Engelmann spruce, giant cedar	Canadian and Transition
C. Northwest Moist Coniferous Forest	Redwood, douglas fir, western hemlock, giant cedar, Sitka spruce	Canadian and Humid Transition
III. Eastern Forests		
A. Mixed Coniferous and Deciduous	Beech, birch, maple, hemlock, white pine	Alleghanian
B. Temperate Deciduous	Beech, maple, oaks, hickories, tulip tree, sassafras	Carolinian
C. Southeast Coniferous Forest	Longleaf, loblolly pine, slash pine, magnolia, live oak, bald cypress	Austroriparian
D. Gulf Coast Forest	Southeast Coniferous Forest with undergrowth of Palmetto	Sabalian or Gulf Strip
IV. Temperate Rain Forest	"Hammock" Country, Florida	Sabalian Zone
V. Sub-tropical Rain Forest	Very rare frost, south tip of Florida	Tropical Zone
VI. Poplar Savanna	Mixture of poplars and tall grasses	Transition and Alleghanian
VII. Oak Savanna	Mixture of Oaks and tall grasses	Alleghanian, Carolinian and Austroriparian
VIII. Rocky Mountain Forest Margin		
A. Chaparral	Brush, as dwarf Oak (Quercus undulatus) and Mountain mahogany (Sercocarpus parvifolius)	Arid transition
B. Woodland	Pinyons and junipers	Upper Sonoran
IX. California region of various vegetation with Summer drouth and Winter Rain		
A. Chaparral	Brush, as Manzanita and Buck brush	Arid transition
B. Woodland	Evergreen oaks, junipers, etc.	Upper Sonoran
C. Coastal sagebrush or "chaparral"	"Old Man" (Artemisia californica) and Salvia	Upper Sonoran
D. Bunch-grass plains in valleys (cultivated)	Tall grass in bunches	Upper and Lower Sonoran

VEGETATION TYPE	COMPOSITION	MERRIAM'S LIFE ZONE
X. Grassland		
A. Prairie	Largely included in Savanna VI and VII	
B. Steppe (Brush–grass-land in part)	Grasses in open sod. Bare ground between plants, or rather short grasses forming sod	Arid Transition and Upper Sonoran
XI. Bush-Steppe		
1. Semi-desert North-west	Mixed grass and sagebrush	Upper Sonoran
2. Semi-desert South-west	Mixed grass and desert shrub	Upper Sonoran
XII. Temperate Desert	Sagebrush-Atriplex-rabbit brush	Upper Sonoran
XIII. Subtropical Desert		
A. California Microphyll Desert	Creosote bush and Sandbur	Lower Sonoran
B. Succulent Desert	Cacti, mesquite, etc.	Lower Sonoran
XIV. Thorn Savanna	Thorn bushes and grass	Lower Sonoran

APPENDIX V (*Continued*)

LANDSCAPE ASPECTS OF AMERICAN TROPICAL REGIONS AND LIFE ZONE EQUIVALENTS

Mangrove Swamps (Tropical Zone as a whole, but as mangrove swamps are not dependent upon rainfall, they occur within the arid or humid divisions of the Lower Tropical section).

Flood Plain Forest (low altitudes)—Lower Tropical Zone.

Luxuriant Tropical Rain Forest—Humid Lower Tropical Zone.

Drier Tropical Rain Forest—Humid Lower Tropical Zone.

Montane or Cloud Forest—Humid Upper Tropical Zone. It includes conifers and oaks in Central America.

Subalpine Evergreen Forest—Temperate Zone. (In Central America.)

Ecuador and British Honduras, ranging in altitudes from 6000 to 7000 ft. in the former country and to 1000 to 4000 ft. in the latter.

The areas in British Honduras extending from 1000 to 4000 ft. altitude would be within the Lower Tropical Zone, associated with an immense number of tropical species. Areas at 6000 to 7000 ft. altitude in Ecuador would probably be assigned to Sub-tropical or Upper Tropical.

Partially Deciduous Forest—Arid Lower Tropical Zone.

Deciduous Thorn Forest—Arid Lower Tropical Zone. In Mexico and in Panama this can not satisfactorily be separated from the preceding, as the regions are coastal plains crossed by streams; and along the streams the vegetation may be only partially deciduous, or near the water line evergreen, while it is completely deciduous away from the water.

(Shrub) Desert—Sonora and Lower California. Lower Austral Zone.

Semi Desert—Lower Austral Zone.

Extreme Desert—Lower Austral Zone. Desert District Vizcaino.

Gallery Savanna—Arid Lower Tropical Zone. A mixture of monsoon forest and savanna. Arid sometimes corresponds to the Lower Tropical Zone.

Grassland, Dry Grassland—Arid Lower Tropical Zone.

Andine bushland Paramillos—Paramo Zone.

APPENDIX VII

Zoological Regions of the World, after Wallace

APPENDIX VIII

Vegetation Regions of the World, after Grisebach '72

ARCTIC

E. CONT. FOREST

MEDITERRANEAN

SAHARA

SUDAN

KALAHARI

CAPE

OCEAN ISL.

ARCTIC

WESTERN CONTINENTAL FOREST

ANTILLES

HYLAEAN

BRAZILIAN

CALIF. ORNAM.

PRAIRIE

MEXICAN

CHILEAN

ANTARCTIC FOREST

EASTERN CONTINENTAL FOREST

STEPPE

INDIAN MONSOON

OCEANIC ISLANDS

AUSTRALIAN

J. RICHARD CARPENTER

NEG. 23237   BUREAU OF AGRICULTURAL ECONOMICS

U.S. DEPARTMENT OF AGRICULTURE.

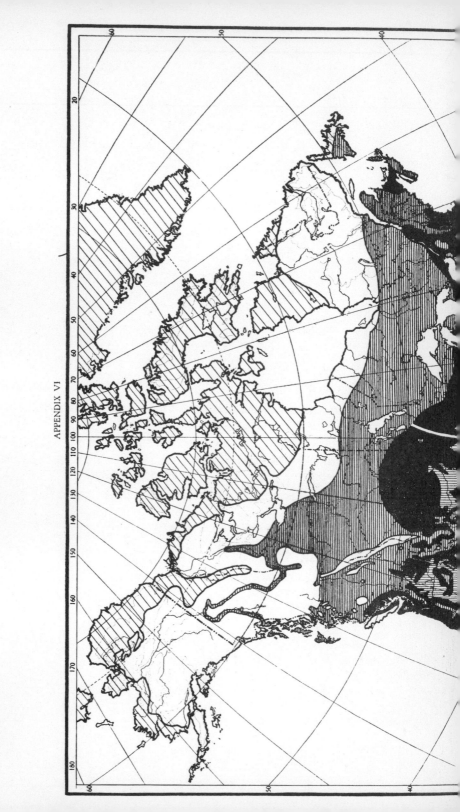

APPENDIX VI

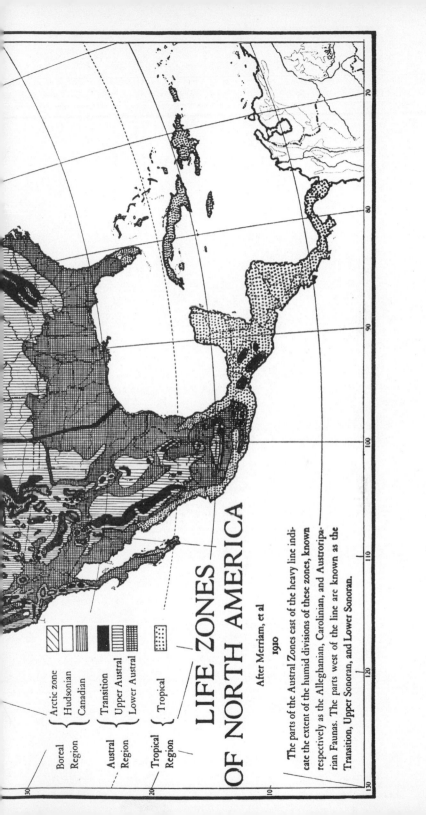

LIFE ZONES
OF NORTH AMERICA

After Merriam, et al

1910

Boreal Region { Arctic zone
Hudsonian
Canadian

Austral Region { Transition
Upper Austral
Lower Austral

Tropical Region { Tropical

The parts of the Austral Zones east of the heavy line indicate the extent of the humid divisions of these zones, known respectively as the Alleghanian, Carolinian, and Austroriparian Faunas. The parts west of the line are known as the Transition, Upper Sonoran, and Lower Sonoran.

APPENDIX IX

MAMMALIAN GEOGRAPHIC REALMS AND REGIONS, AFTER LYDEKKER '96

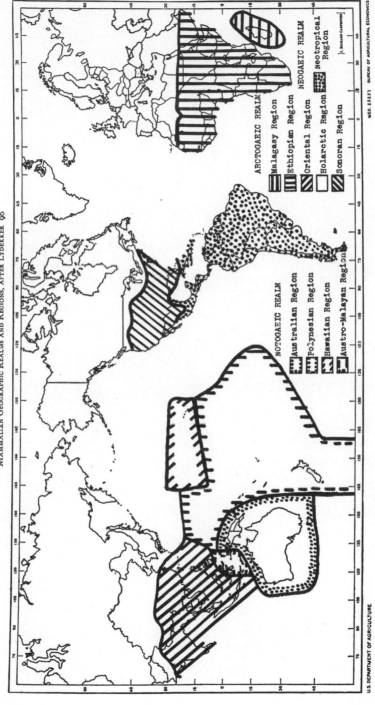

ARCTOGAEIC REALM

Malagasy Region
Ethiopian Region
Oriental Region
Holarctic Region
Sonoran Region

NEOGAEIC REALM

Neotropical Region

NOTOGAEIC REALM

Australian Region
Polynesian Region
Hawaiian Region
Austro-Malayan Region

NEG. 23231   BUREAU OF AGRICULTURAL ECONOMICS

U.S. DEPARTMENT OF AGRICULTURE

Grundlagen einer Ökologischen Tiergeographie

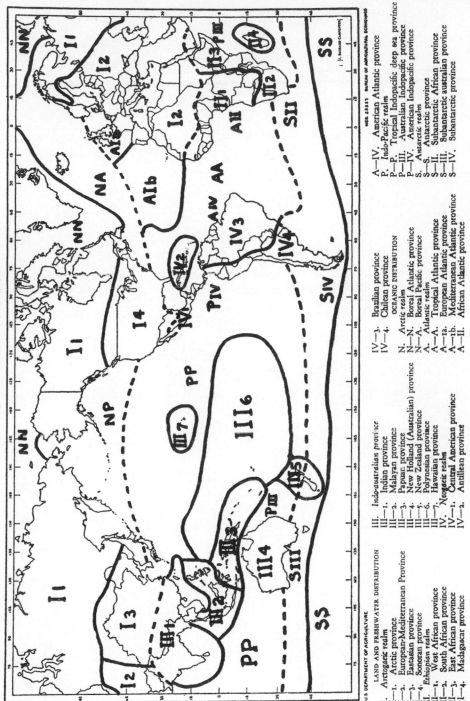

U.S. DEPARTMENT OF AGRICULTURE   NEG. 23317 BUREAU OF AGRICULTURAL ECONOMICS

LAND AND FRESHWATER DISTRIBUTION
I. Arctogaeic realm
I—1. Arctic province
I—2. European-Mediterranean Province
I—3. Eastasian province
I—4. Sonoran province
II. Ethiopian realm
II—1. West African province
II—2. South African province
II—3. East African province
II—4. Madagascar province

III. Indo-australian realm
III—1. Indian province
III—2. Malayan province
III—3. Papuan province
III—4. New Holland (Australian) province
III—5. New Zealand province
III—6. Polynesian province
III—7. Hawaiian province
IV. Neogaeic realm
IV—1. Central American province
IV—2. Antillean province

IV—3. Brazilian province
IV—4. Chilean province

OCEANIC DISTRIBUTION
N. Arctic realm
N—N. Boreal Atlantic province
N—A. Boreal Pacific province
A. Atlantic realm
A—A. Tropical Atlantic province
A—1a. European Atlantic province
A—1b. Mediterranean Atlantic province
A—II. African Atlantic province

A—IV. American Atlantic province
P. Indo-Pacific realm
P—P. Tropical Indopacific deep sea province
P—III. Australian Indopacific province
P—IV. American Indopacific province
S. Antarctic realm
S—S. Antarctic province
S—II. Subantarctic African province
S—III. Subantarctic australian province
S—IV. Subantarctic province

	DOMINANTS		PREDOMINANTS
PERENNIAL NUCLEUS Cercis-Cornus- Cardinalis-Ceratome- gilla ASSOCIES	Cercis canadensis L. Cornus florida L. Ulmus americanus L. Cephalanthus occidentalis Benzoin aestivale L. [L. Fraxinus spp. Crataegus spp.	CARNIVORES	(Taxidea taxus (Schreb.)) (Vulpes fulva (Des (Canis occidentalis (Rich.)) Blarina brevicauda Scalopus aquaticus nus (Haf.)
		OMNIVORES	Didelphys virginiana (Ursus americanus Pallas) (Procyon lotor (L.))
		HERBIVORES	(Marmota monax (L.)) (Odocoileus virgin *Mus norvegicus Erxl. (Erxl.)) Microtus pennsylvanicus Sciurus niger ruf (Ord.) (Geoff.) Peromyscus leucopus nove- S. carolinianus le borensis (Eisch.) (Capper) Microtus austerus (LeC.) Tamias striatus ly Sylvilagus floridanus (Richards) mearnsi (Allen) Citellus franklini (Sabine)
	SUBDOMINANTS		MAJOR INFLUEN
PREVERNAL ASPECT Aesculus-Claytonia- Junco-Corythuca SOCIES	Claytonia virginica L. Trillium spp. Viola spp. Dicentra cucullaria (L.) Aesculus glabra Willd. Dicentra canadensis (Gold.) Collinsia verna Nutt. Ranunculus proserpina- coides Willd.		Bronzed Grackle Robin Towhee Bluebird Brown Thrasher Miscellaneous War Miscellaneous Thr Junco Miscellaneous Spa
VERNAL ASPECT Aesculus-Arisaema- Warbler spp. - Blissus SOCIES	Arisaema triphyllus (L.) Aesculus glabra Willd.		Redstart Whip-poor-will Miscellaneous Spa Wood Pewee Miscellaneous War Catbird Flycatcher Robin Brown Thrasher Towhee
AESTIVAL ASPECT Aesculus-ostrya- Ormensis-Ceresa SOCIES	Aesculus glabra Willd. Ostrya virginica Koch		Miscellaneous Spa Quail Mourning Dove Robin Bronzed Grackle Brown Thrasher
SEROTINAL ASPECT Aesculus-Vernonia- Dicyphus-Apion SOCIES	Aesculus glabra Willd. Vernonia illinoiensis Gleason		Catbird Indigo Bunting Wood Pewee Towhee Redstart Crested Flycatche
AUTUMNAL ASPECT Vernonia-Warbler spp.- Diabrotica-Lygus SOCIES	Vernonia illinoiensis Gleason Miscellaneous Compos- itae		Migrating Warbler Bronzed Grackle Goldfinch Miscellaneous Spa Junco Towhee
HIEMAL ASPECT	Nuthatch - Kinglet - Xysticus		
	HIEMAL PRES- OCIES		White Breasted Nu Junco Ruby Crowned King Goldfinch
	Ceratomegil- la - Blissus Lygus		
	HIBERNAL PRE- SOCIES		

FOREST-EDGE BIOTIC COMMUNITY, Champai

Forms marked by (

	INFLUENTS		
-Tailed Hawk -Shouldered Hawk arp-Shinned Hawk oper's Hawk	Notoxus monodon Fab. Tetragnatha laboriosa Htz. Wala palmarum Ceratomegilla fuscilabris (LeC.)		
ild Turkey) rdinal ickadee tmouse ow ue Jay	Apis mellifica L. Lasius niger sspp. Myrmica spp. Aphaenogaster fulva Roger Andrenidae		
d Headed Wood- pecker d Bellied Wood- pecker wny Woodpecker airy Woodpecker rthern Flicker		Nabis ferus (L.) Corythuca aesculi O. & D. Empoasca viridescens Walsh	Epitrix brevis Schw. Epitrix fuscula Cr. Glyptina spuria LeC.

	MINOR INFLUENTS		
	CARNIVOROUS	SUCKING PHYTOPHAGOUS	CHEWING PHYTOPHAGOUS
	Miscellaneous spiders	Lygus pratensis Say Erythroneura obliqua Say	Phyllophaga spp. Cynipidae Chironomidae spp. Syrphidae spp. Nymphalidae spp. Papilionidae spp. Bombidae spp.
	Reduviid nymphs Miscellaneous spiders	Blissus leucopteris (Say) nymphs Aphidae spp.	Scuddaria nymphs Phalacrus politus Melsh
	Sarcophagidae spp. Chaleidae Miscellaneous spiders Reduviidae	Ceresa bubalis Graphocephala coccinea (Say) Ormensis pruinosa Say Blissus leucopteris (Say) nymphs Jalysus spinosus (Say) Arhidae	Scuddaria furcata Brunn. Photinus scutillans Say Cycloneda sanguinea Thymnes metasternalis Xanthogramma flewipes Anthomyidae spp.
	Reduviidae Miscellaneous spiders	Graphocephala coccinea (Say) Dicyphus gracilentis Parsh Ormensis spp. Ceresa bubalis Nyodocha serripes Oliv	Diabrotica 12-punctata (Fab.)
	Miscellaneous spiders	Triphleps insidiosus Say Lygus pratensis Say	Psilopus nnymph Apion spp. Oecanthus nigricornis F. Walk.
	Xysticus elegans Keys Miscellaneous spiders		
	Ceratomegilla fuscilabris (DeG.) Notoxus monodon Fab.	Blissus leucopteris (Say) Lygus pratensis Say Nyodocha serripes Oliv.	Phyllophaga

linois. Forms in parentheses now extinct.

ative in area.

APPENDIX XII

The Active Process of Erosion
After Malott '28

KIND OF PROCESS	PROCESS OF OBTAINING MATERIAL CARRIED	WEAR BY MATERIAL CARRIED	WEAR OF MATERIAL CARRIED BY MUTUAL CONTACT	SPECIAL PROCESSES
Eolian or Wind Erosion	deflation	corrasion	attrition	
Pluvio-fluvial Erosion by Running Water and Wave Erosion	fluviraption	corrasion	attrition	corrasion
Glacial Erosion	exaration and also plucking	abrasion	abrasion	gouging

From Malott, Clyde A., An Analysis of Erosion, *Indiana Academy of Science Proceedings*, 37;153-163, 1928.